To Laura
from Pop
NYC trip 1/27/89

AMERICAN FOLK TALES AND LEGENDS

AMERICAN FOLK TALES AND LEGENDS

Retold by Niel Grant

PEERAGE BOOKS

First published in Great Britain in 1988 by
Octopus Books Limited,
Michelin House, 81 Fulham Road,
London SW3 6RB

© Octopus Books Limited, 1988

ISBN: 0 7064 3131 6

Printed in Czechoslovakia

50672

ACKNOWLEDGEMENTS
The publishers would like to thank Peter Newark's
Western Americana for supplying the color material
used inside this book.

Black and white illustrations by John Pilley

CONTENTS

Frontier Heroes

Engineers and Steelmen

Indian Myths and Legends

Sailors' Yarns and Fishy Tales

Animal Yarns

The Wild West

Strange Tales

More Superheroes

Witches and Other Devilry

Frontier
Heroes

Johnny Appleseed

The heroes of the old frontier were, most of them, tough characters. Most of the stories about them are stories of great deeds of strength, although sometimes of cunning too. You could say they were men who were not strangers to violence, with knife or gun or fist. There was surely a lot of scrapping on the frontier.

Maybe that's the reason why Johnny Appleseed is such a popular character. You can't imagine Johnny Appleseed strangling a bear with his own hands. He would be more likely to sit down for a quiet talk with the creature. A fur trapper once came upon Johnny playing with three bear cubs while the mother bear looked on happily.

Like Davy Crockett, Daniel Boone and many others, Johnny Appleseed was a real person, although that was not his real name. He was born John Chapman, somewhere around Boston, in 1775, and he died in 1847. He earned his nickname by planting apple trees in what was then wild country in Ohio, Illinois and Indiana, and most of the stories about him are true. At least, they started that way. Some of them may have been stretched a little.

People were telling stories about Johnny Appleseed long before he died, although they weren't written down for a while after then. Vachel Lindsay, a poet who wandered around the country telling poems in exchange for a meal and a bed nearly 100 years after Johnny Appleseed had been living a similar kind of life, wrote several poems about him.

Johnny arrived in western Pennsylvania in 1794 and he soon had a house in Pittsburgh where he planted an apple orchard. He said when he first opened his eyes after he was born the first thing he saw was a branch of an apple tree in bloom right outside the window. He always loved apple trees.

He lived quite some time in Pittsburgh before he had the idea of going west with a load of apple seeds which the settlers could plant around their log cabins. He was first seen in the Territory of Ohio in 1801. He had a big sack of apple seeds, which he got from the cider mills around Pittsburgh, and planted them around Licking Creek. A few years later someone saw him taking a load of apple seeds down the Ohio River with two canoes tied together, but that wasn't Johnny's usual way of traveling. He normally went on his feet, sometimes with a horse, sometimes carrying the seeds on his back. He wore the roughest kind of clothes—in his later years just an old coffee sack with holes for the head and arms—and he often went barefoot.

Now in those days, remember, Ohio was a wilderness. It was full of wild animals, and you could count 100 black rattlesnakes in an acre, or so they say. But Johnny never came to any harm. Once when he was cutting down the grass to make a plot to plant his seeds, he was bitten in the heel by a rattler. Johnny banged the snake with the scythe—about the only time he ever committed a violent act. He was very sorry about it later. "Poor fellow," he said, "he only just touched me, and I gave way to ungodly passion." (Johnny was a very religious man.) "When I came back that way, the poor fellow was dead." He was heartily sorry about killing that rattler.

Another time a hornet got caught under Johnny's coffee-sack coat. It stung him several times because he was so eager to let it free without harming it. "Why didn't you kill it, Johnny?" he was asked. "That wouldn't be right," Johnny replied, "for the poor thing never intended to hurt me."

One cold night when he was camping out, Johnny built a fire to keep warm. But the light of the fire attracted mosquitoes and some of them flew right into the flames and were killed. Right away Johnny put the fire out.

When it was very cold Johnny sometimes made himself a pair of sandals like the Indians wore, but mostly he went barefoot. A settler saw him tramping through the snow one winter, so he gave him a pair of shoes which were too small for him to wear himself. They fitted Johnny all right. But a couple of days later the settler saw Johnny again, and he was barefoot once more. "What have you done with the shoes I gave you, Johnny?" the settler asked. Johnny explained he had met a poor family going west and they were in much greater need than he, so he gave them the shoes.

Johnny wasn't one for fancy hats either. At one time he used to wear the mess tin he cooked his food in. But that wasn't satisfactory, as he explained, because it didn't keep the sun out of his eyes. So he made himself a hat of pasteboard with a great peak in front. He wore that one many a year.

It wasn't that Johnny was poor. He spent so little on himself that he didn't need much money, and he did pretty well at times, selling the young trees he had planted to the settlers who had come to live nearby. Of course, anyone who was too poor got young apple trees from Johnny without paying a bean.

He was a strange-looking fellow. A small man, but wiry, he never cut his hair, which was dark, nor his beard, which was thin. In his strange hat and coat, he was the kind of figure most people would laugh at, but the roughest characters on the frontier always treated with the greatest respect. Not even the children jeered at him. He loved children, especially little girls, and he usually carried a few pretty ribbons or other little presents for them.

The Indians respected him too. They were very kind to him, even when they were planning an attack on some white settlement. During the Indian wars, Johnny wandered about alone and unarmed as usual, and he never came to any harm. He was able to warn many people to get out before they were slaughtered.

One thing the Indians especially admired about Johnny was the way he could stand pain. It seems he just did not feel pain as other folks did. He kept the frontier folk amused by sticking pine needles into his flesh without feeling any pain at all. When he had a sore on his foot, and he had a few of those through walking barefoot through the woods, he would cure it by putting a red-hot iron against it.

Johnny did not eat meat. He believed it was wrong to kill animals for food, and that people should only eat what grew in the ground. Of course he never had a wife. Some said he took to his wanderings in the first place because he had been jilted by a girl in Pennsylvania.

Many of his ideas came from his religion. He was a follower of a Swedish Christian named Emanuel Swedenborg, who wrote books which, he said, were inspired by angels who visited him. Johnny would carry these books around with him and lend them to the folk on the frontier. He hadn't many copies of the books so what he would do was tear the book into pieces and leave one piece at each home. Next time he was passing that way, he collected all the pieces and passed them on to the next family. That way he had a lot of people reading the same book at the same time.

Johnny also talked with angels himself.

When he visited a settler's cabin at the end of a long day's traveling, he would ask the people if they wanted to hear some news fresh from heaven. Then he would get out the Bible, or some other religious book, and read to them. His voice was as loud as the wind and waves, and as soft as the dawn breeze that made the leaves quiver. Mostly, people did not understand much of what he read, but they caught the spirit of it from Johnny's reading. Johnny Appleseed believed it was his religion that kept him from harm. When he was asked if wasn't afraid of being bitten by snakes, he held up a holy book and said, "This is my protection." Johnny was happy in the way he lived because he believed he was living like the first Christians did.

Johnny Appleseed made the west bloom with apple blossom. But some say he was also the cause of the May weed (dog fennel) which became a curse to the Ohio homesteaders in later years. Johnny believed this plant was good for the fever, and he used to scatter seeds of it near every homestead he visited. The weed spread, and although it may have helped to keep down malaria, it was certainly a terrible nuisance to the farmers in other ways.

Johnny planted his apple seeds in places where he reckoned folk would settle. By the time the place was filling up with settlers, the trees were big enough for transplanting. Some people paid for them, some gave him old clothes or a bag of meal, and a great number gave him a note promising future payment. Johnny seemed to think this was the most businesslike way of doing things. It never troubled him if the money was never paid.

He also came by a number of animals, such as old broken-down horses which had been turned loose to die because they couldn't work any more. He would find good pasture for them in the summer, and make a bargain with some settler to feed and look after the horses during the winter.

Wherever he went, Johnny was offered a bed and a meal if they were to be had. He usually liked to sleep outside though, and his meal was mostly bread and milk. He would never sit down to a meal unless he was sure there was enough food in the house to feed the children.

By the time he was 70 years old, Johnny Appleseed had covered around 100,000 square miles of territory. And the proof of it could be seen every spring when the apple trees blossomed pink and white from the Ohio River to the Wabash.

In the summer of 1847, after traveling 20 miles on a warm day, Johnny arrived at the home of an old friend near Fort Wayne, Indiana. He ate his usual meal of bread and milk sitting on the step. Afterwards he read something from the Bible, then he laid down to sleep on the floor. He never woke up. The physician who was called said he'd never seen a dead man so peaceful. There was a glow to him like the glow of a ripening apple on a late summer evening.

There are some people who say Johnny Appleseed was a mite crazy. Maybe he was. And maybe we could do with a whole lot more people crazy like Johnny.

A Comfortable Night

There were many men on the frontier who led a wandering life, though none like Johnny Appleseed. Most of them were down on their luck for one reason or another, but the settlers were hospitable folk mainly, even if they were poor. A man who needed food and a roof for the night was not often turned away.

One fellow was traveling through the country when, about sundown, he came to a log cabin where there was a man and a woman with three children. There was only one bed in the cabin, but the man said they could make room for the traveler. "You take the bed, mister," he said, "and me and my wife will sleep on the pallet on the floor with the three children."

The traveler said this was mighty hospitable. He was tired after traveling all day and soon went to bed. He woke up early in the morning, thinking the bed was rather hard. Then he found he was sleeping on the pallet on the floor, along with the youngsters. The man and his wife were in the bed, snoring hard.

When the man woke up an hour or so later, he said, "You sure wake up early, stranger. If you'd slept a little longer me and my wife would have put you back in the bed again. We always do that with strangers. Mostly they never know the difference."

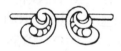

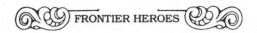

Nail Soup

Sometimes it was the traveler who was the crafty one.

A poor man came once to a big house and asked for something to eat. "There's nothing in this house to eat," said the woman who lived there. "Not so much as a bowl of soup and a crust of bread." She was rich but she wasn't generous.

"OK," said the man. "Then would you have a nail you could give me?"

"What in the world do you want with a nail?" the lady asked.

"Why, so I can make some nail soup."

"Nail soup? I never head of that."

"Oh, you can make a fine bowl of soup with a nail and a pan of water."

The woman was interested, and she went off and fetched a nail and a pan of water. Nail soup, she was thinking, well, that would make a cheap dish. And she watched the man carefully as he put the nail in the pan of water and started to heat it over the fire.

After a while he said, "What this soup needs is a pinch of salt." The woman gave him some salt. Then he said, "I guess a few cabbage leaves or a piece of turnip would help things along." The woman went and got some cabbage leaves and a piece of turnip.

"It'll soon be done," said the man, stirring away. "A little pork fat might help some." The woman brought some pork fat, and he put that in the pan too.

"Nearly ready now," he said. "If I just had a few peas to throw in now, that would finish it off fine." The woman brought him some peas and they went into the pan.

The man asked for two bowls and spoons and, when she had brought them, he poured the soup into the bowls. "Now," he said, "taste that. Ain't it good?"

They drank the soup, and the woman said, "Yes, that is good soup." It wasn't until she'd nearly finished that she said, "What about the nail?"

"Ah." The man dived around in the pan with his spoon and brought up the nail. "Still hard," he said. "Needs more cooking. Add more water. Well, I'll be on my way now."

When he left, the woman was still standing stirring the pan, waiting for the nail to cook.

Davy Crockett

David Crockett was a politician. After twice being elected to the state legislature, he served in the United States Congress as the Representative from Tennessee for six years in the 1820s and 1830s. Is that why we remember him? Well, no, not exactly.

Davy Crockett was first of all a frontiersman and, before he went into politics, he lived the rough-and-tumble life of the pioneer in the backwoods of Tennessee. He ran away from home at 13 and never went to school, but he knew how to hunt bear in the canebrakes and he knew how to tell a good yarn.

As a result of his service under Andrew Jackson in the war against the Creek Indians, he became a hero and then went into local politics. He first stood for Congress because someone suggested it to him as a joke, and he was surprised when he was elected.

The politicians in Washington loved the idea of having a real frontiersman as a lawmaker. (As Davy said, he relied on "natural born sense instead of law learning.") They built up his "image," as we should call it today, as a folksy backwoodsman in a coonskin cap, and lots of stories were published about his adventures. What part Davy himself took in writing these stories isn't certain. Some of them were more or less true and some of them might have been true even if they weren't. But as time went by, the tales grew taller and taller.

After he was defeated in the election of 1835, Davy Crockett went west and joined the Texans fighting against the Mexicans. He was killed at the Alamo, along with Jim Bowie and other western heroes, in 1836, and became after his death the hero of many comic legends.

— □ —

Crockett Gets the Votes

Here are two stories, for a start, about Davy Crockett electioneering. The first one comes from his life story, which he had a hand in though he didn't write all of it himself, and the second is an example of the tall tales which were told, as if by Davy, later.

Davy Crockett had just taken part in a great squirrel hunt and there was a feast afterward at which Davy was called upon to make a speech, because he had recently become a candidate for office. Speech-making then was something of which he was entirely ignorant.

"A public document I had never seen," he tells us, "nor did I know there were such things, and how to begin I couldn't tell. I made many apologies, and tried to get off, for I know'd I had a man to run against who could speak prime, and I know'd, too, that I wasn't able to shuffle and cut with him. He was there, and knowing my ignorance as well as I did myself, he also urged me to make a speech. The truth is, he thought my being a candidate was a mere matter of sport, and didn't think for a moment that he was in any danger from an ignorant backwoods bear hunter. But I found I couldn't get off, and so I determined just to go ahead, and leave it to chance what I should say.

"I got up and told the people I reckoned they know'd what I had come for but, if not, I could tell them. I had come for their votes, and if they didn't watch mighty close I'd get them, too. But the worst of all was that I could not tell them anything about government. I tried to speak about something, and I cared very little what, until I choked up as bad as if my mouth had been jamm'd and cramm'd chock full of dry mush. There the people stood, listening all the while with their eyes, mouths, and ears all open to catch every word I would speak.

"At last I told them I was like a fellow I had heard of not long before. He was beating on the head of an empty barrel near the roadside, when a traveler, who was passing along, asked him what he was doing that for? The fellow replied that there was some cider in that barrel a few days before, and he was trying to see if there was any now, but if there was he couldn't get at it. I told them there had been a little bit of a speech in me a while ago, but I believed I couldn't get it out.

"They all roared out in a mighty laugh, and I told some other stories, equally amusing to them, and believing I had them in a first-rate mood, I quit and got down, thanking the people for their attention and making my way to the liquor stand, for I thought it was time for us all to wet our whistles a little. Most of them followed me, and my competitor had mighty few left to hear him when he got up to speak."

That sounds like a true story. Here is another supposed speech by Davy that is more in the nature of a tall tale.

In one election, Davy Crockett's opponent was a very charming gentleman who had an especially nice and friendly smile. "Yes," said Davy, "he may get some votes by grinning, for he can outgrin me, and you know I ain't slow." And he told this story to show what a fine grin he had himself:

"You all know I love hunting. Well, I discovered a long time ago that a raccoon couldn't stand my grin. I could bring one tumbling down from the highest trees. I never wasted powder and lead when I wanted one of the creatures.

"Well, as I was walking out one night a few hundred yards from my house, looking carelessly about me, I saw a coon planted upon one of the highest branches of an old tree. The night was very moony and clear and old Ratler was with me, but Ratler won't bark at a coon—he's a queer dog that way. So I thought I'd bring the coon down in the usual way—by a grin. I set myself and, after grinning at the coon a reasonable time, found that he didn't come down. I wondered what was the reason, and took another steady grin at him. But he stayed right there. It made me a little mad, so I got an old branch about five feet long so I could rest my chin on it. Then I grinned my best for about five minutes, but the cursed coon hung on.

"Finding I could not bring him down by grinning, I fetched an axe and began to cut down the tree. Pretty soon it came down and I ran forward. Damn, the coon was still there on the branch! Then I looked a little closer and I found that what I had taken for a coon was just a large knot on the branch of the tree. But I had grinned all the bark off it, and left the knot perfectly smooth."

— □ —

The Clever Coon

"Almost everybody who knows the forest understands perfectly well Davy Crockett never wastes powder nor ball, having been brought up to believe it is a sin to waste ammunition. Well, I was out in the forest one afternoon and had just got to a place called the Great Gap when I saw a racoon sitting all alone on a tree. I clapped Brown Betty to my shoulder and was just going to put a piece of lead between his shoulders when he lifted one paw and said, 'Is your name Crockett?'

"'You are right for once,' says I, 'My name is Davy Crockett.'

"'Then,' says the raccoon, 'you needn't take the trouble to shoot, for I might as well come down without another word.' And he walked right down from the tree as if he considered himself shot.

"I stooped down and patted him on the head and said, 'I hope I may be shot myself before I hurt a hair on your head, for I never had such a compliment in my life.'

"'Seeing as how you say that,' says the coon, 'I'll just walk off now lest you should happen to change your mind.'"

———— □ ————

No Credit

One day when Davy Crockett was electioneering, he was due to address a big crowd at a place called the Cross Roads, where Job Snelling, a Yankee, had set up a liquor shop in a shanty especially for the occasion. His opponent was already in full flow when Crockett arrived. A stump had been cut down, and he got up on that and began to "speechify."

He hadn't been speaking long when the crowd became restless. Some of them explained that they couldn't listen to Davy on such a dry subject as the welfare of the nation until they had something to drink. They meant he should buy the drinks. So he led the way to Job's shanty, followed by his supporters shouting, "Hurrah for Crockett!"

Davy went into the shanty and called for a quart of the best rum, but Job just pointed to a board on which he'd chalked up the words, "No Credit." Now, money was always scarce in the west, and it was particularly scarce with Davy at that time.

Davy saw that if he couldn't supply the rum he wouldn't get the votes. So he put his rifle on his shoulder and struck off for the woods. He hadn't been out long before he saw a fat raccoon in a tree. He shot it and stripped the skin off, which he took back to the shanty. In those days a coonskin was as good as money and worth a quart of rum any day.

He threw down the coonskin on Job's bar and Job produced the quart of rum. Now Davy's supporters found their voices again, and when they'd drunk the rum Davy got up on the stump to tell them some more about what he proposed for the good of the nation.

Before he was halfway through, some people said they would rather listen to the rest after they had refreshed themselves again in Job Snelling's bar. They ambled off to the shanty and Davy began to think he'd have to go off into the forest again and shoot another coon.

He was standing at the bar, feeling kind of bashful, with Job's "No Credit" notice staring him in the face, when he noticed a piece of the coonskin sticking out between the logs that supported the bar. Job had put it there out of the way while he was busy supplying drinks. Davy reached down when Job wasn't looking and gave it a tug. It came away in his hand as naturally as if he were its rightful owner, and he slapped it on the bar. Thinking it was another one, Job shoved over another bottle, which was quickly emptied by Davy's supporters, some of whom had seen the trick.

Then the whole party withdrew to resume the discussion of the affairs of the nation, but somehow or other, they soon grew thirsty again and it was necessary to return to the shanty. As luck would have it, the coonskin was still sticking out between the logs, and Davy quickly flung it on the bar again. Before the day was over he had got 10 quarts of rum for that same coonskin. He was especially pleased with his trick because Job, being a Yankee, was considered as sharp as a steel trap and as bright as a pewter button.

The story went around, and people said that anyone who was sharp enough to trick Job Snelling was just the man they wanted to represent them in Congress. The result was Davy won the election by a long way. After it was over, he sent Job the price of the rum, but Job wouldn't take the money, saying it was a good thing for him as a tradesman to be taken in occasionally, as it kept him up to the mark.

— □ —

The Big Freeze

Here is a very tall tale of the kind that was written about Davy Crockett after his death.

"One January morning it was so all-screwed-up cold that the forest trees were so stiff they couldn't shake and the very daybreak froze just as it was trying to dawn. The tinder box in my cabin would no more strike a light than a sunken raft at the bottom of the sea. I thought all Creation was in a fair way to freezing fast.

"'So,' I thinks, 'I must strike a little light from my fingers to light my pipe, travel a few leagues, and see what is going on.'

"Then I banged my knuckles together like two thunder clouds, but the sparks froze before I could catch a light.

"So I walked out, and endeavored to keep myself unfrozen by going at a hop, step, and a jump, and whistling the tune of 'Fire in the Mountains.'

"Well, after I had walked about twenty-five miles up to the top of Daybreak Hill, I soon discovered what was the matter. The earth had actually frozen fast in its axis and couldn't turn around. The sun had

got jammed between two cakes of ice and had been working so hard to get loose he had frozen fast in his own sweat.

"'Creation!' I thought, 'This can't be endured. Something must be done or human-kind is done for.'

"It was then so cold that my upper and lower teeth and my tongue were all frozen together as tight as an oyster. I took a bear off my back that I'd picked up on the road, and beat the animal against the ice until the hot oil began to flow out of him on all sides. Then I took him and held him over the earth's axis and squeezed him till I'd thawed it loose, poured about a ton of it over the sun's face till I got the sun loose, whistled 'Push Along, Keep Moving,' and in about fifteen seconds the earth gave a grunt and began moving. The sun got up beautiful, and I lit my pipe by the blaze of his top-knot. I shouldered my bear and walked home, keeping a piece of sunrise in my pocket with which I cooked my bear steaks, and enjoyed one of the best breakfasts I had tasted for some time."

— □ —

The Death of Colonel Crockett

There's great rejoicing among the bears of Kentucky, and the alligators of the Mississippi roll up their shining ribs to the sun and grow so fat and lazy they will hardly move out of the way for a steamboat. The rattlesnakes come up out of their holes and frolic within 10 feet of the clearings, and the foxes go to sleep in the goose-pens. It is because the rifle of Crockett is silent for ever, and the print of his moccasins is found no more in our woods. His old fox-skin cap hangs up in the cabin, and every hunter never looks at it without turning away his head and dropping a salt tear.

Luke Wing entered the cabin the other day and took down old Kill-Devil to look at it. The muzzle was half stopped up with rust, and a great green spider ran out of it and made his escape in the cracks of the wall. The varmints of the forest will fear it no more. His last act to defend it was when the poor gallant Colonel drew a bead on a Mexican and brought him down. Crockett went to put "Big Butcher" into another, and the feller on the ground turned half over and stuck a knife into him. Another came up behind and ran his bayonet into Crockett's back, for he would as soon have faced 100 live mammoths as to have faced Crockett at any time.

Down fell the Colonel like a lion struck by lightning. He never spoke again. It was a great loss to the country and the world, and to old Kentucky in particular. There was never known such a member of Congress as Crockett, and never will be again. The panthers and bears will miss him, for he never missed them. He was an ornament to the forest, and was never known to refuse whiskey to a stranger.

Daniel Boone

Daniel Boone (1734–1830), the greatest of frontiersmen, is remembered especially as an Indian fighter at a time when, as he said himself, "we Virginians were waging a war of intrusion upon them." He would be sorry about this. Unlike Davy Crockett, who lived a little later, Daniel Boone never became a hero of myth and tall tales. Although many colorful stories were told about him, they were not the kind that said he lit his pipe from the sun or rode to a meeting on a crocodile. The true Colonel Crockett was almost forgotten in the myth of the fantastic superhero, but Daniel Boone has remained more of a historical person in spite of all the legends.

Boone spent most of his life as a wandering hunter. He was not really the "discoverer of Kentucky," as he was sometimes called, because apart from the Indians who had lived there for thousands of years, other white men had been in Kentucky before him. Still, he knew the country better than anyone. In the 1770s, Boone blazed the trail through the Cumberland Gap, now in north-east Tennessee, which became one of the main routes for settlers moving west

He was twice captured by Indians. The second time he was held for five months before he escaped, and the Shawnee chief, Blackfish, adopted him as a son. One of his own sons was killed by the Cherokees, and his daughter was captured—but quickly rescued by Boone. During the Revolutionary War, Boonesboro, which he founded, was attacked by Indian and British forces, but he and a few companions held out successfully during a siege that lasted 10 days.

At the age of 65, Boone moved further west into Missouri, which was then still owned by the Spaniards. When he was asked why, he said that Kentucky had become too crowded. Boone always said that when a man could not cut down a tree for firewood within 10 feet of his house, it was time to move on. When he was a very old man someone asked him how he came to find Missouri. He explained that he had moved from North Carolina to Kentucky seeking peace and quiet from the flood of settlers. But the settlers followed him and he had to move again, to Missouri. "Here I hoped to find rest," he said, "but still I was pursued, for I had not been here two years before a damned Yankee came and settled within 100 miles of me."

An artist from St. Louis came to paint a portrait of the old man, but he couldn't find anyone who knew where he lived. "The nearer I approached the home of the old man," the artist wrote, "the less interest was felt by his neighbors." He spoke to a man who said he did not know any Colonel Boone. But the man's wife butted in, "Why, yes you do. It's that white-headed old man who lives on the bottom, near the river." It was less than two miles away.

The artist himself did not show much interest in the great old frontiersman either, but he did ask him if in all his wanderings he had ever been lost. "No," said Boone, "I can't say as ever I was lost, but I was once bewildered for three days."

In his last years he was much more famous in the east than he was in his own part of the country. People were already writing books about him and his life on the frontier. One day he was given a copy of one of them, but he read it without pleasure. "This book," he said, "represents me as a wonderful man who killed a host of Indians. I don't believe the one has much to do with the other."

—— □ ——

The Young Daniel Boone

Even as a small, rather thin boy, Daniel Boone showed signs of the future frontiersman. When he was no higher than the axe handle, he could chop wood like no other boy. He walked for miles without feeling tired, he swam like a fish the first time he tried, he was dead shot with bow and arrow. When he and his friends were about 12, old enough to carry a rifle, they stumbled on a wildcat in the woods. It turned on them snarling, and they ran—all except Daniel. He stood his ground, squinted through the sights, and shot the wildcat dead in the instant it sprang at him.

The Indians who visited the Quaker settlement where he lived always fascinated him. He saw that they could track game better than any white man, that they were true forest dwellers, and the white man was an alien in their world. He used to follow them, studying their customs and asking questions. Throughout his life, he found that talking to Indians was easier than talking to Whites. He never hated Indians, not even after the Cherokees tortured his young son to death. Daniel Boone never hated anybody.

At the age of 10, Daniel was looking after his father's cattle in a pasture too far away to come home each night. He set out in late spring, stayed in a tiny cabin with his older sister and, although they were often visited by other members of the family, he did not come home until the fall. It was a grand time, and it was in those years that he perfected his skills as a frontiersman.

He had no real schooling, although he could read and write well enough. "Let the girls do the spelling," his father used to say, "Daniel will do the shooting."

From spring to fall he was the family's chief provider of food. There were still buffalo, deer and bear even in eastern Pennsylvania then. He did some cooking, too. He would hang a fat turkey he had shot by its neck over a fire, turning it with a stick so it cooked evenly, and catching the drippings to baste the bird in a piece of curved bark. "Where did you learn that?" his mother asked him. "An Indian told me," Daniel replied.

In the winter he would go trapping, and he once or twice went to Philadelphia to sell his otter and beaver pelts, earning enough money to buy ammunition and hunting knives for his father and brothers as well as himself.

There is a story of Daniel Boone as the age of 17 going to sell furs at a trading post in Salisbury, North Carolina. Two men were hanging around outside the post, and they challenged him to a shooting match. Of course they thought they would easily out-shoot this boy and relieve him of some of the money he would receive for his pelts. They shot at targets cut in trees, and to the great annoyance of the two men, Daniel won $10.

"I'll bet you one-hundred dollars against all your furs on one last shot," one of the men said.

"Are you sure you want to?" Daniel replied.

The man was sure, and the reason he was sure was because he had a set-up especially arranged to trap a young greenhorn, as he supposed Daniel to be. The target had already been cut in the bark, but there was bullet hole right next to the centre. All the man had to do was to aim wide, so he missed the tree altogether, and then claim that the bullet hole was his.

"Good shot!" said Daniel, but he had not been fooled. He had seen the barrel of the man's gun move a fraction just before he fired, and he realized the bullet hole was an old one. But Daniel said nothing. He just lined up his own rifle and sent a ball dead through the center of the target!

Bear Tales

—— ☐ ——

One Way to Skin a Bear

There was a woman in the early days in western Kentucky who set off from her cabin one day to go a christening. She had a bag of food under her arm, and she was just going past a hollow tree when a big bear stepped out in front of her. He looked first at her, then at the food, as if he were trying to make up his mind which to eat first. He stuck his nose out and sniffed at her dinner, which was sausages made of bear meat and crocodile liver.

She stood still just looking at him for a minute, in hopes he would feel ashamed of himself and go off, but then he commenced to sniff at her, and she thought it was time to be making a move. So she threw the dinner down in front of him, and when he put his nose down to it she threw herself on him and caught the scruff of his neck in her teeth.

The bear shot off like a bullet, as her teeth were as long and as sharp as nails. But as he tried to run, she held on hard with her teeth, and stripped the skin right off him. It came right off at the tail and he ran away naked. The bear was seen a week afterward up in Muskrat Hollow, running about without his skin. She made herself a good warm petticoat out of the pesky varmint's hide.

—— ☐ ——

A Bear Hug

"We are great ones for hugging in our parts, and once a couple of us gets into a right good hug it takes us a day to get apart again. But the biggest hug I ever gave was to a great he bear that squeezed me out of nap once as I lay at the foot of an old hollow black oak tree. The cowardly crittur put both his great forepaws around me and clinched them behind my back and began hugging me up to him while wiping his red tongue about in a greedy way. His mouth was watering like a fresh ditch in the spring rains, he couldn't wait to get a taste of my Kentucky tallow.

"But he was presently disappointed, for I grabbed him by the ear, put an arm around his fat body, and with just a single squeeze I hugged him into bear jelly, corked it up in his skin, and took it home for preserves."

The Grizzly's Christmas Present

One winter in the 1860s, a pair of trappers known as Bedrock and Beaver were trapping and prospecting up in Alaska. They hadn't had much good fortune—the snow had driven all the game out of the country—and, except for a few beans and flour, they were out of grub. On top of that, a storm blew up, so bad it looked as though the whole winter's supply of snow was being dumped on them at once. It was so cold even a polar bear would have been looking for cover, so when they stumbled on an old log shack they decided to take shelter.

The cabin was mighty ancient. It had two rooms, but in the rear room the roof had partly given way. The animal smell in the place told them no human had lived there for many a winter. The floor was strewn with pine cones and a few scattered bones, showing it had been the home of mountain rats and squirrels. All in all, it was no palace, but by the time they had got a blaze started in the fireplace and the beans cooking over it, it looked mighty snug after the blizzard outside. The back room had something ghostly about it, and they didn't go in

As they were turning in for the night, Beaver asked what day it was. "Well," said Bedrock, "if I'm right in my dates, it's the night the kids hang up their socks."

"That's what I figured," said Beaver. "Well, this is one camp Santa Claus'll probably overlook."

Both of them went to sleep right away, but Bedrock was woken up in the night by a snuffling noise and something monkeying with the kettle. He raised himself to look, and between him and the fire he saw the form of the biggest silvertip grizzly he'd ever seen. The bear was about the size of a haycart. He was humped over, busy with the beans, snuffling in a pleasant way as though he enjoyed them. Bedrock leant over to nudge Beaver awake. "Santa Claus is here," he said.

Beaver took a look. "Yes," he said, "but he ain't brought nothing but trouble, and more than a sockful of that." He reached for his rifle.

The grizzly heard him and stood up. He was about eight feet tall. Then Beaver fired. The bear went over, upsetting the kettle and putting out the fire. Then he was up again, bellowing and bawling and coming at them in a mighty warlike manner. Bedrock fired, Beaver fired again, and between the smoke of the gunpowder, the barking of the guns and bellowing of the bear, it was like hell on a holiday.

When their magazines were empty, silence fell. "I guess it's all over," said Beaver. When they got the fire lit, they took a look around the battleground. The bear lay stretched out on the floor with his hide so full of holes he wouldn't hold hay.

After all that excitement, they weren't sleepy any more, and they made an early breakfast of bear meat. He was an old bear and tough, but after living on bannocks and beans for a couple of weeks, they weren't particular. Meat was meat.

At daybreak, they decided to look into the back room, where the bear had been hibernating until he was disturbed by the trappers' fire. There was a rusty pick against the wall and a gold pan on the floor, showing that the human who had lived there had been a miner. On the far side, half hidden under the collapsed roof, they found a bunk with an old buffalo robe and some rotten blankets. The body was still there, lying on his side, looking as if he died at peace. An old-fashioned rifle lay across the bunk and a powder horn and bullet pouch hung on the wall. So they knew this man had been a pretty old timer.

Finding the pick and the gold pan made them look more carefully around the shack. They spent the whole day searching but they didn't find any sign of gold. Last of all, they looked at where the bear had made himself a nest, which looked as though it had been occupied for quite a while. The bear had roughed things up a little, and suddenly Bedrock's eye was caught by a hole, half hidden against the wall. In the bottom was a buckskin bag with $500 worth of gold dust inside.

"Old Santa Claus in there," said Beaver, jerking his thumb toward the bear, "didn't fill our socks, but he brought plenty of meat and he showed us the gold, for we'd never have found it if he hadn't kicked the lid off."

The next day they buried the remains of the old prospector, wrapped in a blanket, in the sme hole where they'd found the gold.

"I guess the dust is ours," said Beaver. "There's nothing to show who he was." So they split the pile and left him sleeping in the tomb he had made for himself.

Big-Foot Wallace

William A. Wallace was born in Lexington, Virginia, in 1816. He went to Texas when he was 20 in order, so he said, to take revenge on the Mexicans for the death of his brother and cousin. He went by sea and landed at Galveston, where the only "hotel" in town was the hulk of an old steamboat. Later he settled in San Antonio. He took part in the Mexican wars and was captured for a time. After the wars ended, Wallace became a Texas Ranger and had many fights with the Indians. He was guard on the mail train from San Antonio to El Paso and, in spite of many Indian attacks, it is said he always brought the mail through safely.

—— ☐ ——

How Big-Foot Wallace Got His Name

Wallace gained his nickname while he was a prisoner in Mexico City. The Texan prisoners there were in a poor way. Not one of them had any shoes, and some of the foreign residents in the city got together to collect enough money to buy each of them a pair of shoes. Everyone was fitted up fine—except Wallace. He took a size 13, and he couldn't find even a size 12 anywhere in town. The Mexicans were generally a smaller people than the Americans, and certainly there weren't many as big as Wallace. He was 6' 2", over 200 pounds, and had hands big enough to span a flour barrel. You couldn't say his feet were over-sized, considering his general build.

In the end, Wallace had to buy a piece of leather and get a pair of boots made especially for him. The Mexicans called him "Big-Foot," and the name stuck to him like Texas mud ever afterward. He wasn't too fond of it as a nickname, but as he said, it was better than being called "Lying Wallace" or "Thieving Wallace."

—— ☐ ——

Big-Foot in Disguise

One time Wallace decided to pay a visit back home in Virginia. He wanted to see how people managed to live in the "Old States" without the excitement of an occasional Indian fight, or a scrimmage with the

Mexicans, or even a tussle with a bear now and then to keep their blood in circulation. He thought it must be a mighty humdrum way of living, but then people can get used to anything. He used to say the happiest people he ever saw were the Keechies, who were at war with all the neighboring tribes and ran a great risk of being scalped even when they went to the spring for a drink of water.

His usual dress was a suit of buckskin, with little copper bells that jingled as he walked, and a coonskin hat. But he thought this might not be suitable dress for his visit to Virginia so he asked a city friend to take him around the shops and buy him an outfit for a gentleman: A stovepipe hat, a suit with a long coat and a pair of shiny patent leather shoes—also a pair of gloves, which he only wore once because they were so tight they choked his hands and made him short of breath.

When he tried on his city clothes he found them uncommonly tight. The coat split from stem to stem the first time he sneezed, and he was amazed he managed to get into his shiny shoes without bursting either the shoes or a blood vessel. When he was fully dressed he felt as though he had been coated in plaster which had dried hard in the sun. He couldn't bend his knees or elbows. The only thing he could do was sit bolt upright in a chair with his legs stuck straight out in front of him. Every time he smiled at the ridiculous figure he made, he felt a seam split.

It so happened that while he was togged up like that a friend came to see him about buying a horse. He stared at Big-Foot as if he didn't know him, and at length he asked if Big-Foot was at home. Big-Foot laughed at this, thereby busting two buttons, and his friend finally recognized him. "Why, Big-Foot," he said, "what do you mean by disguising yourself in that way? Are you crazy, or are you going a-courting?"

An acquaintance asked Big-Foot Wallace if he liked a drink. He said he did, providing the liquor wasn't certain death like most of the liquor in Texas. "I once drank some in Castroville," said Big-Foot, "that was so awful bad it burnt a hole in my sleeve when I wiped my mouth afterward."

———— □ ————

Big-Foot the Farmer

After the Mexican war, Big-Foot and his partner Jackson decided to become farmers. It wasn't a success. For one thing, people were crowding into the area as thick as pig tracks around a corn-crib door. If he knew where they'd come from, said Big-Foot, he would go there himself, as the place must be empty by now. Of all things in the world, he hated being fenced in.

Neither Big-Foot nor Jackson knew anything about farming, but they reckoned it would be plain sailing as things in that country appeared to grow pretty much of their own accord anyhow. So they bought 200 acres of land, and they built a shanty and a fence for the vegetable patch. This job right away gave Big-Foot a perfect disgust for farming. The fencing boards split the wrong way, and because of the fact that he worked in the chapparral where the thorns were sharp as cat's claws, Big-Foot ended up tattooed all over.

Big-Foot, however, persevered. He bought a plough, shovels, hoes, and all sorts of farming ammunition. He went to a drug store and bought all kinds of seeds done up in little brown paper packages. He hitched up his old saddle horse to the plough, but that wasn't popular— not popular with the horse, that is. You never saw an animal look so shame-faced. The plough wouldn't behave either. Sometimes it scooted over the top of the ground, sometimes it dove right down into the earth. Looking back at his first furrow made Big-Foot dizzy, it was so monstrously crooked.

Big-Foot and Jackson planted all the seeds. Big-Foot put the seeds labeled "muskmelon" in the richest part of the patch as he was powerful fond of muskmelon. But when they sprouted, they turned out to be bottle gourds, so he rooted them all up.

For a while the corn and everything else grew well. Then the drought set in. It was so dry the frogs turned into toads. The corn turned yellow and wilted. In the end, there were about enough ears of corn for one meal. Big-Foot told Jackson he would go out and shoot a buck, so at least they could have one good meal of meat with fried corn.

He rode all day and never saw a buck. He was about ready to give up when he saw a fine one, which he shot. He skinned it quickly and cut out the "saddle," then headed for home double-quick, for he was as hungry as a coyote. But as he neared the shanty, he smelt a most melancholy smell, the smell of fried corn. He arrived just as Jackson was shoveling the last grains from the skillet down his throat.

All Big-Foot got from that crop was one smell of fried corn, and he wouldn't have got that if the wind hadn't been in the right direction.

Things went from bad to worse. The potatoes took the dry rot (and who could blame them, as it hadn't rained a drop in three months), and everything else they had planted wilted right up. Except the watermelons. They did fine, but what with buying all the ploughs and hoes and all, they had no money left, and they had to live on watermelons. As Big-Foot said, "watermelons are first-rate in their way, but when a fellow has nothing but watermelons for breakfast, watermelons for dinner, and watermelons for supper, he fairly hates the sight of one watermelon after a while."

—— □ ——

Perils of Texas

When Big-Foot Wallace went back east for a spell, everyone asked him a lot of questions about the Texans, the Mexicans, the Indians, and life on the prairies. He found when he gave them true answers they didn't believe him, but when he told them whoppers, they swallowed them down whole.

One young lady wanted to know how many wild horses he had seen in one herd and when he said perhaps 30,000, she replied, "Oh now, Mr. Wallace, don't try to make game of me!" But when he told her there is a spider in Texas as big as a barrel, the poisonous bite of which can only be cured by music, she believed him because she said she'd read it in a book.

There was another varmint, Big-Foot told her, called the Santa Fe which was worse than any poisonous spider because its bite couldn't be cured even by a first-rate brass band. This creature has 100 legs and a sting on each one of them. Besides that it has two stings in its forked tail and a bite like a rattlesnake. When you get stung with the legs, you may live for 15 minutes. When they bite you as well, you turn first blue, then yellow, and then green. Your hair falls out and your nails drop off, and you are dead in five minutes.

"Oh my!" said the young lady. "How can you live in that horrible country?"

Big-Foot explained he had boots made of alligator skin and a centipede hunting shirt made of rattlesnakes' hide, besides which he always chewed tobacco and drank whiskey, which was the best way to keep pests at bay.

There was another young lady, pretty I guess (for you know how Big-Foot liked pretty girls), who asked him if young women were in great demand in Texas.

"I should say they are," said Big-Foot, and he told how the first young woman who came to his settlement had 17 offers of marriage by breakfast time the next morning. Before she could decide which one to choose, one of the young men snatched her and swung her up into his saddle. He rode off full-speed to San Patricio, drew his six-shooter on the minister, and forced him to marry them right there and then. At least she was saved all that trouble choosing.

"How romantic!" said the young lady. "I think I shall have to come to Texas."

"You could do worse," said Big-Foot. "And besides, you might be run away with by some great Comanche chief."

She thought that was even more romantic, so Big-Foot asked her how she would get along without hot rolls for breakfast and baked custard for dinner.

She said she wouldn't mind that at all, and she looked forward to a nice fresh beef-steak before a camp fire.

"Yes," said Big-Foot, "that's reasonable enough, only the Indians don't cook their meat."

"Do they eat it raw?" asked the young lady, losing interest in beefsteak.

"Well," said Big-Foot, "sometimes they fasten a steak under their saddle, and after riding on top of it all day they find it is nicely 'done.' It is a very convenient way of cooking and besides, it's mighty good for a horse with a sore back."

By this time the young lady wasn't so sure she wanted to go to Texas.

By and by she asked Big-Foot if he'd ever seen a mirage on the plains. Big-Foot had no idea what a mirage was, unless it was, maybe, a herd of buffalo or a stampede. "Why, certainly," he replied, "I've seen a thousand of them."

This surprised the young lady because she didn't think mirages were that common, but Big-Foot had her fairly hooked by now.

"Oh yes," Big-Foot went on, "I remember the last one I saw was near Santa Fe, and it kicked up a whole lot of dust as they hadn't had any rain for some time."

"I never heard of a mirage kicking up dust," she said.

"No, in other countries they don't, because the ground is too wet. But in Texas, it's different."

—— □ ——

Big-Foot's Coat of Mail

As everyone knows, the Comanche were expert horse thieves. Big-Foot used to keep his horses in a corral behind his cabin on nights when the moon was full and a raid might be expected. He also had a few dogs roaming around, so he reckoned he was not in much danger of losing his horses.

But one November night, he did. When he woke up in the morning there was a gap in the fence and the horses had gone. The dogs hadn't barked. Some people said the Comanche could put a spell on dogs, and maybe they'd put a spell on Big-Foot's hounds.

He had one old mare still, which he had tethered in the brush a few hundred yards away in case of accidents, so he saddled her up, took Sweet Lips, his muzzle-loading rifle, and Old Butch, his knife, and set off after them. There were moccasin tracks in plenty, in fact too many of them for Big-Foot's liking. Some of the Indians must have been riding horses, so how many of them were there altogether?

He followed the tracks quite a way, until he saw smoke rising ahead of him. The Indians had stopped near a lake, and as Big-Foot came closer he could smell that they were cooking a meal of horse flesh—*his* horse flesh, naturally. He hid up in a wood where many hickory trees were growing, laden with hickory nuts, and he wondered how he was going to cope with a party of Indians who numbered more than 40. Luckily, none of them had guns, but still the odds were a little high. The hickory nuts gave him an idea.

He started picking hickory nuts as fast as he could. He picked them by the hundreds, by the thousands—until he had a great pile of them as high as his knee. Then he tied a piece of rawhide tight around each wrist and each ankle, and started pouring those nuts inside his buckskin breeches and inside his shirt. Big-Foot always wore his clothes loose—remember how he hated tight city clothes—and he filled himself up with nuts until there wasn't a space between his clothes and his skin that wasn't stuffed with those hard-shelled hickory nuts. He even poured some inside his hat.

Big-Foot was ready for battle. He began crawling through the bush, with Sweet Lips in his hand and Old Butch in his belt, until he got to the edge of the clearing where the Indians were lolling about stuffed with horsemeat. Keeping hidden in the grass, he lined up Sweet Lips and—bang!—the Comanches were one down. Before they located him, he dropped another, but then they saw the smoke and grabbing their bows, they came charging at him yelling and howling. Big-Foot had time to load his gun one more time, but this time he didn't fire. The last shot was for emergencies.

Instead, Big-Foot stood up. He was a very big man anyhow, and thickened with those hickory nuts he was a giant, swelled out like a

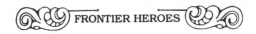

dead mule. The Indians stopped dead, not sure what monster they were attacking. But after a little while, they decided it was just Big-Foot himself, whom they had been half expecting, and they came on again, this time firing their arrows.

They were the best marksmen you could imagine. Every time one of them fired an arrow, it hit Big-Foot, or it should have done. What it actually hit was a hickory nut. It broke the shell and dropped to the ground. In a few minutes there were so many arrows at Big-Foot's feet that when he stepped on top of them he was three inches taller.

The Indians tried coming around from the side, and they came around the back, but the hickory nuts were on all sides too. They got shelled fast, but Big-Foot hardly felt a thing. Except now and then one hit a sensitive spot and tickled, so he had to laugh.

The Indians fired all their arrows, and their target was still standing there, and laughing at that. They stared at him with their eyes rolling and their tongues sticking out, then they turned and started running. They didn't stop 'till they got to the Rio Grande.

When they were out of sight, Big-Foot untied the strings around his wrists and ankles and let the hickory nuts fall out. There wasn't one that wasn't shelled. He made a bag out of the skin of the horse the Comanches had eaten and filled it with the nuts, because they are good for fattening hogs. Then he rode home with all his new horses, which the Comanches had left behind when they ran off.

Jim Bridger

Jim Bridger, also known as Old Gabe and as the "king of the mountain men," was born in Virginia in 1804. He moved west to Kansas as a boy and became a trapper and explorer before he was 18. He is said to have been the first white man to see the Great Salt Lake in Utah in 1824 and later the geysers of Yellowstone National Park. He learned to speak many Indian languages and he knew every tree in country where the only tracks were made by the wolves.

In his old age Jim moved back to civilization, in the shape of St. Louis, Missouri, where he was known as a great story-teller. None of Jim's stories was spoiled by sticking too close to ordinary facts. At Echo Canyon, he said, he never needed an alarm clock, because all he did was yell "Get up, Jim!" when he went to bed and eight hours later the echo woke him up. But like other great spinners of yarns, he used to complain people would believe him when he told them lies and called him a liar when he told the truth. When he described the hot geysers of Yellowstone, they said he was the damnedest liar that ever lived.

When the Union Pacific railroad was being built, they came to a stop in Denver wondering how the heck they were going to lay the track through the Rocky Mountains. Of course in those days Denver was just a small village. One of the settlers there suggested to the Union Pacific engineers they should ask Jim Bridger which was the bst pass for the railroad.

Jim was then an elderly man living in St. Louis, and they sent a request to him by the stage, asking him to come to Denver right away. They didn't say what for. A week or two later, Jim arrived and he asked what was so important he had to travel all the way from St. Louis to Denver. They told him their trouble, and Jim listened in silence, pulling on his old pipe. When they'd finished, he asked for a piece of paper, which he spread out on the table and drew a rough map. He put one finger on a certain spot on the map, then pointed at the horizon, where a peak showed up through the haze. "You fellows can take your railroad across there," he said, "and nowhere else, unless you want to be digging 'till kingdom come." He gazed at them and shook his head. "I could have told you that in St. Louis," he said. "Didn't have to come all this way."

The Survival of Hugh Glass

Some say it was Jim Bridger, when he was a young fellow, who played a part in the story of Hugh Glass, one of the most famous survival stories of the west.

Hugh Glass, a big man with a rough gray beard, was one of a party of trappers making their way along a tributary of the Missouri River looking for buffalo. Trappers and hunters usually like to work alone, or in pairs, but these men were in danger of attack from the Arickarees. They were led by a former army officer, Major Henry, but Glass, an independent-minded man, moved off into the bush on his own.

A little while later, dreadful screams were heard from some way ahead, down by the river. The trappers rushed toward the sound and, breaking through the bush, a terrible sight met their eyes. Looking for a sleepy old cow buffalo Hugh Glass had instead stumbled on a big sow grizzly, 1,000 pounds of angry animal, with two yearlng cubs. He never had a chance to get a shot at her. Her jaws and claws had done such terrible damage.

They shot the grizzly, but it looked like they had arrived too late to save Hugh Glass. Large chunks of his flesh had been torn off, he was covered in blood, and he was not moving. But he was alive. Just.

Now the trappers faced a difficult decision. It was clear to all that the injured man could not last long. But they could not abandon him while he was still alive, nor could they easily take him with them. The nearest place of shelter and security was nearly 300 miles away.

Major Henry asked for two volunteers to stay with the dying man, and give him a proper burial in due course. Every man stared at his feet. To stay even a few hours out in the wilderness with the Arickarees on the warpath was to invite the same fate as old Hugh. Besides, the trapping season was nearly over, and even a day lost meant a loss of valuable trapping time.

"Come on," said the Major. "It won't be more than a few hours."

At length one young fellow said he would stay. "How old are you?" the Major asked. "Nineteen," was the reply.

One older man said he would stay, too, if everyone in the party contributed $40 to compensate him for lost trapping time. This was agreed, and the rest of the party moved off.

Hugh Glass did not die as soon as expected. He was still alive the following day, although he could not speak nor move his legs. He lived, barely, all through that day and the next night. The two men took care of him as best they could, although at the same time they were hoping he would die soon.

Two more days went by and still old Hugh clung on to life. At length the older man said he was not going to stay any longer. Nothing could save Hugh, and it was sheer foolishness for three men to die instead of one. The younger fellow wasn't willing at first, but he was persuaded by the next day, when Hugh's pulse was so faint they couldn't tell easily if he were alive or dead. So they packed up their belongings, including Hugh Glass's rifle and equipment, and they left.

Still Hugh Glass hung on. He was delirious for a time, but then he got better and began to feel hungry. He knew this was a good sign. Dying men don't feel hunger.

He managed to crawl as far as the water and drink from his cupped hands. He found a few berries and roots to eat, and after a few more days he began to crawl. At first he made only a few yards a day, but soon he grew a little stronger. He found a piece of wood he could use as a crutch, and for the first time in many days he could stand upright. He managed to kill a rattlesnake with a stone, and ate it raw. Then he found the remains of a buffalo, killed by hunters or wolves, and there was some meat left on that, although it smelled bad. Now he could travel several miles a day, borne on by his hatred of the men who had left him to die in the wilderness without even his rifle or his knife.

Once he almost blundered right into an Arickaree hunting party, and had to lie still in the long grass all day until a breeze blew up at night to cover the sounds of his retreat. Once he crossed a river, clinging to one stone after another, flung about by the powerful current, swept downstream when his hold broke, but always getting closer to the further bank. Sometimes his wounds reopened, and he had to stop and staunch the flow of blood before he could move on again.

Winter was setting in when he finally reached the nearest trading post, about 300 miles from where he had been attacked by the grizzly. He spent the cold season there, and by the following spring he was almost a fit man again.

The day came when Hugh Glass finally caught up with Major Henry's hunting party. Of the two men who had left him to die, and had afterward reported him dead, only the younger one was present. That was just as well. For months Hugh Glass had killing on his mind. But it was the older man whom he hated, who had persuaded his younger partner to leave Glass, who had taken his kettle, his knife and, above all, his trusty rifle.

By this time, some of old Hugh's hard anger had drained away. When he came face to face with the boy who had deserted him, he found he had nothing to say to him. "I leave you to the punishment of God and your own conscience," he said. "If they forgive you, then so do I."

And the young fellow learned a lesson from it all. He became, in time, a more famous trapper than Hugh Glass, for the youngster's name was Jim Bridger.

As for the older man, some say Hugh Glass found him, too, and got his old rifle back. Some say he was killed by Indians before Glass caught up with him. Others say Glass himself was killed by Arickarees on the Platte River the following year.

Bill Williams

There were many Rocky Mountain men well known in their day if never so famous as Jim Bridger. One of these was Bill Williams, a big man with eyes as blue as the sky and hair as red as flames. I can't say there is a lot known for sure about Bill Williams, for he was a man who kept to himself. He was a strong man, a hard fighter and the kind who can start walking at dawn and still be going at sunset at just the same speed. Folks said he was an educated man, who knew Latin and Greek, and would talk to himself, or to his mustang, in some foreign language. Others said he was a crazy man, who was alone so much he could only talk to himself.

Bill Williams never cared for society, not white men's society that is. He spent many years living with the Osage Indians, married an Osage squaw and had two daughters by her. She was not the only wife Bill Williams had, however.

Some say Bill died when one of his wives shot him. But there is another story, which says that, like a good many other trappers, Bill just disappeared. He'd been seen leaving an encampment with his mustang and a string of mules and, well, he just wasn't seen again. After a time people stopped wondering where he'd got to and assumed he was dead, whether by accident or by Indians or by other means no one could tell. Then, well into the winter of that year, some trappers were pushing up high into the Rockies, higher than they'd been before, when they found old Bill's mustang, ragged and bony and on the verge of death from the cold. Bill had been so fond of that mustang—it was a sad sight.

They looked around a little farther, and weren't too surprised when they found Bill himself. He was sitting by the remains of a fire, half-covered with snow, his rifle by his side all rusted away and his elkskin coat stiff and nearly black. There was a ragged hole in it with a dark stain around it. No one could tell who—or what?—had killed him, nor how long his body had been sitting there frozen stiff.

The trappers buried him, as well as they could, and moved on. I don't know if anyone has visited that place since. I guess Bill Williams's bones are still there at any rate.

Mike Fink

Mike Fink "the last of the keelboatmen" was born in Pittsburgh in the days when it was still called Fort Pitt, about 1770. He became a scout in the Pennsylvania Rangers when he was 17, and later a boatman on the Ohio River. The Ohio and the Mississippi Rivers were the main highways in the development of the frontier. And the life of the boatmen, although it may seem pleasant enough in one way—drifting down the river in beautiful scenery with the sun warm on your back— was also very hard work when going upstream. The boat was moved by men pushing against poles, and it required great strength to keep it moving at all. After a day of this, the boatmen could only replenish their spirits with raw whiskey before flopping out to sleep on the deck. It is not surprising that this life bred a tough race of men, for whom violence was almost a way of life.

But by the 1820s, the steamboat had put the old boatmen out of work. Mike Fink joined a trapping expedition on the Missouri River, and died soon afterward.

Mike Fink was celebrated as the finest marksman with a rifle in North America. He was so good that he was barred from all shooting matches in Pennsylvania, and given a prize for not competing. He was also the roughest, toughest, rudest and crudest man in the west. Many of the legends about him are not very pleasant ones. Burying your wife in a pile of leaves and then setting them on fire to teach her not to make eyes at other men does not seem very funny to us. Nor does shooting off a man's heel just to show how good a shot you are. In figures like Davy Crockett or Big-Foot Wallace there is a good deal of humor and geniality, which balances the cruelty and violence. But Mike Fink, at least in legend, is a less amiable character. He is the kind of man you would walk a long way to avoid meeting.

— □ —

A Deer and an Indian with One Shot

The Pennsylvania Rangers were a body of irregulars who kept watch on hostile Indians in western Pennsylvania, often traveling 40 or 50 miles away from Pittsburgh on their scouting expeditions. Carrying little except a bag of dried corn and their rifles, they lived very like the Indians themselves, and conducted a kind of deadly guerilla warfare on the frontier.

Although he was little more than a boy when he joined them, Mike Fink soon gained a reputation as one of the most fearless and cunning. Many stories were told of his feats. This is one of them.

Mike had been out in the hills for some days when he noticed signs of Indians about. He discovered the fresh blood of a deer on some leaves and, casting about, he found prints of moccasins. He became more cautious than ever, skulking in the deepest thickets and not firing his rifle for several days, which meant he had to go without fresh meat. He lived on dried corn and a little "jerk"—dried meat from an earlier kill.

As he was creeping along one morning with the stealth of a cat, he caught sight of a fine buck browsing on the edge of an open space about 300 yards away. The temptation was too strong for him, and he decided to have a shot at it. He approached soundlessly, until he reached a spot where he could take aim. Just as he was about to raise his rifle, he saw an Indian approaching from a different direction, intent on the same buck. Mike slipped behind a tree, and kept an eye on the stalking Indian. When he was no more than 50 yards from Mike, the Indian stopped and leveled his gun at the deer. Mike aimed his at the Indian. An instant after the Indian fired—so close you could barely detect two shots—Mike fired too, and both deer and Indian fell dead.

Mike reloaded his rifle and remained where he was for some minutes in case there were more Indians in the area. Then he stepped over to make sure the man was dead, and finding he was, he began to cut up the deer.

———— □ ————

Shooting for a Cup

You remember the tale of William Tell and the apple which he shot from his son's head? You might have seen something like it on the banks of the Ohio River nearly 200 years ago, if you had been one of a party of British tourists who happened to come across Mike Fink when he was about to "shoot at the tin cup for a quart."

Followed by several of his crew, Mike led the way to a beech grove a little way from the landing. On arriving at the spot, a stout, bull-headed boatman, who might have been recognized as Mike's brother, drew a line in the ground with his toe and stepped off 30 yards. Then, turning around to face his brother, he put a tin cup on the top of his head. Even those who had seen this feat performed before felt a little uneasy, but the man said, "Blaze away, Mike, and let's have the quart."

Some of the tourists looked as though they would like to intervene, but Mike, bracing his legs apart, leveled his rifle at the head of his brother. For some seconds the weapon and Mike's arm remained so immovable it was hard to believe there was so much as a pulse beat in that arm.

Then came a sharp crack of the rifle, and the cup flew off 30 or 40 yards—rendered unfit for future service. There was a cry of admiration from the strangers, who pressed forward to see if the foolhardy boatman was safe. He remained as immovable as if he had been carved out of stone. He had not even winked when the ball struck the cup within two inches of his skull.

As for the boatmen, they acted as if nothing more than a common bet had been won, and they hurried back to the boat, giving the spectators an invitation to partake of the quart, which, however, was declined. A few minutes afterward, the keelboat could be seen wheeling into the current, the gigantic form of Mike Fink bestriding the steering oar and the others arranging themselves in their places.

— □ —

Fink vs. Crockett

Another story of Mike Fink's skill with a rifle also concerns Davy Crockett. It happened like this.

There are those who say Davy Crockett was never beaten in a contest with the rifle. Others say Mike Fink beat him. But did he? Well, judge for yourself.

Mike Fink was living in a little cabin at the head of the Cumberland River with a woman whom some say was his wife. One day he ran into Davy Crockett in the woods nearby, and invited him to sleep the night in his cabin. In the morning Mike announced, in his usual modest manner, "I've got the handsomest wife and the fastest horse and the sharpest shooting iron in all Kentucky, and if any man dare doubt it, I'll be in his hair quicker than hell can scorch a feather."

This kind of brag was a challenge, of course, and you can bet Crockett did not fail to answer it. "Well, Mike," he said, "your wife is a handsome woman, and Mrs. Crockett ain't here, and I haven't got any horses. But, although I don't care to say you are a liar, what you say about your rifle is not the truth and I will prove it."

They took a step outside and Crockett said, "Do you see that cat sitting on the rail of your potato patch?" It was about 150 yards away. "If he ever hears again, it'll be without ears."

Then Crockett blazed away and the ball cut off both the old tom cat's ears close to his head, and shaved the hair off across the skull as clean as a razor. The cat never stirred, and he never knew he'd lost his ears 'till he tried to scratch 'em. "Now, what was it you said about your rifle, Mike?" said Crockett.

"Do you see that sow over there with a litter of piglets around her?" was Mike's reply. It was about the same distance. Mike started shooting, reloading and firing for dear life, till he had shot off the tail on every one of those pigs. "Now," Mike said, "can you put them tails on again, Colonel?"

"That's impossible Mike," said Crockett, "but I see you have left one of 'em about an inch, and if it had been my work, I wouldn't have been so careless." Then he let fly and cut off the stump of tail, so close that tail might have been driven in with a hammer.

That made Mike a little mad. His wife came out at that moment with a gourd she was going to fill with water at the spring. Mike took a bead on her and shot off half the comb she was wearing on her head without stirring a single hair. "There you are, Colonel," said Mike, "I'd be obliged if you would remove the other half."

The woman stood still as a post. She was used to Mike's tricks by this time. But Crockett declined the challenge. "No, Mike," he said, "for the hand of Davy Crockett would surely shake if his shooting iron were pointed within a hundred yards of a woman. You win, Mike, and now let's have something to get the fog out of our throats and then we'll disperse."

□

Mike Fink, Bull-fighter

"I can out-run, out-shoot, out-brag, out-drink, an' out-fight any man on both sides of the river from Pittsburgh to New Orleans and back again to St. Louie."

That was Mike Fink. In his later days he once admitted losing a single contest—to a bull.

It was an awful hot day in August, and Mike was thinking he'd have a dip in the creek before he melted. There was a nice place for it at the bottom of Deacon Smith's meadow, so he went down there and got undressed in the bushes, pulling off the red shirt he always wore and thinking how scrumptious it would feel to be wallowing around in the water. He was just about to go in when he saw the deacon's brindle bull making a beeline for him.

This old bull had scared more people in the parish than all the deacon's talk of hellfire, and come near killing a few. Mike knew him well, and the bull knew Mike. He was pawing the ground as though he were digging Mike's grave.

Mike had no time to get his clothes on and reckoned he'd have to try the varmint naked. "Come on, you bellowin' old heathen," he said, "don't be just a-standing there, for as the old deacon says of the Devil, 'you are not comely to look upon'."

The bull charged at Mike and Mike slipped aside so he went straight past him. Then it was about-face for another charge. Mike dodged him again, but he came near to driving his big horns into Mike's bowels, so Mike thought he'd better try something else.

The next time the bull charged, Mike grabbed a hold of his tail, and he swore he wouldn't let go till the bull's tail came adrift from his backbone. The bull stopped to get his wind, and Mike judged him to be thinking up something devilish by the way he stared. He didn't want to shout for help. It was against his principles, for one thing, and he didn't want the deacon and his whole congregation to come down and see him in this dreadful predicament.

Then the bull set off. He dragged Mike over every briar and stump in the field until he was sweating and bleeding like a fat bear with a pack of hounds at his heels. They went so fast, Mike and the tail were sometimes strung out in a straight line behind the bull.

By and by he slackened off a little, and Mike got himself lodged behind a stump. "Now," he said, "you can pull up this here oak, or you can break your tail—or you can hold on while I get my wind."

Well, Mike couldn't figure out how he was going to get out of this, so, looking at the question from every viewpoint, he came to the conclusion that he'd better let someone know where he was. He let out a yell louder than a locomotive whistle, and in half a minute he saw the deacon's two dogs coming down as if they were in a race.

This was no help at all. Mike knew well enough those dogs would be on the side of the bull, for they were awful venomous and had a spite against him.

Riding is as cheap as walking, Mike decided, and he leapt on top of the bull's back. The bull took off again, faster than before, with Mike sitting astride and the two dogs snapping at his feet on either side.

They went on in this way about an hour, when the old bull thought it was time to stop and take a breath or two. He happened to stop under a tree. "Now," said Mike, "this is where you lose a passenger," and he grabbed a branch above his head and hauled himself up into the tree. He calculated he'd roost up there 'till he starved rather than ride around on the bull any longer.

But when he started climbing up, he changed his mind. He heard an awful buzzing overhead, and looked up to see the biggest hornet's nest ever built. It struck him that he'd have a better chance on board the bull, so he said, "Hold on old fellow, I guess I'll ride to the next station."

Off they went again, this time with the hornets after them. Some of them went for the dogs, about quarter struck Mike, and the rest were after the bull. The dogs led the way, streaking for the deacon's house, Mike and the bull came next, and the hornets directly after.

They were about 200 yards from the house when the deacon heard them and came out. He took one look, raised his hands, and turned white. Then the whole congregation come out after him, and all hands went to yelling.

They thought they were seeing an apparition. They didn't realize that Mike Fink and the bull were not one creature, until the bull came up against a fence and stopped short so Mike was pitched over his head. Until then, all thought that Mike and the bull belonged together. But when the old bull walked off by himself, they saw how things were, and one of them said, "Mike Fink has got the worst of the scrimmage for once in his life."

—— □ ——

The Death of Mike Fink

There are many legends about how Mike Fink met his death. This one was told by a man who claimed to have known him.

After the steamboats took over on the Mississippi, Mike Fink took a job with the Mountain Fur Company, at St. Louis, and he went as a trapper and hunter to the fort at the mouth of the Yellowstone River, which was commanded by Major Henry. But by this time Mike was getting on in years, and he had become a slave to drink. Whiskey wasn't allowed in the trading posts along the Missouri, and that was a sore grievance to Mike. He was known to march into the fort and demand whiskey, and when he was not given it, he drilled a hole through the cask with his rifle and walked up to help himself to the spirits as they leaked out.

Time went by and Mike's behavior did not improve. The state of relations between him and Major Henry was not good, but most of the other trappers began to lose patience with Mike, too. In the end he left the fort and made himself a cave in the river bank, and there he spent the winter. He had a plentiful supply of whiskey, and he didn't seem to need much else.

What he did need was brought to him by his one companion. This was a young man named Carpenter, whom Mike had raised from a child. Some said he was Mike's own child, but most likely he was not.

As the months passed, with Mike hardly leaving his cave and not getting any more pleasant, relations between him and Carpenter soured a little. There were some in the fort who tried to get the youngster to leave Mike, saying he was a bad influence on the boy.

In the spring, things improved a little, as they usually do. Mike and Carpenter had a bit of a frolic up in the fort, which, said Mike, was a skunk-hole and he'd rather live with the bears. Something was said between the two of them, which seemed to show that Mike was a little sore at the youngster whom, he said, he loved like his own cub. But it wasn't anything too bad, because they went on drinking together. After a while, Mike filled up his can, walked 30 or 40 yards, and told Carpenter to take his rifle. This shooting of cans off heads was a favorite with Mike, as we know. Maybe Mike proposed it this time to show that, whatever had been said, he still trusted Carpenter.

Carpenter was as drunk as a skunk, but then so were most of the others. He snatched up his rifle, leveled it at Mike, and fired. The can flew off his head and a few cheers were heard. But not from Mike. He was standing dead still with kind of a staring look on his face that wasn't pleasant to see.

It seemed the ball had grazed the top of Mike's head, just breaking the scalp, and the thought of treachery was in his mind.

Meanwhile Carpenter, still laughing, had put a can on his own head and was telling Mike to fire, if he knew how.

"I taught you to shoot differently from that last shot," Mike growled. "You *missed*, but you won't ever miss again." Then he fired, and the ball hit Carpenter in the very center of his forehead.

Afterward, Mike went back to his cave. There he skulked, speaking to no one, and only coming out once in a while to hang around the grave of his boy, whom he'd killed—by accident or design no one rightly knew.

There was a lot of talk up at the fort, naturally. A man by the name of Talbott was particularly hot against Mike, calling him a murderer, who had killed the youngster because he was jealous of his youth. Mike got to hear of this, and he swore that he would take the life of Talbott for those words.

But time went by and these words were almost forgotten when one day Mike came into the fort. Talbott, who was sitting mending a rifle, saw him coming. Mike looked old, and ill, and thin, and there was no look of violence about him. But he was carrying his rifle, as he always did, and Talbott was not a brave man.

He snatched up a pair of pistols and shouted. "Fink, if you come three steps nearer, I'll fire!"

"Talbott," Mike answered in a weary voice, "you needn't fear me. I've come to talk about Carpenter, my boy—"

But Talbott was feeling mighty nervous, and he repeated his warning. "Three steps nearer, and I'll fire!"

Mike was carrying his rifle across his arm, not like he was getting ready to use it. "You've accused me of murdering my boy that I raised from a child, but I couldn't have done that. I'd rather have died than done it..."

But he kept on walking. One, two, three—and Talbott fired both pistols into his chest. Before he died, he whispered, "I didn't mean to kill my boy."

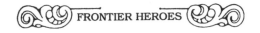

The Haunted Barrel

A man who made good use of the stories of the Mississippi in the old frontier days was Samuel Clemens, better known as the writer Mark Twain. He grew up on the banks of the river at Hannibal, Missouri, and turned his own adventurous boyhood into his stories of Huck Finn and Tom Sawyer. There are more tales, some true, some "tall," in his book, *Life on the Mississippi*. Here are some examples.

"In the heyday of the steamboats, the river from end to end was flanked with coal fleets and timber rafts, all managed by hand, and employing hosts of the rough characters whom I have tried to describe. I remember the annual processions of mighty rafts that used to glide by Hannibal when I was a boy—an acre or so of white sweet-smelling boards on each raft, a crew of two dozen men or more, three or four wigwams scattered about the raft's vast level space for storm-quarters—and I remember the rude ways and the tremendous talk of their big crews, the ex-keelboatmen and their successors..."

As an example of this "tremendous talk," here is a Mississippi boatman spoiling for a fight.

"Whoop—oop! I'm the old original iron-jawed, brass-mounted copper-bellied corpse-maker from the wilds of Arkansaw! Look at me! I'm the man they call Sudden Death and General Desolation! Fathered by a hurricane, mothered by an earthquake, half-brother to the cholera, nearly related to the smallpox on my mother's side! Look at me! I take nine alligators and a barrel of whiskey for breakfast when I'm in robust health, and a bushel of rattesnakes and a dead body when I'm ailing. I split the everlasting rocks with my glance, and I squench the thunder when I speak! Whoo—oop! Stand back and give me room according to my strength! Blood's my natural drink, and the wails of the dying is music to my ear. Cast your eye on me, gentlemen! And lay low and hold your breath, for I'm about to turn myself loose!"

Here is one of Mark Twain's raftsmen with a strange tale to tell.

"Five years ago I was on a big raft, and right along here it was a bright moonshiny night, and I was on watch and boss of the starboard oar forrard, and one of my pards was a man named Dick Allbright, and he come along to where I was sitting, forrard—yawning and stretching he was—and stooped down on the edge of the raft and washed his face in the river, and come and set down by me and got out his pipe, and had just got it filled, when he looks up and says:

"'Why, looky here,' he says, 'ain't that Buck Miller's place over yonder in the bend?'

"'Yes,' says I, 'it is—why?'

"He laid his pipe down and leaned his head on his hand, and says: 'I thought we'd be further down,' he says.

"'I thought it too, when I went off watch'—we was standing six hours on and six off—'but the boys told me,' I says, 'that the raft didn't seem to hardly move for the last hour,' says I, 'though she's a-slipping along all right now,' says I.

"He gave a kind of groan, and says, 'I've seen a raft act so before, along here,' he says, 'appears to me the current has most quit above the head of this bend during the last two years,' he says.

"Well, he raised up two or three times, and looked away off and around on the water. That started me at it too. A body is always doing what he sees somebody else doing, though there mayn't be no sense in it. Pretty soon I see a black something floating on the water away off to starboard and quartering behind us. I see he was looking at it too. So I says, 'What's that?'

"He says, sort of pettish, 'Tain't nothing but an old empty barrel.'

"'An empty barrel!' says I, 'Why,' says I, 'a spy-glass is a fool to *your* eyes. How can you tell it's an empty barrel?'

"He says, 'I don't know. I reckon it ain't a barrel, but I thought it might be,' says he.

"'Yes,' I says, 'so it might be, and it might be anything else, too. A body can't tell nothing about it, such a distance as that,' I says.

"We hadn't nothing else to do, so we kept on watching it. By and by I says, 'Why, looky here, Dick Allbright, that thing's a-gaining on us, I believe.'

"He never said nothing. The thing gained and gained, and I judged it must be a dog that was about tired out. Well, we swung down into the crossing, and the thing floated across the bright streak of the moonshine, and by George, it *was* a barrel.

"Says I, 'Dick Allbright, what made you think that thing was a barrel, when it was half a mile off?' says I.

"Says he, 'I don't know.'

"Says I, 'You tell me, Dick Allbright.'

"Says, he, 'Well, I know'd it was a barrel. I've seen it before. Lots has seen it, they call it a haunted barrel.'

"I called the rest of the watch, and they come and stood there and I told them what Dick said. It floated right along abreast now and didn't gain any more. It was about twenty foot off. Some was for having it aboard, but the rest didn't want to. Dick Allbright said rafts that had fooled with it had got bad luck by it. The captain of the watch said he didn't believe in it. He said he reckoned the barrel gained on us because it was in a little better current than what we was. He said it would leave by and by.

"So then we went on talking about other things, and we had a song, and then a breakdown, and soon after that the captain of the watch called for another song. But it was clouding up now, and the barrel stuck right there in the same place, and the song didn't seem to have much warm-up to it somehow, and so they didn't finish it, and there weren't any cheers, but it sort of dropped flat, and nobody said anything for a minute. Then everybody tried to talk at once, and one chap got off a joke, but it weren't no use, they didn't laugh, and even the chap that made the joke didn't laugh at it, which ain't usual. We all just settled down glum, and watched the barrel, and was uneasy and uncomfortable. Well, sir, it shut down black and still, and then the wind began to moan around, and next the lightning began to play and the thunder to grumble. And pretty soon there was a regular storm, and in the middle of it a man that was running aft stumbled and fell and sprained his ankle so that he had to lay up. This made the boys shake their heads. And every time the lightning come, there was that barrel, with the blue lights winking around it. We was always on the lookout for it. But by and by, toward dawn, she was gone. When the day come we couldn't see her anywhere, and we weren't sorry, either.

"But next night about half past nine, when there was songs and high jinks going on, here she comes again, and took her old roost on the starboard side. There weren't no more high jinks. Everybody got solemn. Nobody talked. You couldn't get anybody to do anything but set around moody and look at the barrel. It began to cloud up again. When the watch changed, the off watch stayed up, instead of turning in. The storm ripped and roared around all night, and in the middle of it another man tripped and sprained his ankle, and had to knock off. The barrel left toward day, and nobody saw it go.

"Everybody was sober and down in the mouth all day. I don't mean the kind of sober that comes of leaving liquor alone—not that. They was quiet, but they all drunk more than usual—not together, but each man sidled off and took it privately, by himself.

"After dark, the off watch didn't turn in, nobody sang, nobody talked.

The boys sort of huddled together, forrard, and for two hours they sat there perfectly still, looking steady in the one direction, and heaving a sigh once in a while. And then, here comes the barrel again. She took up her old place. She stayed there all night—nobody turned in. The storm came on again after midnight. The captain ordered the watch to man the sweeps aft and nobody would go—no more sprained ankles for them, they said. They wouldn't even *walk* aft. Well then, just then the sky split wide open, with a crash, and the lightning killed two men of the after watch, and crippled two more. Crippled them how? Why, sprained their ankles!

"The barrel left in the dark betwixt lightnings, toward dawn. Well, not a body ate a bite at breakfast that morning. After that the men loafed around in twos and threes, and talked low together. But none of them herded with Dick Allbright. They all give him the cold shake. If he come around where any of the men was, they split up and sidled away.

"After night come, you could see pretty plain that there was going to be trouble if that barrel come again. There was such a muttering going on. A good many wanted to kill Dick Allbright, because he'd seen the barrel on other trips, and that had an ugly look. Some wanted to put him ashore. Some said, 'Let's all go ashore in a pile if the barrel comes again.'

"This kind of whispers was still going on when, lo and behold, here comes the barrel again. Down she comes, slow and steady, and settles into her old tracks. You could have heard a pin drop. Then up comes the captain, and says. 'Boys, don't be a pack of children and fools. I don't want this barrel to be dogging us all the way to Orleans, and *you* don't. Well then, how's the best way to stop it? Burn it—that's the way. I'm going to fetch it aboard,' he says. And before anybody could say a word, in he went.

"He swum to it, and as he come pushing it to the raft, the men spread to one side. But the old man got it aboard and busted in the head, and there was a baby in it! Yes sir, a stark naked baby. It was Dick Allbright's baby; he owned up and said so.

"'Yes,' he says, a-leaning over it, 'yes, it is my own lamented darling, my poor lost Charles William Allbright deceased,' says he—for he could curl his tongue around the bulliest words in the language when he was of a mind to 'Yes,' he said, he used to live up at the head of this bend, and one night he choked his child, which was crying, not intending to kill it—which was probably a lie—and then he was scared, and buried it in a barrel, before his wife got home, and this was the third year that the barrel had chased him.

"He said the bad luck always begun light, and lasted till four men were killed, and then the barrel didn't come any more after that. He said if the men would stand it one more night—and was a-going on like that—but the men had got enough. They started to get out a boat to take him ashore and lynch him, but he grabbed the little child all of a sudden and jumped overboard with it, hugged up to his breast and shedding tears, and we never seen him again in this life, poor old suffering soul, nor Charles William neither."

The great danger for boats navigating the Mississippi in the days of the old paddle steamers was of going aground. To prevent this, a man sounded the bottom with a lead weight at the end of a rope, which was marked to show the depth of water. He called out the soundings to the pilot in a kind of chant. As the boat moved from deep into shallow water, the leadsman's chant would go like this:

"No bottom—Mark four—Quarter less four—Quarter less five—Half twain—Quarter twain—Quarter less four—Half twain—Quarter twain—Mark twain—Quarter less twain—Nine feet—Eight and a half feet."

It was from the call of the leadsmen on the Mississippi boats that Samuel Clemens took his pen name, Mark Twain. The next story is also by him.

Huck, Tom, and the Murderer

In this extract, which comes from *The Adventures of Tom Sawyer* (1876), Mark Twain recounts an episode in the lives of Tom and his friend Huckleberry Finn; an incident which, like the rest of the book, is a reflection of his own boyhood in Hannibal, Missouri, and of the legends which flourished there at that time.

At half-past nine that night, Tom and Sid were sent to bed as usual. They said their prayers, and Sid was soon asleep. Tom lay awake and waited in restless impatience. When it seemed to him that it must be nearly daylight, he heard the clock strike 10! This was despair. He would have tossed and fidgeted, as his nerves demanded, but he was afraid he might wake Sid. So he lay still and stared up into the dark. Everything was dismally still.

By-and-by, out of the stillness little scarcely perceptible noises began to emphasize themselves. The ticking of the clock began to bring itself into notice. Old beams began to crack mysteriously. The stairs creaked faintly. Evidently spirits were abroad. A measured, muffled snore issued from Aunt Polly's chamber. And now the tiresome chirping of a cricket that no human ingenuity could locate, began. Next the ghastly ticking of a death-watch in the wall at the bed's head made Tom shudder—it meant that somebody's days were numbered. Then the howl of a far-off dog rose on the night air and was answered by a fainter howl from a remoter distance. Tom was in an agony. At last he was satisfied that time had ceased and eternity begun; he began to doze in spite of himself; the clock chimed 11, but he did not hear it. And then there came, mingling with his half-formed dreams, a most melancholy caterwauling. The raising of a neighboring window disturbed him. A cry of "Scat! You devil!" and the crash of an empty bottle against the back of his aunt's woodshed brought him wide awake, and a single minute later he was dressed and out of the window and creeping along the roof of the "ell" on all fours. He "meow'd" with caution once or twice as he went; then jumped to the roof of the woodshed, and thence to the ground. Huckleberry Finn was there, with his dead cat. The boys moved off and disappeared in the gloom. At the end of half-an-hour they were wading through the tall grass of the graveyard.

It was a graveyard of the old-fashioned western kind. It was on a hill, about a mile and a half from the village. It had a crazy board fence around it, which leaned inward in places, and outward the rest of the time, but stood upright nowhere. Grass and weeds grew rank over the whole cemetery. All the old graves were sunken in. There was not a tombstone on the place, round-topped worm-eaten boards staggered over the graves, leaning for support and finding none. "Sacred to the memory of" so-and-so had been painted on them once, but it could no longer have been read, on the most of them, now, even if there had been light.

A faint wind moaned through the trees, and Tom feared it might be the spirits of the dead complaining at being disturbed. The boys talked little, and only under their breath, for the time and the place and the pervading solemnity and silence oppressed their spirits. They found the sharp new heap they were seeking, and ensconced themselves within the protection of three great elms that grew in a bunch within a few feet of the grave.

Then they waited in silence for what seemed a long time. The hooting of a distant owl was all the sound that troubled the dead stillness. Tom's reflections grew oppressive. He must force some talk. So he said in a whisper:

"Hucky, do you believe the dead people like it for us to be here?"

Huckleberry whispered:

"I wisht I knowed. It's awful solemn like, ain't it?"

"I bet it is."

There was a considerable pause, while the boys canvassed this matter inwardly. Then Tom whispered:

"Say, Hucky—do you reckon Hoss Williams hears us talking?"

"O' course he does. Least his spirit does."

Tom, after a pause:

"I wish I'd said *Mister* Williams. But I never meant any harm. Everybody calls him Hoss."

"A body can't be too particular how they talk 'bout these yer dead people, Tom."

This was a damper, and conversation died again. Presently Tom seized his comrade's arm and said:

"*Sh!*"

"What is it, Tom?" And the two clung together with beating hearts.

"*Sh!* There 'tis again! Didn't you hear it?"

"I—"

"There! Now you hear it!"

"Lord, Tom, they're coming! They're coming, sure. What'll we do?"

"I dono. Think they'll see us?"

"Oh, Tom, they can see in the dark the same as cats. I wish I hadn't come."

"Oh, don't be afeard. I don't believe they'll bother us. We ain't doing any harm. If we keep perfectly still, maybe they won't notice us at all."

"I'll try to, Tom, but Lord, I'm all of a shiver."

"Listen!"

The boys bent their heads together ad scarcely breathed. A muffled sound of voices floated up from the far end of the graveyard.

"Look! see there!" whispered Tom. "What is it?"

"It's devil-fire. Oh, Tom, this is awful"

Some vague figures approached through the gloom, swinging an old-fashioned tin lantern that treckled the ground with innumerable little spangles of light. Presently Huckleberry whispered with a shudder:

"It's the devils, sure enough. Three of 'em! Lordy, Tom, we're goners! Can you pray?"

"I'll try, but don't you be afeard. They ain't going to hurt us. 'Now I lay me down to sleep, I—'"

"Sh!"

"What is it, Huck?"

"They're *humans!* One of 'em is, anyway. One of 'em's old Muff Potter's voice."

"No—'tain't so, is it?"

"I bet I know it. Don't you stir nor budge. He ain't sharp enough to notice us. Drunk, same as usual, likely—blamed old rip!"

"All right, I'll keep still. Now they're stuck. Can't find it. Here they come again. Now they're hot. Cold again. Hot again. Red hot! They're pointed right, this time. Say, Huck, I know another o' them voices; it's Injun Joe."

"That's so—that muderin half-breed! I'd druther they was Devils a dern sight. What kin they be up to?"

The whispers died wholly out now, for the three men had reached the grave, and stood within a few feet of the boys' hiding-place.

"Here it is," said the third voice; and the owner of it held the lantern up and revealed the face of young Dr. Robinson.

Potter and Injun Joe were carrying a handbarrow with a rope and a couple of shovels on it. They cast down their load and began to open the grave. The doctor put the lantern at the head of the grave, and came and sat down with his back against one of the elm-trees. He was so close the boys could have touched him.

"Hurry, men!" he said in a low voice. "The moon might come out at any moment."

They growled a response and went on digging. For some time there was no noise but the grating sound of the spades discharging their freight of mold and gravel. It was very monotonous. Finally a spade struck upon the coffin with a dull, woody accent, and within another minute or two the men had hoisted it out on the ground. They prised off the lid with their shovels, got out the body and dumped it rudely on the ground. The moon drifted from behind the clouds and exposed the pallid face. The barrow was got ready and the corpse place on it, covered with a blanket, and bound to its place with the rope. Potter took out a large spring-knife and cut off the dangling end of the rope, and then said:

"Now the cussed thing's ready, Sawbones, and you'll just out with another five, or here she stays."

"That's the talk!" said Injun Joe.

"Look here; what does this mean?" said the doctor. "You required your pay in advance and I've paid you."

"Yes, and you done more than that" said Injun Joe, approaching the doctor, who was now standing. "Five year ago you drove me away from your father's kitchen one night when I came to ask for something to eat, and you said I weren't there for any good; and when I swore I'd get even with you if it took a hundred years, your father had me jailed for a vagrant. Did you think I'd forget? The Injun blood ain't in me for nothing. And now I've got you, and you got to *settle*, you know!"

He was threatening the doctor with his fist in his face by this time. The doctor struck out suddenly, and stretched the ruffian on the ground. Potter dropped his knife, and exclaimed:

"Here, now, don't you strike my pard!" and the next moment he had grappled with the doctor, and the two were struggling with might and main, trampling the grass, and tearing the ground with their heels. Injun Joe sprang to his feet, his eyes flaming with passion, snatched up Potter's knife, and went creeping, catlike, and stooping round and round about the combatants, seeking an opportunity. All at once the doctor flung himself free, seized the heavy headboard of William's grave and felled Potter to the earth with it; and in the same instant the half-breed saw his chance, and drove the knife to the hilt in the young man's breast. He reeled and fell partly upon Potter, flooding him with his blood, and in the same moment the clouds blotted out the dreadful spectacle, and the two frightened boys went speeding away in the dark.

Presently, when the moon emerged again, Injun Joe was standing over the two forms, contemplating them. The doctor murmured inarticulately, gave a long gasp or two, and was still. The half-breed muttered:

"That score is settled, damn you."

Then he robbed the body. After which he put the fatal knife in Potter's open right hand, and sat down on the dismantled coffin. Three—four—five minutes passed, and then Potter began to stir and moan. His hand closed upon the knife, he raised it, glanced at it, and let it fall with a shudder. Then he sat up, pushing the body from him, and gazed at it and then around him confusedly. His eyes met Joe's.

"Lord, how is this, Joe?" he said.

"It's a dirty business," said Joe, without moving.

"What did you do it for?"

"I! I never done it!"

"Look here! that kind of talk won't wash."

Potter trembled and grew white.

"I thought I'd got sober. I'd no business to drink tonight. But it's in my head yet—worse'n when we started here. I'm all in a muddle; can't recollect anything of it hardly. Tell me, Joe—*honest*, now, old feller—did I do it, Joe? I never meant to; 'pon my soul and honor I never meant to, Joe. Tell me how it was, Joe. Oh, it's awful—and him being so young and promising."

"Why, you two was scuffling, and he fetched you one with the headboard, and you fell flat; and then up you come, all reeling and staggering like, and snatched the knife and jammed it into him just as he fetched you another awful clip, and here you've laid dead as a wedge 'till now."

"Oh, I didn't know what I was doing. I wish I may die this minute if I did. It was all on accounts of the whiskey and the excitement, I reckon. I never used a weapon in my life before, Joe. I've fought, but never with weapons. They'll all say that. Joe, don't tell! Say you won't tell, Joe; that's a good feller. I always liked you, Joe, and stood up for you too. Don't you remember? You won't tell, will you, Joe?" And the poor creature dropped on his knees before the stolid murderer, and clasped his appealing hands.

"No, you've always been fair and square with me, Muff Potter, and I won't go back on you. There, now, that's as fair as a man can say."

"Oh, Joe, you're an angel. Ill bless you for this the longest day I live," And Potter began to cry.

"Come, now, that's enough of that. This ain't any time for blubbering. You be off yonder way and I'll go this. Move, now, and don't leave any tracks behind you."

Potter started on a trot that quickly increased to a run. The half-breed stood looking after him. He muttered:

"If he's as much stunned with the lick and fuddled with the rum as he had the look of being, he won't think of the knife 'till he's gone so far he'll be afraid to come back after it to such a place by himself—chicken-heart!"

Two or three minutes later the murdered man, the blanketed corpse, the lidless coffin, and the open grave, were under no inspection but the moon's. The stillness was complete again, too.

Engineers
and
Steelmen

Casey Jones

The Ballad of Casey Jones is probably the most famous of the many ballads of the railroads. It tells of the fatal last run of the engineer Casey Jones, in a locomotive carrying the western mail and running eight hours late. His effort to arrive on time ends in a terrible head-on collision with another train. There are several versions of the ballad, both words and music, and no one can say for certain who wrote it or when, though the most likely author was a black railroad worker named Wallace Saunders.

The story is probably based on a real crash which took place on the Chicago-to-New Orleans run of the *Cannonball Express* in 1900. The name of the engineer killed in that crash was John Luther Jones, who was born in Cayce, Kentucky, from which (it is said) he got the nickname "Casey."

—— ▢ ——

Come all you rounders for I want you to hear
The story of a brave engineer;
Casey Jones was the fellow's name,
A big eight-wheeler of a mighty fame.
Caller called Casey at half-past four,
He kissed his wife at the station door,
Mounted to the cabin with orders in his hand,
And took his farewell trip to the promised land.
  Casey Jones, he mounted to the cabin,
  Casey Jones, with his orders in his hand!
  Casey Jones, he mounted to the cabin,
  Took his farewell trip into the promised land.

Put in your water and shovel in your coal,
Put your head out the window, watch the drivers roll,
I'll run her 'till she leaves the rail,
'Cause we're eight hours late with the western mail!
He looked at his watch and his watch was slow,
Looked at the water and the water was low,
Turned to his fireboy and said,
'We'll get to 'Frisco, but we'll all be dead!' (*Chorus*)

Casey pulled up Reno Hill,
Tooted for the crossing with an awful shrill,
Snakes all knew by the engine's moans
That the hogger at the throttle was Casey Jones.
He pulled up short two miles from the place,
Number Four stared him right in the face,
Turned to his fireboy, said 'You'd better jump,
'Cause there's two locomotives going to bump!' (*Chorus*)

Casey said, just before he died,
"There's two more roads I'd like to ride."
Fireboy said, "What can they be?"
"The Rio Grande and the Old S.P."
Mrs. Jones sat on her bed a-sighing,
Got a pink that Casey was dying,
Said, "Go to bed, children; hush your crying,
'Cause you'll get another papa on the Salt Lake line."
  Casey Jones! Got another papa!
  Casey Jones, on the Salt Lake Line!
  Casey Jones! Got another papa!
  Got another papa on the Salt Lake Line!

John Henry, the Steel-Driving Man

John Henry is surely one of the greatest heroes in North American legend—the man who fought the machine and won, but gave up his life in the process. The "real" John Henry has long been lost in legend. There are stories about him in which he becomes a supernatural "superhero" of the Paul Bunyan type, which is a pity in a way. For John Henry was a *natural* man.

He is also one of the first black American folk heroes who was a hero of all men and all races and was neither a criminal nor an amiable idiot.

When John Henry went to work on the Big Bend Tunnel of the Chesapeake and Ohio Railroad, he told the captain (foreman), "I is bigger and stronger than any man working in the Big Bend Tunnel. Bring me a twelve-pound hammer and get me a shaker, and stand out of my way, 'cause I can drive more steel than any nine men at work in this here tunnel."

The captain thought he was bragging, until he saw John Henry at work. Then he had to admit John Henry was the best steel-driving man he had ever seen.

The job of the men in the Big Bend Tunnel in West Virginia was to drive long steel rods deep into the rock. When the holes were made, explosives were sunk in them and the explosion dislodged a mass of rock. It was a job that took great strength, but also rhythm. When he was at work, John Henry would sing as he swung his hammer:

> Oh, my hammer (BANG!)
> Sounds like silver (BANG!)
> Yes, my hammer (BANG!)
> Sounds like silver (BANG!)
> Oh, my hammer (BANG!)
> Sounds like silver (BANG!)
> It feels like gold (BANG!)
> Yes, it feels like gold (BANG!)

The captain was mighty pleased when he saw how John Henry was a natural-born steel-driving man, and John Henry went to work in the Big Bend Tunnel. The company gave him $4 a day and a house and vittles for himself and pretty Polly Anne, John Henry's loving wife. And John Henry said to his captain, "When you next go to town, get me two twenty pound hammers, so I can hear that steel ring."

It was hard work in the tunnel. The dust from the hard rock and the smoke from the lamp were so thick that a man couldn't see his own feet, when he looked down. It was hot too, and dark, and dirty. But John Henry could sink a hole quicker than nine men. He could sink it down, or sideways or any way, in soft rock or in hard—made no difference. When he was swinging those 20-pound hammers, one in each hand, the whole mountain seemed to ring.

Then one day a man came along who was trying to sell a new-fangled machine called a steam drill. He had pictures of his machine in a book, and he showed 'em to the captain. "This here steam drill," he said, "will drill holes faster than any twenty men, and it don't have to stop and rest. It will save you a heap of money."

The captain was not too eager to buy, but the salesman was a slick-talking fellow, and in the end the captain said, "I'll tell you what we'll do. You bring your machine and set it going', an we'll set it against John Henry, for he is the best steel-driving man in the world."

"I heard about John Henry," the man said, "and I know he is good. But he ain't but a man, and this machine of mine can't be beat by a man."

Then the captain went to John Henry and asked him if he would take on the race with the steam drill for a bonus of $100. John Henry said he would race that machine and he would beat it. For if he did not, then he and a whole lot of others would be out of work. "Yes, sir," said John Henry, "before I let that steam drill beat me down, I'll die with my hammer in my hand."

The people came from miles around to see John Henry race the steam drill. The race was held outside the tunnel so they all could see. The steam drill was on the right-hand side, and John Henry was on the left. The blacksmiths had sharpened piles of drills, and the carriers were ready, with pads on their backs, to carry the sharpened steels from the shop and the dull ones back to be sharpened. The machine had got up steam in its boiler, and John Henry picked up his hammer. The captain blew a whistle, and the race began.

Then John Henry swung his hammer, and he said to his shaker (the man who holds the steel rods), "Bill, you'd better pray, 'cause if I miss this piece of steel, tomorrow will be your buryin' day."

The steam drill started pounding and John Henry started swinging, and pretty soon he was ahead. The salesman wasn't worried, though. "That's a mighty man," he said, "but when he hits the hard rock he'll weaken."

When they reached the hard rock, John Henry kept driving as fast as before, and the salesman said, "That's a mighty man, but he can't keep it up. He'll start to weaken soon, and the steam drill won't. My machine don't feel no pain, no weariness in the bones."

John Henry showed no sign of weakening. He swung his hammer in a steady rhythm, and he sang as he drove the steel, and the steel sounded like silver. He stopped just a moment about once an hour to take a drink that Polly Anne brought him in a dipper. One hour, two hours, three hours, four hours... The shaker was worn out and another man had to take over, but John Henry kept driving that steel.

Six hours, seven hours, eight hours... John Henry was still going strong, and the rhythm of his swing was the same as at the start.

In the last hour, John Henry began to show signs that he was tired, and the captain came and asked him how he was doing. "This rock is hard," John Henry said, "this steel is tough, this hammer is heavy, but before I let that steam drill beat me down, I'll die with my hammer in my hand."

John Henry stopped singing. He was having trouble keeping time. The ring of the hammer on the steel was not so loud, and the chugging of the steam drill was louder.

At the end of the ninth hour, the captain blew his whistle. The race was over. The hammer was still, the steam drill was silent. It was so quiet you could hear the crunch of the captain's boots as he went to look at the result. Then he said, loud so the crowd could hear, "John Henry has won—three holes more than the steam drill!"

A mighty cheer went up. The steel-driving men flung their hats in the air, for they did not love that steam drill any more than John Henry did.

Then everyone grew quiet all of a sudden. For they saw John Henry lying on the ground. Polly Anne was holding his head and giving him a drink of water from the dipper, and she was crying. His eyes were shut, but those nearby could just hear him say, "Before I let that steam drill beat me down, I'll die with my hammer in my hand."

They buried John Henry on the mountain, with a hammer in his hand and a steel rod across his breast. For John Henry was a steel-driving man.

Everyone knows the ballad of John Henry, of which there are several versions (two verses are printed on the following page).

John Henry told his captain,
A man ain't nothing but a man,
But before I let that steam drill beat me down,
I'll die with my hammer in my hand,
O Lord!
I'll die with my hammer in my hand.

Well, every Monday morning,
When the bluebirds begin to sing,
You can hear those hammers ring a mile or more,
You can hear John Henry's hammer ring,
O Lord!
You can hear John Henry's hammer ring.

Joe Baldwin's Lamp

Many of the great railroad legends are about train wrecks. *Joe Baldwin's Lamp* also begins with a train wreck, but it turns out to be something else as well.

In the early days of railroads, there was a small line that ran through Wilmington, North Carolina, westward, toward Augusta, Georgia, although at that time it did not go so far. As you know, a lot of that is swamp country and building the railroad wasn't easy. Still they built it, although the traffic was not very heavy.

Joe Baldwin was a conductor on that line in 1867, the year we bought Alaska from the Russians. One night he was in the rear car when he noticed the noise of the locomotive getting fainter. At the same time the car was, very slightly, slowing down. He guessed what had happened. The car had become uncoupled, and the rest of the train was leaving it behind.

This wouldn't have been too serious—the engineer was bound to notice he had shed a car pretty soon as it was not a long train—but for one thing: Another train was due pretty soon going in the same direction. Joe grabbed a signal lamp and hurried to the platform at the rear.

The headlight of the other train was already in sight. It was gaining fast on the rogue car and, as the car was going slower and slower, the gap was narrowing faster and faster. Joe swung his lamp back and forth, but the train kept on coming. It didn't slow down at all. It was obvious that Joe's signal had not been seen.

They say Joe kept swinging his lamp right up to the instant when the train piled into the runaway coach with an almighty crash. Of course Joe was killed. In fact his head was cut right off. They found the body, but the head was lost in the swamp. Someone who was there said that at the moment of the crash Joe's lantern had been flung through the air and landed some way off. It went out for a moment, then kindled again and burned for some time.

And that was that. A sad story. But at least no one else was killed. There were a lot of railroad accidents in the early years, almost as many as there are songs about them.

Some time later, another train was coming up the line toward Maco station, where the accident happened. The engineer noticed a signal lamp swinging up ahead, and he slowed down and stopped. The light stopped swinging to and fro, and shone there for a while, but before

anyone could get down and find out what was going on, it disappeared.

After then the light appeared frequently. At Maco station the signalman took to carrying two signal lamps, red and green, so he would not be confused with the ghost light of Joe Baldwin. People used to come from some distance to see the light. They would bring a picnic and sit in their cars—more than 50 years after the accident happened.

I haven't heard of the light being seen lately, but now it is hard to tell just where the old railroad track ran. Maybe the light still shines, or maybe the ghost of Joe Baldwin has at last found his head.

Slow Trains

Most legends about railroad trains are about expresses, or long-distance freight trains, but there are some stories of slow trains, too.

There was a slow train in Indiana which was said to stop at every house. When it came to a place with two houses, it stopped twice.

A slow train in Arkansas made so many stops, a passenger asked the conductor what it was stopping for. "There are some cattle on the line," he said. A little while later the train stopped again. "Why are we stopping now?" asked the passenger, "We have caught up with those darned cattle again," the conductor explained.

One old country train kept stopping in the middle of nowhere and showed no inclination to get going again. A passenger asked the conductor if he might get off to pick some flowers. "No flowers around here," said the conductor. "Never mind," said the passenger, "I have brought some seeds with me."

Another time the conductor became a little irritated by all the complaints. "If you don't like this train," he said to a passenger who had been pestering him, "you can get off and walk." "I would," said the passenger, "but somebody is meeting me at the station, and he won't get there until the time the train is due."

"Tickets, please," said the conductor to a lady and a young man. "One of these is a half-fare. You can't have a half fare unless you are under twelve." "My son *was* under twelve when we got on," said the lady.

The conductor was a very tall man. He said this was because he'd had his leg pulled so often.

The conductor came by punching tickets. There was a woman with a baby who didn't have a ticket. She said the baby had swallowed it, so the conductor punched the baby.

There was the man who tried to commit suicide by laying his head on the line before the train was due. He died all right—of starvation.

One of the slowest trains ran—well, *ambled* is more like it—out of Salmon City in northern Idaho. It used to carry hay in open wagons from Kamiah to Lewiston, but the cars were always empty by the time they arrived, all the hay having been eaten by cows along the way.

"I struck a train in Indiana that was sure enough slow. I asked the conductor whose dead body he'd got on board. He said, 'Nobody's, why?' I said, 'Because you're running so slow I thought maybe you were running a funeral procession.' He got real mad and we had a fight—we jumped out of the train first, of course. I knocked the breath out of him

70

and ran down to a pond and got my hat full of water and poured it in his face and brought him to. We both caught the hind end of the train as it came by."

"I went to the conductor next day and apologized for banging him up. He said, 'Oh, that's all right. The only thing I regret is, I lost my cap back there where we had the fight.' I said, 'I'll go back and get it.' He said, 'Don't put yourself to any trouble.' I said, 'It won't be any trouble.' I went back and got his cap and caught up with the train at the next station."

"A fellow got took with typhoid fever on that train just after I got on, and when I got off at the end of my journey, he was sound and well, and he had a long siege of it too."

A man was traveling in the front car on the old S & L Railroad. As the train left the station he was leaning out the window and saw a friend of his arrive just in time to jump aboard the last car. Without thinking, he hung his hat on a post the train was just passing, and he walked back to the last car to look for his friend. Then he remembered what he'd done with his hat, and he leaned out of the window in the last car to look for it. It hadn't arrived yet, however.

Kate Shelley Saves the Express

This is a true story, which tells of events on a stormy night in Iowa in July, 1881.

> Have you heard how a girl saved the lightning express,
> Of Kate Shelley whose father was killed on the road?
> Were he living today he'd be proud to possess
> Such a daughter as Kate. Oh, 'twas grit that she showed
> On that terrible evening, when Donahue's train
> Jumped the bridge and went down in the darkness and rain!

Kate Shelley was the eldest child of an Irish railroad worker, a foreman on the Chicago and Northwestern Railway. He was killed in an accident when Kate was 12, leaving his wife to bring up Kate and her four brothers and sisters in a little house about 20 miles north-west of Des Moines. The railroad ran near the house and crossed a creek, which joined the Des Moines River a mile or two downstream.

On July 6, 1881, when Kate was 15, an almighty storm blew up in central Iowa. Big black clouds had been rolling up for some time, and when the storm began, around sunset, it blew and it rained harder than people could remember in those parts. The sky was black as pitch, the thunder rolled all around like a great battle in the sky. It had been a rainy summer so far, but nothing like this had been seen yet. Looking out of the windows through a sheet of rain that poured over the gutters, Kate and her mother could not see much except when the lightning flashed. Then they saw that the creek was in roaring flood, bringing down trees and bushes and already overflowing its banks.

Kate went out to turn loose the horses and cows—they'd be safer in the open—and was drenched to the skin before she had gone five yards from the door. She and her mother knew a good deal about railroads and they were worried about a possible accident.

The railroad crossed the creek near the house. Further up the line, toward Moingona, it also crossed the Des Moines River—on an old wooden bridge that was probably a little frail.

It was getting on toward midnight when they heard the sound of a locomotive chuffing slowly up the line. It was a "pusher," the kind of locomotive kept to give trains an extra push on steep grades or with extra-heavy loads. They could see it moving along in reverse, quite slowly. It had been sent from Moingona to check for damage to the track in the storm. Obviously, it had crossed the Des Moines bridge safely, and they watched it through the darkness and rain as it rolled on to the bridge over the creek.

Suddenly, the engine's bell clanged in alarm, and an instant later there was a mighty crash, and locomotive and bridge disappeared together into the creek.

In the Shelley home there was a moment of complete silence. Then Kate screamed: "They've gone down!"

Her first thought was for the men in the locomotive. But there was a bigger danger now looming. In less than one hour's time the midnight express would be coming through. Once across the Des Moines river it would be putting on speed, expecting to race across the creek near the Shelleys' house—on a bridge that wasn't there!

No one else had seen the crash. Kate knew it was up to her. Her mother would have stopped her, but there was no one else who had seen the bridge go, no one else who could possibly get to Moingona in time to stop the express.

Kate pulled on her coat and a straw hat—that wouldn't be much good in a storm but it was all she had—and she took an oil lamp, the kind that miners used in those days. Once outside in the raging storm, she found the water was so deep around the house she couldn't get to the creek direct, but had to go a long way around on higher ground. When she did get there, she saw the two men from the wrecked locomotive clinging to trees which had been swept down the creek and lodged against the wreck of the bridge. She shouted down to them, and they shouted up to her, but neither could hear a word—the storm was making far too much noise. Anyhow, there was nothing Kate could do for the men in the creek except to get help.

She began to run along the track, toward the Des Moines River bridge. It happened there was a lull in the storm at that time, and she may have thought it was easing up, making her job not so difficult. But the lull did not last. In a few minutes, the storm came on fiercer than before. The night was blacker, the rain harder, the thunder louder, and the wind fiercer.

A terrible decision awaited Kate at the bridge. It was a typical wooden trestle bridge of the early railroads, a simple straight deck that was carried across the river on wooden piers for about 500 yards. It had a catwalk alongside the track, but the railroad company had deliberately ripped out a number of planks in the catwalk to make it difficult to cross. They didn't want trespassers. That made it a dangerous walk on a calm, sunny day. In the middle of the night and in a furious storm, well, it looked like suicide.

But there was no other way. She got down on her knees and prepared to crawl along the catwalk. Hardly had she started, when an extra-strong blast of wind blew out her lamp. She was now in complete darkness, and had to feel for the planks ahead of her, in case they were not there. Splinters ran into her hands and knees, but they were a minor problem. It was slow going, and if the express were on time, she might be too late. She might be caught on the bridge as it rushed down on her. But she could not hurry.

About halfway across, a tremendous flash of lightning, quickly followed by more flashes just as bright, showed Kate a nasty sight. A huge tree was coming roaring down the river, toward the bridge. If it smashed into one of the piers, surely nothing could prevent it collapsing! Each lightning flash showed the tree coming nearer. Kate could even see the fresh soil in its roots. For a moment she held herself rigid, waiting for the crash, but luck, or maybe it was God, to whom Kate prayed, sent the great tree through between two of the piers and it rushed on harmlessly down the river.

Kate began crawling again. The bridge seemed to be 100 miles long. Sometimes she felt she had been crawling along it all night. Sometimes she felt she never would reach the other side.

But she did—without knowing it at first. So black was the night that it was not until she felt firm ground under her groping hands that she knew she was on the other side.

She struggled upright and started running again. But now there wasn't far to go. The station at Moingona was only about a quarter of a mile from the bridge, and a few minutes later Kate saw its lights ahead.

She staggered in soaked-through, white-faced, with blood on her hands and knees and too out-of-breath to make much sense for a second or two. The first thing the men thought when they saw her was, the girl is crazy, but one of them recognized her as Mike Shelley's daughter, and understood what she was trying to tell them. He grabbed a red lamp and made for the track—none too soon, for at the same moment the headlight of the approaching express came into sight.

The engineer was none too pleased to be stopped at an unscheduled halt, but when he found out why, he took a different tone. A hat was passed round among the passengers, who were as generous as you could expect, seeing Kate had saved their lives. But Kate was off again. She was guiding the rescue locomotive across the Des Moines bridge to rescue the crew of the pusher locomotive from the waters of the creek.

Kate Shelley became a national heroine. That may sound nice but it has its drawbacks. All the fuss and bother, reporters around the house all day, didn't do Kate any good, and sad to say she went down with a nervous illness. Probably it was partly caused by her experience on the bridge, but partly too by people not letting her alone when she needed peace and quiet. Luckily, she got better after a few months, and some years later she became the station agent at Moingona.

The railroad was very grateful, as you can imagine. When a new, iron bridge was built over the Des Moines River, it was named after Kate Shelley. The railroad company also gave her a life pass, which meant she never had to pay for a ticket on that line again, and it issued an order that whenever Kate was traveling to Boone to do the shopping, the train should make a special stop outside her front door.

Kate Shelley died when she was only 37 years old. She had heart trouble, which some say was the result of her efforts to stop the express in 1881. I need hardly tell you, that her coffin was carried on its journey by a special train of the Chicago and North-Western Company.

No Way to Run a Railroad

If you think of crooks in connection with railroads, you probably think of Jesse James and other bandits who followed the career of train robber. But some of the biggest bandits connected with railroads were not outlaws on horseback, they were respectable gents in stove-pipe hats who worked in offices in Wall Street. They were fellows like Jim Fisk, who built an opera house for his girl friend to sing in, and Jay Gould, who sat on a stool tearing up little bits of paper and planning how to capture the world supply of gold. When they thought of railroad companies, they did not think of people and locomotives, they thought only of making money. And in those days the rules of business were not as strict as they are now. Fraud was not too difficult. It was amazing how easily fortunes could be made by some skilful paperwork.

These bandits did not need guns. Their weapons were stocks and shares, bond issues and legal injunctions. They "owned" several members of the legislature and local judges, thanks to handsome "presents" (did I hear the word *bribe*?) but they did not *break* the law unless it was necessary. They were able to *bend* it pretty freely when they wanted.

For years Fisk and Gould ran the Erie Railroad as their private hobby. They made a lot of money—and they ruined the railroad. Of course there were a lot of scandals along the way, and the worst of them was what led to the Battle of Binghamton.

There was a little local line called the Albany and Susquehanna (A & S) Railroad, which ran between Albany, New York, and Binghamton, New York, where it connected with the bigger Erie Railroad. It offered a lot of advantages to the Erie, so Gould and Fisk set out to gain control of it. To do this they had to hold a majority of stock in the company. This would entitle them to appoint directors at the annual election who would do what they were told. They could buy some stock in the ordinary way on the stock market, and in the summer of 1869 the price of Albany and Susquehanna stock went up from 20¢ to 65¢ as a result of buying by the Erie.

The "father" of the A & S, and president of its board of directors, was Joseph H. Ramsay. He was determined to preserve his darling from the unwelcome grasp of the Erie, i.e. Mr. Fisk and Mr. Gould.

Now, Fisk and Gould had not been able to buy enough stock on the open market to give them control of the company, but some of the A & S directors were opposed to Ramsay and likely to vote with the

Erie interests. Even if you put the Erie and the hostile directors together, they did not represent a majority of the stock, but Ramsay was not quite safe.

Most of the remaining stock was owned by towns that stood along the railroad. This stock was guarded by certain rules to prevent local officials doing any private deals to their own benefit. It could only be sold at par value, i.e. 100¢, which was way above the market price, and it could only be sold for cash on the barrel.

Before the battle for control of the railroad began, of course, no one would have dreamed of buying this stock—remember it was only 25¢ on the open market. But now agents of the Erie began to pop up in all these little New York towns with bags of money, offering to buy the stock on the terms laid down. A few towns did sell, but then Ramsay's men arrived, also carrying heaps of cash, and the price went so high Gould and Fisk decided they would have to find less expensive ways to gain control.

They promised to buy the towns' stock, at their price, after the meeting to elect directors of the A & S, which would decide who controlled the company. All the towns had to do was to ensure that their representatives voted on the Erie's side at the election. Anyone who relied on a promise by Fisk and Gould had to be wet behind the ears, but some towns went along.

But Ramsay also had a trick up his sleeve. There was still some stock, which had never been issued, in the A & S treasury, and Ramsay now issued it—to friends of his, on rather favorable terms. They only had to put 10 per cent down, and Ramsay kindly undertook to lend them that amount out of his own pocket. Thus they actually paid not so much as a wooden nickel. This was the kind of trick at which Fisk and Gould were past masters, and it looked as if Old Joe Ramsay was fast learning their methods.

The battleground now shifted to the courts. The Erie side got an injunction (a court order) to stop Ramsay's friends voting. Ramsay got an injunction to stop Erie boys taking over the towns' stock. The Erie then got an order to stop Ramsay acting as a director of the A & S.

The directors were equally divided between the supporters of Ramsay and the supporters of the Erie, so this latest move gave the Erie a majority. All they had to do now was to call a directors' meeting, at which they would be able to get hold of the Company's books. They could then transfer stock more or less how they liked, making certain of their control.

The meeting took place in Albany on Thursday, August 5th. That was just two days before the last day on which such transfer of stocks could be legally made—until after the election that would decide the fate of the company. It was a very noisy meeting, and in the end the police had to be called. When they met again next day, Ramsay's lawyers turned up with a nice new set of injunctions, which stopped four of the Erie directors acting in that capacity.

Injunctions, enjoinders, and every other type of legal missile were now fired thick and fast. Pretty soon things were in such a mess that nobody was entitled to do anything. The management of the railroad had collapsed, and both sides demanded the appointment of a receiver (someone to manage the property). Did this mean they agreed about something? Well, no. They wanted different men appointed as receiver. The Erie's man was none other than Jim Fisk, whom some suspicious spectators might suspect to be a little biased. Anyhow, Jim had a legal order appointing him to the post, signed by the Erie's tame judge, Judge Barnard. Quite how Judge Barnard managed to sign it in New York City while he was at his sick mother's bedside in Poughkeepsie 70 miles away nobody could rightly explain, but why worry over trifles?

Fisk left New York for Albany on the night train along with a fair flock of lawyers and a number of other gentlemen of much rougher appearance. When they arrived at the A & S offices next morning, they found Ramsay's men in occupation. They had got their own receiver appointed by an Albany judge.

Fisk demanded the company books, which had in fact been removed from the office by Ramsay's agents the night before. When he tried to enter the room where they were supposed to be kept, there was a tussle, and the Erie men were pushed down the stairs and into the street. "I'll be damned!" said Jim Fisk, who was puffing badly. The overworked Albany police were called again, and they arrested Fisk because they reckoned he was the chief cause of the riot. He got out of jail pretty quickly and went back to the A & S offices, where he suggested to Ramsay in a friendly way (for Jim was always a genial soul) they should play cards to decide who should control the railroad.

Ramsay did not think much of that suggestion, and a new battle of writs (written commands from courts) began. Judge Barnard issued a whole lot of orders from New York very helpful to the Erie. They were sent by telegraph from New York, although the good Judge was actually still in Poughkeepsie. One of his orders put the Albany sheriff under the orders of the Erie receiver, which the sheriff didn't much like, and in the end a kind of truce was arranged, whereby both sides agreed to do nothing until after the weekend.

The Erie party returned to New York for a council of war. They went back to Albany on the Sunday night, but once again they found Ramsay was one jump ahead of them. The Albany judge, just as obliging to Ramsay as Judge Barnard was to Fisk, had dissolved all Judge Barnard's injunctions and summoned Fisk to appear in court for interference with justice. It looked like Fisk was stymied in Albany. But, as he remarked, a railroad has two ends.

The orders of the Albany judge had the effect of putting the railroad into the hands of the Ramsay receiver. Those orders were put on the first train leaving Albany at 8 a.m. on Monday morning, to be communicated to all the stations on the line to Binghamton. (Although it was called the Albany and Susquehanna, the railroad terminated at Binghamton.) The train was due to reach Binghamton at 3 p.m.

But there were faster ways of communicating than by train, and the Erie group in New York could get in touch with Binghamton by telegraph. So, although the writ of the Albany judge was law on most of the stations down the line, at Binghamton the writ of Judge Barnard ruled. The Binghamton sheriff took possession of all the railroad's property on behalf of the Erie. It included a train that was just getting up steam to set off for Albany, and the passengers had to get off and go home. There were also three other locomotives at Binghamton. The sheriff took over two of them, but an official who was loyal to the Ramsay management stopped him getting the third by switching the points so the train on which the sheriff was traveling was diverted into a siding, and the third locomotive slipped past him and escaped east into A & S territory.

Now the lines were drawn up for battle. At Albany, the Ramsay side was in full control, but at the other end Binghamton was secured for the Erie. Two trains set off, one from each terminus, each carrying the writs of rival judges. It looked as though a big clash would occur somewhere east of Binghamtpon. The Albany train was ahead, but when it came to Harpursville, about 25 miles from Binghamton, it stopped. All other traffic on the line had stopped on orders from Albany, and anyone who had the bad luck to be traveling on the railroad that day must have had a puzzling time of it. Now a special train was sent from Albany, which contained 150 muscular mechanics from the Albany workshops. Ramsay wasn't relying on writs alone.

Meanwhile, the Erie's train had started from Binghamton. On board were the Binghamton sheriff and a dozen or so Erie men. They stopped at each station to turn out the Albany men and replace them with Erie officials, on the orders of Judge Barnard. They went slowly, as it was now getting dark, and when they reached Bainbridge their locomotive gave a lurch and came off the rails. The line had been booby-trapped by the Albany men. Just behind them, the Albany train slid out of a siding where it had been waiting out of sight and carried on down the line toward Binghamton, stopping at each station to throw out the Erie men and put back the Albany officials. They got as far as a tunnel about 15 miles from Binghamton. On the other side of the tunnel were a band of Erie men, armed with clubs.

Now came a pause. For several hours nothing happened, except that each party, on either side of the tunnel, received reinforcements from special trains coming up from behind while they waited for orders from headquarters. The night passed.

About 7 a.m. the next morning, the Erie men got an order to advance. Their train chugged carefully through the tunnel and, as no one interfered, kept going on the steep downward grade on the other side. As it came round a curve, it met the Albany train coming up. Now at this stage, the Erie men out-numbered the Albany men about two-to-one, but the Albany men were better armed (it was said that some had guns) and they were also more angry. The Albany men were loyal to the Ramsay management, while the Erie men were just hired hands who had no love for genial Jim Fisk or his pal back in New York, the grim-faced Gould.

It appeared that the Albany train was not going to stop. The Erie train tried to go into reverse, but it was hard for the wheels to get a grip on the steep grade and before it could get going the Albany train piled right into it. Of course, that gave it just the start it needed, and it continued backward at a spanking pace, though now without its cow-catcher, headlights or smokestack.

Everyone piled out of the trains, but the Erie men were in no mood for a fight, especially as the rumor about guns proved true: A bullet had gone through the engine cab. They ran for it. Some clambered back on the train before it vanished backward into the tunnel.

The collision had derailed the Albany locomotive, but Ramsay's men managed to get it back on the track and set off in pursuit of the Erie train. News came, however, that the Governor of the State had called out the state troopers so, leaving a freight car across the line to block it, Ramsay's men went back to Albany, where they were welcomed as heroes.

The Lightning Express Trains: Leaving the Junction, published by Currier & Ives, 1864

Across the Continent: Westward the Course of Empire Takes its Way, by Fanny Palmer, published by Currier & Ives, 1868

Fisk wasn't beaten yet. On the Tuesday evening he again tried to get into the A & S offices in Albany, but Ramsay had it well guarded. Fisk was arrested and charged with attempted burglary. Out on bail, he hightailed it for New York, while Judge Barnard, still issuing writs like a hero, had Ramsay and his chief associates arrested for contempt of court.

The Governor of New York then said if the two sides couldn't come to an agreement, the State would take over the railroad until they did. They couldn't, so the State did. The battle of the judges died away in a rumble of false evidence, phony affidavits, explanations, orders and counter-orders, and the telegraph wires grew cool again.

But the matter was still undecided. The election which would decide who gained control was getting near. The Erie men badly wanted to get a look at the company books, so they could see how the land lay in the matter of stock-holding. But they were not to be found. Ramsay had them hidden in an Albany churchyard, and they were smuggled back into the office the day before the election in a basket let down from a third-floor window.

The meeting was a complete muddle, with writs and counter-writs flying again, Fisk sending in a gang of toughs to vote in his place, and Ramsay arrested on some charge or other. At the end, both sides declared they had won.

Not before time, the State Attorney-General stepped in. In front of an independent judge at Rochester, he gained the verdict that the election of the pro-Erie directors was "irregular, fraudulent and void" (that meant—crooked). Still, you couldn't write off Fisk and Gould. They were all set to appeal against the judgement, when Ramsay played his trump card. He leased his railroad to the Hudson & Delaware Canal Company, a much bigger outfit with which Fisk and Gould did not care to tangle.

Joe Magarac, the Steel Man

Joe Magarac is the hero of steel workers, especially of those immigrant workers from Central Europe who worked in the steel mills of Pittsburgh and other places in Western Pennsylvania. The name *magarac*, in Hungarian, means a donkey, and a donkey is a creature that does not care about anything except eating and working—like Joe.

Joe Magarac is a figure of pure legend, a "superhero" like Paul Bunyan, whose acts are fantastical, tall tales told for amusement. There may have been a Hungarian or Slovak steel worker who was the original for Joe Magarac, or there may not. It doesn't matter. The stories of Joe Magarac have nothing to do with history. The same stories are (or were) told by Irish steelworkers, but in them the name of the hero is Joe McGarrick.

A long time ago, there was a steel worker named Steve Mestrovich who had a mighty pretty daughter. Oh my! Mary was pretty! Big blue eyes, long yellow hair, strong white teeth and dainty hands—it was no wonder all the young men at the mill wanted to marry her. Mary was 17 and she wanted to get married, too, but Steve always said she must marry the strongest man around. He put a lot of importance in that. Mary herself wasn't worried about strength so much. She chiefly wanted to marry Pete Pussick.

Although so many young men wanted to marry his daughter none of them came up to the standard Steve had set, so he decided he would give a party and hold a trial of strength among all-comers. He had two barrels of beer sent from Pittsburgh on a truck and his wife got busy making prune-jack, which is home-made plum brandy. The word went around, and next Sunday all the young men from the steel mills all over western Pennsylvania came to Steve Mestrovich's party, which was held in a field near the river. They had all been practicing lifting dolly bars, which are steel bars used for riveting, to get themselves ready for the trial of strength.

Pete Pussick was one of the favorites. He could pick up those dolly bars as if they were toothpicks, although each weighed 350 pounds. But others thought the winner would be Eli Stanoski.

The contest began with the 350-pound dolly bars. Pete stepped forward, stripped off his shirt, and picked it up easily. Eli followed him, and he picked it up even easier. Then came some young men from Homestead or Monesson or from Duquesne, from all the steelmaking places in the Monongahela valley. They were eager to show everyone how strong they were, and especially to impress Mary, who was looking as pretty as a picture in a white dress made from her mother's old wedding gown. But not many of them could lift the dolly bar off the ground.

Those who had succeeded next tried to lift the 500-pound dolly bar. There was only three of them could do that: Pete, Eli, and a man from Johnstown. This Johnstown man was a big fellow, and he lifted the 500-pound dolly bar with no trouble. It looked like he might be the winner, which didn't please most of the people there. They wanted Pete or Eli to win. They didn't want any stranger carrying Mary off to Johnstown.

Pete told them not to worry. He took a big drink of prune-jack, and he spat on his hands. Then he bent down to the third dolly bar, which weighed 850 pounds. He grabbed a-hold of it. His arm cracked like a paper bag, his eyes stuck out like apples, and sweat ran down his face as if he were working in a steel furnace in July. But that big dolly bar did not move.

Then Eli stepped forward, but he couldn't move it either. Then it was the turn of the man from Johnstown. He took two big drinks of prune-jack, he twisted up his moustache to show he was confident, he gave everyone a big wave, he shuffled his feet to get a firm grip, he bent down and grabbed hold of the dolly bar and he gave it one big pull. Nothing happened. He pulled again, and his hand slipped and he fell over. He got up cursing, grabbed hold of the dolly bar again . . . nothing doing.

Then from somewhere in the crowd came a big laugh. "Ho! Ho! Ho!" "Who's laughing at me?" yelled the man from Johnstown. "If the fellow who laughed thinks he is such a big strong man, let him come out here and pick up those dolly bars—and after that I'll break his neck!"

A man came out from the crowd. He was the biggest man you ever saw. His back was bigger than a door, his neck was like a bull's, and his arm was as thick as most people's waist.

"Who is that fellow, anyhow?" Everybody shook their heads. No one had seen him before.

The big fellow walked over to the dolly bars. He was still laughing, and the man from Johnstown was so angry he took a slug at him. The big man didn't stop laughing, but he picked up all three dolly bars in one hand and the man from Johnstown in the other hand. He held them all above his head and gave them a shake.

Everybody went as white as a sheet. Nobody had ever seen such strength. But he put down the fellow from Johnstown as gently as a mother puts down her baby, and he said: "Nobody need be afraid. I don't want to make trouble—just have a little bit of fun, that's all."

Steve Mestrovich walked up to him and asked, "What kind of man are you? Where are you from?"

And the fellow answered, "My name is Joe Magarac."

Then everyone laughed, because *magarac* means a jackass. A man who called himself Joe Jackass had to be all right.

Joe grinned and said, "Yes, Joe Magarac, that's me. All I do is eat and work, like a donkey. I'm the only steel man in the whole world. Look here, I'll show you something." And he pulled off his shirt. By gosh, he wasn't lying—he was a steel man all right. He was made of steel—steel hands, steel body, steel everything. "I was born inside an ore mountain many years ago," he said, and he laughed, and twisted the dolly bars in two.

Steve Mestrovich was smiling like a man who has just been given a cold beer on a hot day. He took Mary by the hand and led her over. He had found the best possible husband in the whole country.

Joe looked at Mary and he said, "Oh boy, I never saw such a pretty girl, but marriage is not the business for me. I've got no time to sit around the house with a woman. I've only got time for working. Better if Mary has another husband, and I've seen her looking at Pete. Now Pete is the best man in the country after me, so he should marry Mary."

Well, that made nearly everybody happy. The man from Johnstown was not too happy, and he stormed around a bit, but he was afraid to say anything to the man made of steel and in the end he went off.

Mary and Pete got married pretty soon after that, and Joe Magarac went down to a boarding-house by the gate of the steel mill to find a place to eat. "Howdy, Mrs. Horkey," he said to the lady who ran the boarding house. "I don't want a room because I don't sleep, but I'm going to work in the mill and I need five big meals a day."

So Joe worked in the mill and he ate at Horkey's boarding house. He worked all night and all day and he never got tired. He used to stir up the molten steel with his hands, and scoop it up in big handfuls when it was ready to be poured into the mold. He used to shape steel rails just by drawing a steel bar through his fingers—eight rails at a time, four between the fingers of each hand. Pretty soon he was making more steel than all of the other furnaces put together. The boss of the mill had a big sign made which he put up outside the mill. The sign said: "The Home of Joe Magarac."

Joe Magarac worked all day and all night at the mill, only stopping for his five big meals a day. Pretty soon, the pile of rails in the yard got so big there was no place to put anything else. Pretty soon after that, there was nowhere to put more rails either. Joe Magarac just laughed and worked harder than ever.

So one day they decided to shut the mill down early for the week. They closed it on a Thursday night and planned to start again on Monday morning. When they told Joe Magarac, he looked like he wanted to say something, but then he shut his mouth and said nothing.

When Monday morning came around, Joe Magarac was not at work on No. 7 furnace. Another man had to take over, as Joe Magarac was nowhere to be found.

By and by the foreman came along to see how things were going at No. 7. "How's it looking?" said a voice he thought he knew. "Is that you, Joe Magarac?" he said. "Where are you?"

"I'm inside the ladle." And sure enough he was sitting in the big ladle, with molten steel up to his neck. The foreman was so shocked his voice was shaking. "What are you doing in there, Joe Magarac?" he said. "You'd better get out of there right away or you are going to get melted up."

Joe Magarac just winked at the foreman. "That's fine," he said. "That's just what I want. By gosh, I was sick at the mill closing down Thursday to Monday. What am I going to do with my time while the mill is shut down? But I heard the big boss say they were going to pull this mill down to build a new one, the best in the whole Monongahela valley. That plant must be made from the best steel. So I got this plan. I jumped in the furnace to get melted up to make steel to build the mill. You make that steel mill out of me and you are going to have the best steel mill in the whole world. Goodbye!"

Then he sat down in the ladle until he was all melted up. They poured him in the mold, rolled him out and cut him up—and they had the best steel that ever was made, not a seam, not a fault in it. And they took that steel and built the finest steel mill in the whole world.

Indian Myths
and
Legends

Myths are much more than stories. They are closer to religion than to folk tales. Myths give the answers to such questions as: "Who made the world?" or "Why is the sky blue?"

The white settlers in North America came from a society with an established religion and a good deal of scientific knowledge. Such a society has no need for mythology. Stories like the one which explains why there are no trees in the plains (see Paul Bunyan) are simple entertainment, not to be taken seriously. (Of course, to non-Christians, the Bible is simply a collection of myths.)

The Africans brought to North America as slaves came from a different kind of society, in which myths played an important part. Although some African myths and legends survived in North America, the Blacks in general adopted—willingly or not, and sometimes in different forms—the beliefs of ruling white society.

The real native myths of North America are therefor to be found only among the Indians. They had a great number of imaginative stories which explained the workings of nature and made gods out of forces like the rain and the sun. They had many mythical heroes, part human, part god, who were regarded as the first men and had marvelous magic powers. They believed that everything in nature, animals, plants, stones—every blade of grass or breath of wind—is inhabited by a mysterious power or spirit. Among the Algonquin peoples of the northeast, the most powerful is the Great Spirit, who has always existed (and was therefore never "made") and is the father of all forms of life.

Tales of Creation

In another Algonquin myth, the father of the race is Michabo, the Great Hare (who can, however, change himself into any other kind of animal), who also created water and the fish. One story about him tells how he restored the earth after a great flood.

Once, Michabo went hunting with the wolves, his hunting dogs. When they came to a great lake, the wolves dived in and disappeared. Michabo searched for them without success, and a bird told him they were lost in the middle of the lake. He was about to plunge in after them when the lake rose and covered the whole earth.

Michabo decided to remake the world, and told a raven to bring him a lump of clay. The raven could not find any, so he sent an otter to dive for it. But the otter also returned with no clay, and finally Michabo sent muskrat. The muskrat brought him a handful of clay, with which he remade the earth.

Many similar Indian myths tell how the earth and people were created by the wife or daughter of the Chief of Heaven.

At that time, although heaven was inhabited, the earth was nothing but water. The earth was dark, but heaven was lit by the Tree of Light, with its luminous blossoms, which grew outside the lodge of the Chief of Heaven. But the Chief became very angry, because he believed his wife had been unfaithful to him, and in his anger he tore up the Tree of Light by the roots, leaving a great hole in the floor of Heaven. He pushed his wife (or, as some versions of the myth say, his daughter) into the hole.

As she fell, she saw nothing but water beneath her, but the creatures that lived in the water, and the birds that lived in the air, decided to take a hand. The birds came together with outstretched wings and helped to slow down the fall of the Sky Woman, while the animals tried to make some dry land for her. They searched for soil, and only the muskrat was successful in finding some. (Here we have an echo of the myth of Michabo's recreation of the earth.) They put the earth on the back of the Great Snapping Turtle, which came to the surface and grew very large.

An island was formed, on which the Sky Woman landed after the birds had brought her down safely. She scattered the earth about, the island grew and grew until the horizon was out of sight, and thus the earth was created.

The Sky Woman had a daughter and the daughter had two sons, Good and Evil. They began to quarrel even before they were born, and this caused the death of their mother. When she died, she was buried in a shallow grave, and from her body grew five plants, tobacco, corn, squash, beans and potatoes. This was the origin of the most important food plants, although another version of the myth says that these things, and others, were thrown through the hole in the sky by the Chief of Heaven after he had thrown out the Sky Woman.

The Sky Woman was angry at the death of her daughter and asked the twin sons who was responsible. Evil blamed Good and as a result, Good was driven out of the world. However, he did not die, but grew to be a man, discovering among other things that his father was the West Wind. His father taught him how to build a house, how to tend plants, and how to make fire. He went back into the world, to make it ready for mankind, and did many good things, though in everything he did, his brother, Evil, tried to make trouble.

For example, Good made all streams with a current running in both directions, but Evil made the current run in one direction only, and filled the streams with annoying rapids and waterfalls. Good made fish for men to eat, and Evil filled the fish with small bones for men to choke on.

However, Good had the best of the contest, even though Evil was aided by the Sky Woman. He made the animals, and stole the secret of medicine from the dwarf who is responsible for all diseases. He took the sun and the moon away from the Sky Woman and Evil, and put them in their places in the sky. Finally, he created mankind. Evil also tried to make his own creatures, which were monsters, and in the end he was defeated by his brother, Good.

How Fire Came

There were many legends to explain how fire first came to the earth. This one was told by the Cherokee.

The earth was a very cold place before fire came. The birds needed all their feathers to keep warm, and the animals needed their fur. Even so, they shivered, and the thunder god, feeling sorry for them, sent down a bolt of lightning which set fire to a tree growing on an island.

The animals could see the advantage of the fire. They could feel its warmth all the way across the water. But the fire was no good to them on an island, so they decided they would bring a piece of it to the mainland.

First to volunteer was the raven. He flew over and dived boldly into the flames. But he was driven back at once, burned black by the fire.

Next the owl said he would try. But the smoke hurt his eyes, burning rings around them which he still has, and making him blink whenever the light is bright.

Next the blacksnake went. He swam over to the island and tried to reach the burning tree, but he was burnt as black as the raven, and came back without any fire.

None of the animals knew what to do. There they were, shivering with cold, and there was the fire, giving out a lovely warmth. But they couldn't capture a piece of the fire.

At last a very small animal spoke up—the water spider. She said she thought she could bring back a piece of the fire. She spun a little bowl and put it on her back, then she scampered across the surface of the water to the island where the tree still burned. She caught a tiny live coal from the burning tree in her bowl and scampered back again. The animals had fire at last, and the water spider had a mark on her back from the bowl that you can still see if you look at her.

The Pipe of Peace

The origin of the famous ceremony of smoking the pipe of peace is explained by the Lenni Lenape ("true men") or Delaware Indians in this way.

One day, all the nations of the north gathered together in council and decided to wage war upon the Lenni Lenape and destroy them forever. Suddenly, a huge bird of brilliant white appeared in the sky and came to hover above the head of the only daughter of the Paramount Chief. Through her, the bird spoke. It said: "Bring together all the warriors, and tell them that the heart of the Great Spirit is sad, and has gone to dwell in a dark cloud, because they would destroy the oldest of his people and drink their blood. Therefore, to appease his anger and to bring joy back into his heart, all the warriors wash their hands in the blood of a fawn, then let them bring presents and go to their elders (i.e. the Delaware) and smoke with them the great pipe of peace and brotherhood, which will unite them for ever."

It is in memory of this first ceremony of smoking the pipe of peace in honor of the Great Spirit that—according to the Delaware Indians—the practice continues.

Why the Helldiver has Red Eyes and No Tail

Many Indian legends are about animals, and many, especially in the west, are about a tribal hero who saves his people by cunning trickery. Among the Menominee Indians of Wisconsin, the name of this trickster is Manabozho.

Manabozho was walking along the shore of a lake. He was tired and hungry. Ahead of him, on a sand bar, he saw hundreds of waterfowl gathered, and he thought, "Now I shall have a feast!"

He went into the woods and hung his medicine bag on a tree. He stripped some bark from the trees and rolled it into a bundle to make a drum. Then he returned to the lake shore and began to walk slowly toward the birds.

The birds saw him and recognized him. Some of them were suspicious and moved away. One of the swans called out, "Where are you going, Manabozho?" He replied, "I am going to have a sing-song. Come with me, my brothers, and let us sing and dance."

The birds followed him to a space on the shore where there was room to dance. Manabozho put his dark drum on the ground and took out his drum sticks. "Now," he said, "dance around me in a circle while I play the drum. Sing as loud as you can, but keep your eyes closed. The first one who opens his eyes will have sore red eyes for ever."

He began to play on his birchbark drum, while the birds, with eyes closed, danced around him singing as loudly as they could.

Manabozho kept drumming with one hand, but the other hand reached out and grabbed a swan. He wrung its neck, but not before the swan had managed to give a screech. "That's right, my brother," Manabozho called out, "sing as loud as you can!"

A few minutes later he killed another swan in the same way, and then a goose, and then more. Then the Helldiver opened his eyes to see why fewer birds were singing than before. He saw Manabozho with a pile of dead birds beside him, and cried out, "Manabozho is killing us! Manabozho is killing us!" He ran for the water, and the other birds followed him.

But the Helldiver is not a fast runner, and Manabozho overtook him. "I won't kill you," he said, "but because you opened your eyes, they will remain always red and the other birds will laugh at you." And he gave the Helldiver such a kick that he knocked his tail off.

That is why the Helldiver has red eyes and no tail.

Tales of the Blackfeet

Nearly 100 years ago Walter McClintock, a U.S. forestry official, was introduced to the Blackfeet by William Jackson, or Siksikakoan (Blackfoot Man), the famous Indian scout who played a heroic part in Custer's last stand. McClintock lived with the Blackfeet for four years, and wrote about the time a book called *The Old North Trail*. Among those McClintock met was a noted medicine man, Spotted Eagle.

"We found Spotted Eagle reclining on his bed of robes and blankets, fanning himself with a large eagle wing. Commanding in person, and with a face indicating much force and strength of character, he had an imposing presence—a most valuable qualification for a medicine man. His hair, now streaked with gray over his temples, was separated into braids by bands of otter skin.

"Spotted Eagle was accustomed to give special attention to his toilet. We found him pulling out straggling hairs from his face with a small pair of tweezers (the Blackfoot substitute for shaving), and dressing his hair with a comb made of porcupine's tail, ornamented with beadwork, and a hair brush made of the skin of a buffalo tongue. These toilet articles were not modern, but they served the purpose equally as well. The making use, or wearing as an ornament, of any part of an animal, was often the Indian's way of honoring that animal. Spotted Eagle's comb and brush (especially the latter) had a superior value for a medicine man's toilet over the best comb and hair brush to be had from the Indian trader's stock.

"Spotted Eagle had quite a reputation as a wit, and was widely known as a joker. He was fond of telling stories about the marvelous adventures of Old Man (Napi), a mythical character of the Blackfeet, whose contradictory qualities are difficult to understand, or reconcile. Old Man was also known to other plains tribes and by different names.

"Many of the legends about him are vulgar and even obscene, and cannot appear in a book for general circulation. Spotted Eagle had a fondness for them because they had been handed down from the ancients, and he also had that common trait, which finds enjoyment in hearing and telling such stories, because of a keen sense of the humor in them.

"The character of Old Man, as revealed even in the more serious of these myths, is a strange mixture of opposing attributes, of power and weakness, of wisdom and passion, of benevolence and malevolence. He associated intimately with the birds and animals. He conversed with

93

them and understood their thoughts and language, and they understood him. Although believed to be the creator of all things, and as having power over all things, he was often helpless and in trouble, and compelled to seek the aid of his animal friends.

"Spotted Eagle said of him: 'Old Man first came to the Blackfeet from the south. The last we heard of him, he was among the Crees, and disappeared toward the east, whence he is not likely ever to return.'"

The following myths were some of those about Old Man related by Spotted Eagle.

"Old Man came to a place where many ground squirrels were seated around a fire, playing a game. They would bury one of their number in the ashes, until he squealed, when they pulled him out. Old Man said that he would like to learn the game.

"The squirrels explained that it was very easy, and invited him to take part. He asked them to bury him first, but as soon as he was covered over, he yelled, and they quickly pulled him out. Old Man then said that it was the squirrels' turn, but since there were so many of them, it would save time to bury them all at once. They agreed, so he covered them all over him hot ashes, excepting one mother squirrel, who was afraid. He warned her to run away, so that there might be other squirrels, but he left the others in the ashes, until they were well roasted. He ate so many of the roasted squirrels that he fell asleep, when a lynx came along and ate up the others. Old Man followed the lynx, until he came upon him fast asleep. He was so angry that he seized him by the ears and shortened his head by hammering it against a stone. He pulled out his long tail and, breaking it in two, stuck the brush part on his rump, making a bobtail. He stretched his legs and body, making them long and slender, and then cast him upon the ground, saying, 'You bobcats will always look like this, and you will always be so short-winded that you will never be able to run far'.

"Old Man, having been burned by the fire, called upon the wind to blow. The cool air made him feel better, so he continued calling upon it to blow harder and harder, until there came such a fierce wind that he was blown away. Every tree that he caught hold of was torn up by the roots, and he could not stop himself, until he lay hold of a birch tree. When the wind went down and he was rested, he denounced the birch, saying, 'Why have you such strong roots that you cannot be pulled up like other trees? I was having a good time being blown around by the wind, and you spoiled my fun.' He was so angry that he drew his stone knife and gashed the birch all over.

.·"This is the reason why the bark of a birch tree always has a gashed appearence."

"Old Man came to the lodge of a man who owned a wonderful pair of leggings. Wherever he went they set fire to the grass. If he wished to kill buffalo, he had only to walk around them when they would be caught in a circle of fire. Old Man wanted these leggings very much. He said that he had come a long journey to get them, but the owner refused to give them up. Old Man then decided to remain all night in the lodge. When the owner and his wife were sound asleep, Old Man stole the leggings. After running a long distance he became tired and lay down to sleep in a thicket with the leggings under his head. But, when he awoke in the morning, he found to his surprise that he was back again in the lodge. When the owner asked him how it happened that he had his leggings under his head, Old Man told him a lie, saying, 'I had nothing else, so I used them for a pillow.'

"On the following night, Old Man made another attempt to carry off the leggings, but morning found him back again in the lodge where the leggings belonged. The owner then told Old Man that, if he wanted the leggings so badly, he would give them to him. He warned him, however, not to make use of them more than three times.

"Old Man was so proud of the fire-leggings that he put them on to show off in every camp he entered and paid no heed to the warning of the owner. He used them three times successfully, but the fourth time he put them on he set fire to the grass wherever he stepped. The grass burned so fiercely that Old Man became frightened and started to run. The fire followed him wherever he went, burning his clothes and his hair, until he was compelled to jump into a river. But the magical leggings were burned up."

The Sea Maiden of the Biloxi

The Biloxi were a small tribe who lived at one time on an island in the Bay of Biloxi, Mississippi, from which they seem to have been expelled in early colonial times. This legend of the fate of the Biloxi was told to Carl Carmer in the 1920s by many different people in the region.

A long time ago, a tribe of Indians, named the Biloxi, lived on this island. They believed themselves to be children of the sea, and they worshipped a sea maiden. But the Spaniards came and they forced the Indians to give up their belief and take the Christian religion. A Spanish priest went among them with his cross and bell and box and the Indians had to bow to him and his God. One night the priest was wakened by a sound of stirring waters. He looked out and saw dark waves risen into a trembling mound that almost reached the clouds. At its peak, close against the blue moon, stood the sea maiden. She sang:

> Come to me, children of the sea.
> Neither book, nor bell, nor cross
> Shall win you from your queen.

Then, before the priest could interfere, he saw the natives fling themselves into the water and swim toward the maiden, leaving behind them great streaks of fire. When they had circled the column of waves, it burst with a great hissing roar, engulfing the whole tribe in the subsiding waters.

The priest who saw this strange thing happen believed that it was due to the fact that he was not himself in a true state of grace. On this deathbed he said that if a priest would row to the spot where the music sounded and drop a cross into the water, all the souls at the bottom would be redeemed, although the priest himself would be swallowed up by the waves.

No one has ransomed the souls of the Biloxi. The sad music that haunts the Bay today, rising through the waters when the moon is out, comes from the sea caves down below where they live.

American Indians, by George Catlin

Game of the Arrow: The Plains Indians at Play, by George Catlin

Hiawatha's Fishing

Henry Wadsworth Longfellow's poem *The Song of Hiawatha* was first published in 1855. It brings together many Indian legends in the story of the Indian hero, Hiawatha. It is a very long poem, and the following section, which describes how Hiawatha overcame Mishe-Nahma, the great sturgeon, King of Fishes, is only a small part.

Forth upon the Gitche Gumee,
On the shining Big-Sea-Water,
With his fishing line of cedar,
Of the twisted bark of cedar,
Forth to catch the sturgeon Nahma,
Mishe-Nahma, King of Fishes,
In his birch canoe exculting
All alone went Hiawatha.

Through the clear, transparent water
He could see the fishes swimming
Far down in the depths below him:
See the yellow perch, the Sahwa,
Like a sunbeam in the water,
See the Shawgashee, the craw-fish,
Like a spider on the bottom,
On the white and sandy bottom.

At the stern sat Hiawatha,
With his fishing line of cedar:
In his plumes the breeze of morning
Played as in the hemlock branches;
On the bows, with tail erected,
Sat the squirrel, Adjidaumo;
In his fur the breeze of morning
Played as in the prairie grasses.

On the white sand of the bottom
Lay the monster Mishe-Nahma,
Lay the sturgeon, King of Fishes:
Through his gills he breathed the water,
With his fins he fanned and winnowed,
With his tail he swept the sand-floor,

There he lay in all his armor:
On each side a shield to guard him,
Plates of bone upon his forehead,
Down his sides and back and shoulders
Plates of bone with spines projecting!
Painted was he with his war-paints,
Stripes of yellow, red, and azure,
Spots of brown and spots of sable:
And he lay there on the bottom,
Fanning with his fins of purple,
As above him Hiawatha
In his birch canoe came sailing,
With his fishing-line of cedar,
"Take my bait!" cried Hiawatha
Down into the depths beneath him,
"Take my bait, O Sturgeon, Nahma,
Come up from below the water,
Let us see which is the stronger!"
And he dropped his line of cedar
Through the clear, transparent water,
Waited vainly for an answer,
Long sat waiting for an answer,
And repeating loud and louder,
"Take my bait, O King of Fishes!"

Quiet lay the sturgeon, Nahma,
Fanning slowly in the water,
Looking up at Hiawatha,
Listening to his call and clamor,
His unnecessary tumult,
Till he wearied of the shouting:
And he said to the Kenozha,
To the pike, the Maskenozha,
"Take the bait of this rude fellow,
Break the line of Hiawatha!"

In his fingers Hiawatha
Felt the loose line jerk and tighten:
As he drew it in, it tugged so
That the birch canoe stood endwise,
Like a birch log in the water,

With the squirrel. Adjidaumo,
Perched and frisking on the summit.

Full of scorn was Hiawatha
When he saw the fish rise upward,
Saw the pike, the Maskenozha,
Coming nearer, nearer to him,
And he shouted through the water,
"Esa! esa! shame upon you!
You are but the pike, Kenozha,
You are not the fish I wanted,
You are not the King of Fishes!"

Reeling downward to the bottom
Sank the pike in great confusion,
And the mighty sturgeon, Nahma,
Said to Ugudwash, the sun-fish,
"Take the bait of this great boaster,
Break the line of Hiawatha!"

Slowly upward, wavering, gleaming
Like a white moon in the water,

Rose the Ugudwash, the sun-fish,
Seized the line of Hiawatha,
Swung with all his weight upon it,
Make a whirlpool in the water,
Whirled the birch canoe in circles,
Round and round in gurgling eddies.
Till the circles in the water
Reached the far-off sandy beaches,
Till the water-flags and rushes
Nodded on the distant margins.

But when Hiawatha saw him
Slowly rising through the water,
Lifting his great disc of whiteness,
Loud he shouted in derision,
"Esa! esa! shame upon you!
You are Ugudwash, the sun-fish,
You are not the fish I wanted.
You are not the King of Fishes!"

Wavering downward, white and ghastly,
Sank the Ugudwash, the sun-fish,
And again the sturgeon, Nahma,
Heard the shout of Hiawatha,
Heard his challenge of defiance,
The unnecessary tumult,
Ringing far across the water.

From the white sand of the bottom
Up he rose with angry gesture,
Quivering in each nerve and fibre,
Clashing all his plates of armor,
Gleaming bright with all his war-paint:
In his wrath he darted upward,
Flashing leaped into the sunshine,
Opened his great jaws, and swallowed
Both canoe and Hiawatha.

Down into the darksome cavern
Plunged the headlong Hiawatha,
As a log on some black river
Shoots and plunges down the rapids,

Found himself in utter darkness,
Groped about in helpless wonder,
Till he felt a great heart beating,
Throbbing in that utter darkness.

And he smote it in his anger,
With his fist, the heart of Nahma,
Felt the mighty King of Fishes
Shudder through each nerve and fibre,
Heard the water gurgle round him
As he leaped and staggered through it,
Sick at heart, and faint and weary.

Crosswise then did Hiawatha
Drag his birch canoe for safety,
Lest from out the jaws of Nahma,
In the turmoil and confusion,
Forth he might be hurled and perish
And the squirrel, Adjidaumo,
Frisked and chattered very gaily,
Toiled and tugged with Hiawatha
Till the labor was completed.

Then said Hiawatha to him,
"O my little friend, the squirrel,
Bravely have you toiled to help me:
Take the thanks of Hiawatha,
And the name which now he gives you:
For hereafter and for ever
Boys shall call you Adjidaumo,
Tail-in-air the boys shall call you!"

And again the sturgeon Nahma,
Gasped and quivered in the water,
Then was still and drifted landward
Till he grated on the pebbles,
Till the listening Hiawatha
Heard him grate upon the margin,
Felt him strand upon the pebbles,
Knew that Nahma, King of Fishes,
Lay there dead upon the margin.

Then he heard a clang and flapping,

As of many wings assembling,
Heard a screaming and confusion,
As of birds of prey contending,
Saw a gleam of light above him,
Shining through the ribs of Nahma,
Saw the glittering eyes of sea-gulls,
Of Kayoshk, the sea-gulls, peering,
Gazing at him through the opening,
Heard them saying to each other,
"Tis our brother, Hiawatha!"

And he shouted from below them,
Cried exulting from the caverns,
"O ye sea-gulls! O my brothers!
I have slain the sturgeon, Nahma;
Make the rifts a little larger,
With your claws the openings widen,
Set me free from this dark prison,
And henceforward and for ever
Men shall speak of your achievements,
Calling you Kayoshk, the sea-gulls,
Yes, Kayoshk, the Noble Scratchers!"

And the wild and clamorous sea-gulls
Toiled with beak and claws together,
Made the rifts and openings wider
In the mighty ribs of Nahma,
And from peril and from prison,
From the body of the sturgeon,
From the peril of the water,
Was released my Hiawatha.

He was standing near his wigwam,
On the margin of the water,
And he called to old Nokomis,
Called and beckoned to Nokomis,
Pointed to the sturgeon, Nahma,
Lying lifeless on the pebbles,
With the sea-gulls feeding on him.
"I have slain the Mishe-Nahma,
Slain the King of Fishes!" said he;

"Look! the sea-gulls feed upon him,
Yes, my friends Kayoshk, the sea-gulls;
Drive them not away, Nokomis,
They have saved me from great peril
In the body of the sturgeon.
Wait until their meal is ended,
Till their craws are full with feasting,
Till they homeward fly, at sunset,
To their nests among the marshes;
Then bring all your pots and kettles,
And make oil for us in Winter."

And she waited till the sunset,
Till the pallid moon, the night-sun,
Rose above the tranquil water,
Till Kayoshk, the sated sea-gulls,
From their banquet rose with clamor,
And across the fiery sunset
Winged their way to far-off islands,
To their nests among the rushes.

To his sleep went Hiawatha,
And Nokomis to her labor,
Toiling patient in the moonlight,
Till the sun and moon changed places,
Till the sky was red with sun-rise,
And Kayoshk, the hungry sea-gulls,
Came back from the reedy islands,
Clamorous for their morning banquet.

Three whole days and nights alternate
Old Nokomis and the sea-gulls
Stripped the oily flesh of Nahma,
Till the waves washed through the rib-bones,
Till the sea-gulls came no longer,
And upon the sands lay nothing
But the skeleton of Nahma.

Peboan and Seegwun

Many of the legends which Longfellow worked into his poem, *The Song of Hiawatha*, he took from the writings of H. P. Schoolcraft (1793–1864), at one time Superintendent of Indian Affairs and the author of many books about the Indians. One of these legends was reprinted by Mark Twain in his *Life on the Mississippi*, and as he said, it is worth reading in its original form, if only to see "how effective a genuine poem can be without the helps and graces of poetic measure and rhythm." *Peboan*, as you will guess, means winter, and *seegwum* means spring.

An old man was sitting alone in his lodge by the side of a frozen stream. It was the close of winter, and his fire was almost out. He appeared very old and very desolate. His locks were white with age, and he trembled in every joint. Day after day passed in solitude, and he heard nothing but the sound of the tempest, sweeping before it the new-fallen snow.

One day, as his fire was just dying, a handsome young man approached and entered his dwelling. His cheeks were red with the blood of youth, his eyes sparkled with animation, and a smile played upon his lips. He walked with a light and quick step. His forehead was bound with a wreath of sweet grass, in place of a warrior's headband, and he carried a bunch of flowers in his hand.

"Ah, my son!" said the old man, "I am happy to see you. Come in! Come and tell me of your adventures, and what strange lands you have been to see. Let us pass the night together. I will tell you of my prowess and exploits, and what I can perform. You shall do the same, and we will amuse ourselves."

He then drew from his sack a curiously fashioned anitque pipe, and having filled it with tobacco, rendered mild by a mixture of certain leaves, handed it to his guest. When this ceremony was concluded they began to speak.

"I blow my breath," said the old man, "and the stream stands still. The water becomes stiff and hard as clear stone."

"I breathe," said the young man, "and flowers spring up all over the plain."

"I shake my locks," retorted the old man, "and snow covers the land. The leaves fall from the rees at my command, and my breath blows them away. The birds rise from the water, and fly to a distant land. The animals hide themselves from my breath, and the very ground becomes as hard as flint."

"I shake my ringlets," rejoined the young man, "and warm showers of soft rain fall upon the earth. The plants lift up their heads out of the earth, like the eyes of children glistening with delight. My voice recalls the birds. The warmth of my breath unlocks the streams. Music fills the groves wherever I walk, and all nature rejoices."

At length the sun began to rise. A gentle warmth came over the place. The tongue of the old man became silent. The robin and bluebird began to sing on the top of the lodge. The stream began to murmur by the door, and the fragrance of growing herbs and flowers came softly on the breeze.

Daylight fully revealed to the young man the character of his entertainer. When he looked upon him, he had the icy visage of *Peboan*. Streams began to flow from his eyes. As the sun increased, he grew less and less in stature, and soon had melted completely away. Nothing remained on the place of his lodge fire but the *miskodeed*, a small white flower with a pink border, which is one of the earliest of northern plants.

Sedna and the Fulmar

The goddess Sedna holds an important place in the myths of the Inuit and other Eskimo peoples. She is the goddess of the sea and of the sea animals, sometimes thought of as a giantess with one eye. She is not very friendly to the human race, and the Inuit used to make many sacrifices to her in hope of gaining her good favor. As you might expect of such a frightening goddess, her story is a grim and gruesome one.

Sedna was a very beautiful girl, whose mother died soon after she was born. She lived alone with her father, who was naturally very fond of her. When she reached marrying age, many young men came to court her, from her own tribe and from other tribes far away. But she would have none of them. She seemed to delight in being rude to them.

Then, one day in spring, there arrived from a distant land a new suitor, a young and handsome hunter dressed in the most splendid furs and carrying a spear made of ivory. He sang to Sedna a most alluring song as he floated in his canoe close to the shore. "Come with me," he sang, "to the land of the birds where there is never any hunger. You shall have a beautiful tent made of soft skins, you shall lie on warm bear skins, your lamp will be always filled with oil, and your plate with meat."

Sedna was drawn to the young stranger at once, but at first she rejected his proposal. He told her she would wear the most beautiful ivory necklace and be dressed in the feathers of the birds. Little by little, Sedna was drawn down to the edge of the sea, and at last she agreed to get into the canoe. At once the young man paddled away and they were soon out of sight.

He was not really a young man at all, but a phantom whose natural form was that of a fulmar. He could take on the form of any bird—or of a man. When Sedna discovered her mistake, she was desolate. Still more reason for regret was that the luxuries she had been promised did not exist in the land of the birds. Her new home was not built of soft furs but of fishskins, full of holes that let in the wind and snow. Her bed was made not of thick bearskins but of old walrus hides, and instead of a plate always filled with meat she had to live on scraps of fish that the birds brought her.

Meanwhile, her father was grieving over the loss of his daughter. One day he set out for the distant land where she had been taken. When he arrived, he found her in deep despair and, carrying her to his boat, he sailed away with her toward their old home.

When the fulmar-spirit returned, he looked in vain for his wife. The birds told him how her father had come and taken her away in his boat. He followed in his canoe, taking again the form of a man, and when he caught up with them he demanded to see Sedna, whom her father had hidden under some skins in the boat. But her father would not listen to him, and he took on the form of a great bird, soaring up into the sky and uttering strange cries, before he disappeared in the distance.

No sooner had he gone than a great storm blew up. The sky turned black and the waves rose up in anger, demanding that Sedna should be surrendered to them. Her father, in terror, decided to sacrifice his daughter, and, seizing her, he hurled her into the sea.

She tried to climb back into the boat, but her father chopped off the fingers which clung to the boat's side. From the joints of her fingers the seals grew. A second time she tried to climb in, and her father chopped off another joint of her fingers. From them the walrus grew. A third time she tried, and her father chopped off the third joint of her fingers. From them the whales grew. Then she sank below the surface of the sea.

At once the storm died away and the waves were quiet. The father continued his journey alone, and at last reached his tent. He fell asleep at once, and while he slept the sea rose and covered the land, sweeping away the sleeping man in his tent and Sedna's dog, which was tied to the tent pole. The man and the dog were reunited with Sedna in the depths of the ocean, and ever since they have lived with her in her kingdom of Adliden, where the souls of the dead go to pay for the sins they committed while they lived.

The White Buffalo

In the legends of North American Indians, animals play a large part. They usually have supernatural powers, and are sometimes a spirit within the skin of an animal. Among the Fox (Muskwaki), whose original homeland was central Wisconsin, an especially important spirit was that of the White Buffalo.

Wisaka was blessed by the White Buffalo before he was born, so everyone knew he would be a remarkable person. When he was a small baby fox his mother, carrying him on her back in the usual way, wandered away from the camp one day and became lost. She slept on the prairie with her baby, and when she awoke she was shocked and frightened to find that they were surrounded by a herd of buffalo. But the buffalo did not harm them, and allowed them to walk away.

Some time later they ran into a party of Sioux, enemies of the Fox, and as they were about to be killed, the herd of buffalo came galloping up and put the Sioux to flight. Soon afterward, Wisaka and his mother were found by a Fox search party. It was clear that Wisaka was a guardian spirit, who had summoned the buffalo to their aid.

Wisaka grew up into a handsome young man and a leader of his people. He was seen to meet and talk with the White Buffalo, for instance when a member of the tribe was sick. He also had the power to change into a white buffalo himself.

There are many stories told about Wisaka and the White Buffalo.

Once, his people were attacked by the Sioux, who were moving into their homeland in large numbers. Wisaka said he could not take part in the forthcoming battle himself, but he told his people they should fight, and perhaps they would be able to kill the Sioux, although there were so many of them.

The battle began and the Fox did indeed kill many of the Sioux warriors, but many of them were killed also, and it looked as if the Sioux would win.

When Wisaka saw how the battle was going, he said, "Then I shall have to kill them all myself." At once he turned into a white buffalo, a huge and mighty beast, and charged down into the fight. The Sioux shot many arrows and threw many spears at him, but they could do him no harm. He charged among them, tossing them on his horns and trampling them with his hooves. He killed them all.

Then he changed back into his human shape again and returned to his marveling people. "There," he said, "that's the way you should have done it!"

Many tales are told of the marvelous deeds of Wisaka. One day, when he was an old man, his people woke up one morning to find that he had disappeared. He was never seen again.

The White Bear

This story comes from a modern novel, *The White Bear* by Gail Trenton, and is therefore not an authentic legend (i.e. a story told by the Indians themselves). The narrator, Silas, is a mysterious old man who lives in the Green Mountains of Vermont, and Fay is a young visitor from England.

The sunlight glittered on the water flowing steadily southward. Silas guided the canoe into the main current. There was no need to paddle, except to keep a course in the current, and they glided easily downstream.

"The old people lived hereabouts," said Silas.

"Old people?"

"Indians. Their village was up behind that bluff."

Fay followed his glance. "Wonderful place for it."

He agreed.

"Who were they?"

His deep blue eyes fastened upon her. "They were a small tribe—clan is a better word. An offshoot of one of the Iroquois nations. And around here that meant trouble. This was borderland between Iroquois and Algonquin. Life wasn't as peaceful as it ought to have been.

"These people fought with the British during the Revolution, and they were sent packing by the settlers afterwards. Some of them ended up on a reservation in Ontario."

"Is that what happened to this village?"

"No, they disappeared before all that. There's an old story about it . . ." He smiled at her. She looked expectant.

"The chief had a beautiful daughter, named Miawani. She was tall and slim and graceful, and she ran through the forest like a deer. The people believed that she brought them good luck.

"But there was another tribe, moving up from somewhere to the south, a larger tribe, looking for land, and hostile. They were led by a famous warrior.

"One day this warrior saw Miawani bathing in the river and he fell in love with her. He came in peace to ask her father if he would give her to him.

"But Miawani did not love the warrior, and she did not wish to leave her people. The chief was in sore doubt. If he did not do as the warrior wished, surely his village would be destroyed.

"He told Miawani she must marry his people's enemy, to prevent war.

That night she went down to the river again. She did not come back. The river had carried her away. For many days and nights her people lamented her.

"At last the expected attack came from the south. The village was burned and the people fled. Their attackers pursued them, and all would have been killed. As dusk was falling they were surrounded, their backs to the river.

"At that moment a great white bear appeared. The attackers, terrified by this apparition, turned and ran.

"When they had gone, the bear stood still for some time before the transfixed villagers, then slowly turned and made its way into the trees, toward the west.

"The villagers believed the white bear was the spirit of Miawani, who had come to save them. Next day, collecting their few possessions, they followed the track of the bear through the woods. Thus they left their village for ever, and followed the white bear to a happier land beyond the mountains."

The Dun Horse

This Pawnee folktale was first printed by George Bird Grinnell, a naturalist who was with General Custer in Dakota, in 1889. Grinnell was a naturalist who wrote many books about the Indians, especially the Pawnee and Cheyenne.

Many years ago there lived in the Pawnee nation an old woman and her grandson, a boy about 16 years old. These people had no relations and were very poor. They were so poor that they were despised by the rest of the tribe. They had nothing of their own and always, after the village started to move camp from one place to another, these two would stay behind the rest to pick up anything that the others had thrown away as worn out or useless. In this way they would sometimes get pieces of buffalo robes, worn-out moccasins, and bits of meat.

Now, it happened one day, after the village had moved away from the camp, that this old woman and her boy were following along the trail behind the rest when they came upon a miserable old worn-out dun horse, which they supposed had been abandoned by some Indians. He was thin and exhausted, blind in one eye, had a sore back, and a swollen foreleg. In fact, he was so worthless that none of the Pawnee had been willing to take the trouble to try to drive him along with them. But when the old woman and her boy came along, the boy said, "Come now, we will take this old horse, for we can make him carry our pack." So the old woman put her pack on the horse, and drove him along, but he limped and could only go very slowly.

The band moved up on the North Platte River until they came to Court House Rock. The two poor Indians followed them and camped with the others. One day while they were there, the young men who had been sent out to look for buffalo came hurrying into camp and told the chiefs that a large herd was nearby, and that among them was a spotted calf.

The Paramount Chief of the Pawnee had a very beautiful daughter, and when he heard about the spotted calf, he said that the man who killed the spotted calf should have his daughter for a wife. For a spotted robe is big medicine.

The buffalo were feeding about four miles from the village, and the chiefs decided the charge should be made from there. In this way, the man who had the fastest horse would be the most likely to kill the calf. Then all the warriors and the young men picked out their best and fastest horses, and made ready to start. Among those who prepared for the charge was the poor boy on the old dun horse. But when they saw him, all the rich young braves on their fast horses pointed at him and said, "Oh look! There is the horse that is going to catch the spotted calf!" And they laughed at him, so that the poor boy was ashamed, and rode off to one side of the crowd, where he could not hear their jokes and laughter.

When he had ridden off some little way, the horse stopped, and turned his head, and spoke to the boy. He said, "Take me down to the creek, and plaster me all over with mud. Cover my head and neck and body and legs." When the boy heard the horse speak, he was afraid, but he did as he was told. Then the horse said, "Now, mount, but do not ride back to the warriors, who laugh at you because you have such a poor horse. Stay here, until the word is given to charge."

Presently, all the fine horses were drawn up in line and pranced about, so eager to go that their riders could hardly hold them in. At last the chief gave the word go, and with a great yell, away they went.

Suddenly, away off to the right, was seen the old dun horse. He did not seem to run. He seemed to sail along like a bird. He passed all the fastest horses, and in a moment he was among the buffalo. He picked out the spotted calf and charged up alongside it. Straight flew the arrow, and the calf fell. The boy drew another arrow, and killed a fat cow that was running by. Then he dismounted and began to skin the calf before any of the other warriors had come up. But when he got off the old dun horse, how changed the animal was! He pranced about and would hardly stand still. His back was all right again, his legs were well and fine, and both eyes were clear and bright.

The boy skinned the calf and the cow that he had killed, and then he packed all the meat on the horse, and put the spotted hide on top of the load, and started back to the camp on foot, leading the dun horse. Even with this heavy load, the horse pranced all the time. On the way to camp, one of the rich young chieftains of the tribe rode up to the boy and offered him 12 good horses for the spotted robe, so that he could marry the Paramount Chief's beautiful daughter. But the boy laughed at him and would not sell the robe.

Now, while the boy walked to the camp leading the dun horse, most of the warriors rode back, and one of those who came first to the village went to the old woman and said, "Your grandson has killed the spotted calf." And the old woman, said, "Why do you come to tell me this? You ought to be ashamed to make fun of my boy because he is poor." The warrior said, "What I have told you is true," and he rode away. After a little while another brave rode up to the old woman, and said, "Your grandson has killed the spotted calf." Then the old woman began to cry, she felt so badly because everyone made fun of her boy, because he was poor.

Pretty soon the boy came along, leading the horse up to the lodge where he and his grandmother lived. It was a little lodge, just big enough for two, and was made of old pieces of skin that the old woman had picked up, and was tied together with strings of rawhide and sinew. When the old woman saw her boy leading the dun horse with the load of meat and the robes on it, she was very much surprised. The boy said to her, "Here, I have brought you plenty of meat to eat, and here is a robe, that you may have for yourself. Take the meat off the horse."

Then the old woman laughed and was glad, but when she went to take the meat from the horse's back, he snorted and jumped about, and acted like a wild horse. The old woman looked at him in wonder, and could hardly believe it was the same horse.

That night the horse spoke again to the boy. It said, "Tomorrow the Sioux are coming—a large war party. They will attack the village, and you will have a great battle. Now, when the Sioux are drawn up in line of battle and ready to fight, you jump on my back and ride as hard as you can, right into the middle of the Sioux, and up to their Paramount Chief, and kill him, and then ride back. Do this four times, and kill four of the bravest Sioux, but don't go a fifth time. If you do, you may be killed, or else you will lose me. Remember!" And the boy promised.

The next day it happened as the horse had said, and the Sioux came down and formed in line of battle. The boy took his bow and arrows, and jumped on the dun horse, and charged into the midst of them. And when the Sioux saw that he was going to strike their Paramount Chief, they all shot their arrows at him, and the arrows flew so thickly that they darkened the sky, but none of them hit the boy. And he killed the Chief and rode back.

After that he charged again among the Sioux, where they were gathered thickest, and killed their bravest warrior. And then twice more, until he had gone four times, as the horse had told him.

But the Sioux and the Pawnee kept on fighting, and the boy stood and watched the battle. At last he said to himself, "I have been four times and have killed four Sioux, and I am all right. I am not hurt anywhere— why may I not go again?" So he jumped on the dun horse and charged again. But when he got among the Sioux, one Sioux warrior drew an arrow and shot. The arrow struck the dun horse behind the forelegs and pierced him through. And the horse fell down dead. But the boy jumped off and fought his way through the Sioux, and ran as fast as he could to the Pawnee.

As soon as the horse was killed, the Sioux said to each other, "This horse was like a man. He was brave. He was not like a horse." And they took their knives and hatchets, and hacked the dun horse, and cut him into small pieces.

The Sioux and the Pawnee fought all day long, but toward night the Sioux broke and fled.

The boy felt very badly that he had lost his horse. After the fight was over, he went out from the village to where it had taken place, to mourn for his horse. He went to the spot where the horse lay, and gathered up all the pieces of flesh, which the Sioux had cut off, and the legs and the hoofs, and put them all together in a pile. Then he went off to the top of a hill nearby, and sat down and drew his robe over his head, and began to mourn for his horse.

As he sat there, he heard a great wind storm coming up, and it passed over him with a loud rushing sound, and after the wind came rain. The boy looked down from where he sat to the pile of flesh and bones, which was all that was left of his horse. He could just see it through the rain. And the rain passed by, and his heart was very heavy, and he kept on mourning.

Pretty soon came another rushing wind, and after it rain, and as he looked through the driving rain toward the spot where the pieces lay, he thought that they seemed to come together and take shape, and that the pile looked like a horse lying down. But he could not see well in the thick rain.

After this came a third storm like the others, and now when he looked toward the horse he thought he saw that its tail moved from side to side two or three times, and that it lifted its head from the ground. The boy was afraid, and wanted to run away, but he stayed.

And as he waited, there came another storm. And while the rain fell, looking through the rain, the boy saw the horse raise himself up on his forelegs, and look about. Then the dun horse stood up.

The boy left the place where he had been sitting on the hill-top, and went down to him. When the boy had come near, the horse spoke and said, "You have seen how it has been this day, and from this you may know how it will be from now on. But the Great Spirit has been good, and has let me come back to you. After this, do what I tell you. Not any more, not any less." Then the horse said, "Now lead me off, far away from the camp, behind that big hill, and leave me there tonight, and in the morning come for me." And the boy did as he was told.

When he went for the horse in the morning, he found with him a beautiful white gelding, much more handsome than any horse in the tribe. That night, the dun horse told the boy to take him again to the place behind the big hill, and to come for him the next morning. When the boy went for him again, he found with him a beautiful black gelding.

And so for 10 nights he left the horse among the hills, and each morning he found a different colored horse, a bay, a roan, a gray, a blue, a spotted horse, and all of them finer than any horses that the Pawnee had ever had before.

Now the boy was rich, and he married the beautiful daughter of the Paramount Chief, and when he grew older he became Paramount Chief himself. He had many children by his beautiful wife, and when his oldest boy died, he wrapped him in the spotted-calf robe and buried him in it. He always took good care of his old grandmother, and kept her in his own lodge until she died. The dun horse was never ridden, except at feasts, and when they were going to have a dance, but he was always led about with the Chief, wherever he went. The horse lived in the village for many years, until he became very old and, at last, died.

The Deer

Among the Pawnee there is a ceremonial dance called the deer dance. This story explains how it was begun.

A long time ago, as the tribe were on their summer hunt, a man and his wife began to quarrel. They had a child, a boy about 10 months old. It was while they were traveling along, going from one camp to another, that they began to quarrel. At last the wife became very angry, and threw the baby to the man, saying, "You take that baby. It belongs to you, for it is a man child. I am not going to nurse it for you any longer." Then she went away.

The man took the child and carried it along with him. He felt very badly, both on his own account and on account of his child. He was so unhappy that he almost wanted to kill himself. It was a disgrace that he, being a man, should have to take care of his child until it was grown up, by he had no female relatives to rear the child for him. He decided to leave the tribe and wander off on his own, far from his people.

He carried the child on his back, as a woman does. But when it cried for its mother's milk, he had none to give it. He could only cry with the child. He hated the idea of killing it or leaving it on the prairie to die, but what else could he do? He wandered off to the south, traveling for some time until he came near to where the buffalo were. By this time the fat baby had grown into a thin one, because it had no milk. When he got to the buffalo, he killed a cow, and took its udder and while it was fresh he let the child suck it, until it became sour. Then he killed another cow, and did the same thing. In every way he did his best to nourish the child. Sometimes he would get a slice of meat and half cook it, and let the child suck the juice. The child began to improve, and to grow a little stronger. In this way the father supported the child for quite a long time, and it did pretty well, and at last it got used to this food, and became strong and healthy.

At length the man found that the child could sit up alone. He began to give it all sorts of playthings so that it could amuse itself. First he made for it a little bow and some arrows, and taught it how to use them. He made other things for the child to play with, and at last it grew to be happy playing alone. Then the father would leave the child for a few minutes, and go off a little way, perhaps to the top of a hill nearby, to look over the country, but he would look back at the child every few steps to see that it was all right. When he came back he would find the child safe, playing by itself and perfectly contented.

After a while he got so that he would leave it for about an hour, and when he came back he would always find it safe and happy. By this time the child had begun to walk. Finally, the father went off once for half a day, and when he came back, he found the child still playing and safe. It did not seem to mind much when its father was away. About this time he killed a buffalo cow, and made some dried meat, and put it in a certain place, showing the child where it was. When the child was hungry, it could go and get a piece of meat.

Now he went off for a whole day, and when he came back at night the child was safe. Then he made preparations and went off to stay overnight, and was gone two days. When he came back, the boy was asleep. He went away a second time and was gone for two days, going quite a long distance. When he came back he found that the child's face was painted with white clay. The father thought this was strange. He said to himself, "Something must have come and talked to my child, and is taking care of him while I am gone."

When he came back the third time after a two days' journey, he found that the child had a string of beads made from wild currants strung around his neck. The fourth long journey he took lasted three days, and when he returned he found his boy still wearing the beads and with a feather tied in his hair. Now his father knew that something was looking after his child when he was away, and when he went off he would pray that whatever was taking pity on his child would also take pity on him.

The child had now grown big enough to talk with his father, and one day it said, "Father, you go away and be gone for four days. I shall be all right here. When you come back, you will find me safe."

The man went. He started to go way down south, to be gone four days. After he had traveled for two days and two nights, he saw signal smoke and went toward it. As he looked over a hill, he saw far off a lot of people and horses coming toward the river which lay between him and them. He lay on the hill for a long time, watching to see where they would camp. When they had made camp, he went down into a ravine and crept closer, until he could see that the camp was just one lodge, and that all round it was a great herd of horses. He waited till evening and then went over to the lodge. He had never seen so many horses. He crept closer and, looking into the lodge through an opening by the door, he saw lying down inside a great big man, with a woman on either side of him. As he looked at them, he thought he recognized one of the women. He started at her and at last he remembered who she was. She had been captured a long while before from the Pawnees. Her family were still living. The man, he saw, was a Comanche.

While he watched, the man inside the lodge asked for something, and the captive woman stood up to go out of the lodge, and the Pawnee man stepped to one side, out of sight. The woman came out into the darkness and went among the horses. The Pawnee stepped up behind her very softly and put his hand on her shoulder, saying to her in Pawnee, "Friend, do you belong to my tribe?" The woman started to scream, but he put his hand on her mouth, and said to her, "Be quiet. Keep still and do not call out." She answered him, "Yes, I belong to your tribe." Then he asked her, "Who is that other woman I saw in the lodge?" She answered him, "She also belongs to our tribe, and is a prisoner too." Then the Pawnee said, "I am going to kill that man." The woman said, "That is good. That is good. This man is the biggest man among all the Comanches. He has come first to this place, and the rest of the Comanches are coming here to meet him. I am glad that my people are living, and that I am going back to see them once more. Do not fail to kill the Comanche. I shall tell the other woman to be ready, that our friend is here, and we will wait and watch."

When the woman went back into the lodge, she whispered to the other woman, "Be ready. A friend who belongs to our tribe is here. Take your hatchet, and be prepared to help to kill this Comanche."

The two women waited, and the Pawnee made ready to shoot the Comanche with his bow and arrow. The woman had said to him, "Push aside the door a little, and be ready." He made a little opening by the door, just big enough to let an arrow pass through, and when the time came he let it go. The arrow flew straight, and pierced the Comanche through the heart. So he died, and the Pawnee took his scalp.

The women were so glad to meet a friend that they put their arms around the man and embraced him. They were going home to see their relatives. They asked him, "How many of you are here?" and they were very surprised when he answered, "I am alone."

They took down the lodge, and packed everything on the horses, and drove off the herd, leaving the dead body of the enemy behind. All night they traveled, and all the next day, and as they went, the man told them how it came about that he was alone. They told him that there were about 300 horses in the herd they had with them.

When they were pretty close to the place where he had left the child, he told them about the boy being alone there all the while, and the women galloped their horses to get to the boy. Whichever got their first, he should be hers. They arrived together, took the boy in their arms and petted him, and took him as their own.

Now the father was no longer sad. He had regained two captured women, he had killed an enemy, and he had taken a great many horses.

They went on, and traveled far, and at length, one night, they came up with the Pawnee tribe and camped with them. The horses surrounded the lodge so thickly that you could only see the top of it above their backs. The next morning all the people wondered who these strangers might be. They found out that the man and child who were lost had returned, and with them the two women who had been lost, captured long ago by the Comanches. And there was great joy in the tribe.

The man gave his relatives many horses. In those days the Pawnees had few horses, and it seems that this man brought good luck in horses to the tribe, for ever since then the Pawnees have had many horses. The mother of the child came to see him, but she was driven out of the lodge.

When the child grew up, he told the father how, ever since he could remember, a buck deer had come to him, talked to him, and taken care of him. It had saved him from danger, and brought them both good fortune. In order that this might be remembered, he established a dance, called the deer dance, which was kept up ever afterward.

The Mink and the Wolf

This story and the two that follow it are Indian legends retold by the Scottish-born author Andrew Lang (1844–1912). Lang wrote a huge number of books in his lifetime, but most of them are now forgotten. It is his books of fairy stories and legends that have lasted best.

In a big forest in the north of America lived a quantity of wild animals of all sorts. They were always very polite when they met; but, in spite of that, they kept a close watch one upon the other, as each was afraid of being killed and eaten by somebody else. But their manners were so good that no would ever have guessed that.

One day a smart young wolf went out to hunt, promising his grandfather and grandmother that he would be sure to be back before bedtime. He trotted along quite happily through the forest till he came to a favorite place of his, just where the river runs into the sea. There, just as he had hoped, he saw the chief mink fishing in a canoe.

"I want to fish too," cried the wolf. But the mink said nothing, and pretended not to hear.

"I wish you would take me into your boat!" shouted the wolf, louder than before, and he continued to beseech the mink so long that at last he grew tired of it, and paddled to the shore close enough for the wolf to jump in.

"Sit down quietly at that end or we shall be upset," said the mink; "and if you care about sea urchins' eggs, you will find plenty in that basket. But be sure you eat only the white ones, for the red ones would kill you."

So the wolf, who was always hungry, began to eat the eggs greedily; and when he had finished he told the mink he thought he would have a nap.

"Well, then, stretch yourself out, and rest your head on that piece of wood," said the mink. And the wolf did as he was bid, and was soon fast asleep. Then the mink crept up to him and stabbed him to the heart with his knife, and he died without moving. After that he landed on the beach, skinned the wolf, and taking the skin to his cottage, he hung it up before the fire to dry.

Not many days later the wolf's grandmother, who, with the help of her relations, had been searching for him everywhere, entered the cottage to buy some sea urchins' eggs, and saw the skin, which she at once guessed to be that of her grandson.

"I knew he was dead—I knew it! I knew it!" she cried, weeping bitterly, till the mink told her rudely that if she wanted to make so much noise she had better do it outside as he liked to be quiet. So, half-blinded by her tears, the old woman went home the way she had come, and running in at the door, she flung herself down in front of the fire.

"What are you crying for?" asked the old wolf and some friends who had been spending the afternoon with him.

"I shall never see my grandson any more!" answered she. "Mink has killed him. Oh! Oh!" And putting her head down, she began to weep as loudly as ever.

"There! there!" said her husband, laying his paw on her shoulder. "Be comforted; if he *is* dead, we will avenge him." And calling to the others they proceeded to talk over the best plan. It took them a long time to make up their minds, as one wolf proposed one thing and one another; but at last it was agreed that the old wolf should give a great feast in his house, and that the mink should be invited to the party. And in order that no time should be lost it was further agreed that each wolf should bear the invitations to the guests that lived nearest to him.

Now the wolves thought they were very cunning, but the mink was more cunning still; and although he sent a message by a white hare,

122

that was going that way, saying he should be delighted to be present, he determined that he would take his precautions. So he went to a mouse who had often done him a good turn, and greeted her with his best bow.

"I have a favor to ask of you, friend mouse," said he, "And if you will grant it I will carry you on my back every night for a week to the patch of maize right up the hill."

"The favor is *mine*," answered the mouse. "Tell me what it is that I can have the honor of doing for you."

"Oh, something quite easy," replied the mink. "I only want you—between today and the next full moon—to gnaw through the bows and paddles of the wolf people, so that directly they use them they will break. But of course you must manage it so that they notice nothing."

"Of course," answered the mouse, "nothing is easier; but as the full moon is tomorrow night, and there is not much time, I had better begin at once." Then the mink thanked her, and went his way; but before he had gone far he came back again.

"Perhaps, while you are about the wolf's house seeing after the bows, it would do no harm if you were to make that knothole in the wall a little bigger," said he. "Not large enough to draw attention, of course; but it *might* come in handy." And with another nod he left her.

The next evening the mink washed and brushed himself carefully and set out for the feast. He smiled to himself as he looked at the dusty track, and perceived that though the marks of wolves' feet were many, not a single guest was to be seen anywhere. He knew very well what *that* meant; but he had taken his precautions and was not afraid.

The house door stood open, but through a crack the mink could see the wolves crowding in the corner behind it. However, he entered boldly, and as soon as he was fairly inside the door was shut with a bang, and the whole herd sprang on him, with their red tongues hanging out of their mouths. Quick as they were they were too late, for the mink was already through the knothole and racing for his canoe.

The knothole was too small for the wolves, and there were so many of them in the hut that it was some time before they could get the door open. Then they seized the bows and arrows which were hanging on the walls and, once outside, aimed at the flying mink; but as they pulled the bows broke in their paws, so they threw them away, and bounded to the shore, with all their speed, to the place where their canoes were drawn up on the beach.

Now, although the mink could not run as fast as the wolves, he had had a good start, and was already afloat when the swiftest among them threw themselves into the nearest canoe. They pushed off, but as they dipped the paddles into the water, they snapped as the bows had done, and were quite useless.

"I know where there are some new ones," cried a young fellow, leaping on shore and rushing to a little cave at the back of the beach. And the mink's heart smote him when he heard, for he had not known of this secret store.

After a long chase the wolves managed to surround their prey, and the mink, seeing it was no good resisting any more, gave himself up. Some of the elder wolves brought out some cedar bands, which they always carried wound around their bodies, but the mink laughed scornfully at the sight of them.

"Why I could snap those in a moment," said he. "If you want to make sure that I cannot escape, better take a line of kelp and bind me with that."

"You are right," answered the grandfather, "your wisdom is greater than ours." And he bade his servants gather enough kelp from the rocks to make a line, as they had brought none with them.

"While the line is being made you might as well let me have one last dance," remarked the mink. And the wolves replied: "Very good, you may have your dance; perhaps it may amuse us as well as you." So they brought two canoes and placed them one beside the other. The mink stood up on his hind legs and began to dance, first in one canoe and then in the other; and so graceful was he, that the wolves forgot they were going to put him to death, and howled with pleasure.

"Pull the canoes a little apart; they are too close for this new dance," he said, pausing for a moment. And the wolves separated them while he gave a series of little springs, sometimes pirouetting while he stood with one foot on the prow of both. "Now nearer, now further apart," he would cry as the dance went on. "No! further still." And springing into the air, amidst howls of applause, he came down head foremost, and dived to the bottom. And though the wolves, whose howls had now changed into those of rage, sought him everywhere, they never found him, for he hid behind a rock till they were out of sight, and then made his home in another forest.

An Indian Brave

A long, long way off, right away in the west of America, there once lived an old man who had one son. The country around was covered with forests, in which dwelt all kinds of wild beasts, and the young man and his companions used to spend whole days in hunting them, and he was the finest hunter of all the tribe.

One morning, when winter was coming on, the youth and his companions set off as usual to bring back some of the mountain goats and deer to be salted down, as he was afraid of a snowstorm; and if the wind blew and the snow drifted the forest might be impassable for some weeks. The old man and the wife, however, would not go out, but remained in the wigwam making bows and arrows.

It soon grew so cold in the forest that at last one of the men declared they could walk no more, unless they could manage to warm themselves.

"That is easily done," said the leader, giving a kick to a large tree. Flames broke out in the trunk, and before it had burnt up they were as hot as if it had been summer. Then they started off to the place where the goats and deer were to be found in the greatest numbers, and soon had killed as many as they wanted. But the leader killed most, as he was the best shot.

"Now we must cut up the game and divide it," said he. And so they did, each one taking his own share, and, walking one behind the other, set out for the village. But when they reached a great river the young man did not want the trouble of carrying his pack any further, and left it on the bank.

"I am going home another way," he told his companions. And taking another road he reached the village long before they did.

"Have you returned with empty hands?" asked the old man, as his son opened the door.

"Have I *ever* done that, that you put me such a question?" asked the youth. "No, I have slain enough to feast us for many moons, but it was heavy, and I left the pack on the bank of the great river. Give me the arrows, I will finish making them, and you can go to the river and bring home the pack!"

So the old man rose and went, and strapped the meat on his shoulder; but as he was crossing the ford the strap broke and the pack fell into the river. He stooped to catch it, but it swirled past him. He clutched again; but in doing so he overbalanced himself and was hurled into some rapids, where he was knocked against some rocks, and he sank and was drowned, and his body was carried down the stream into smoother water when it rose to the surface again. But by this time it had lost all likeness to a man, and was changed into a piece of wood.

The wood floated on, and the river got bigger and bigger and entered a new country. There it was borne by the current close to the shore, and a woman who was down there washing her clothes caught it as it passed, and drew it out, saying to herself, "What a nice smooth plank! I will use it as a table to put my food upon." And gathering up her clothes she took the plank with her into her hut.

When her supper time came she stretched the board across two strings which hung from the roof, and set upon it the pot containing a stew that smelt very good. The woman had been working hard all day and was very hungry, so she took her biggest spoon and plunged it into the pot. But what was her astonishment and disgust when both pot and food vanished instantly before her!

"Oh, you horrid plank, you have brought me ill luck!" she cried. And taking it up she flung it away from her.

The woman had been surprised before at the disappearance of her food, but she was more astonished still when, instead of the plank, she beheld a baby. However, she was fond of children and had none of her own, so she made up her mind that she would keep it and take care of it. The baby grew and throve as no baby in that country had ever done, and in four days he was a man, and as tall and strong as any brave of the tribe.

"You have treated me well," he said, "and meat shall never fail to your house. But now I must go, for I have much work to do."

Then he set out for his home.

It took him many days to get there, and when he saw his son sitting in his place his anger was kindled, and his heart was stirred to take vengeance upon him. So he went out quickly into the forest and shed tears, and each tear became a bird. "Stay there till I want you," said he, and he returned to the hut.

"I saw some pretty new birds, high up in a tree yonder," he remarked. And the son answered, "Show me the way and I will get them for dinner."

The two went out together, and after walking for about half an hour the old man stopped. "That is the tree," he said. And the son began to climb it.

Now a strange thing happened. The higher the young man climbed

126

the higher the birds seemed to be, and when he looked down the earth below appeared no bigger than a star. Still he tried to go back, but he could not, and though he could not see the birds any longer he felt as if something were dragging him up and up.

He thought that he had been climbing that tree for days, and perhaps he had, for suddenly a beautiful country, yellow with fields of maize, stretched before him, and he gladly left the top of the tree and entered it. He walked through the maize without knowing where he was going, when he heard a sound of knocking, and saw two old blind women crushing their food between two stones. He crept up to them on tiptoe, and when one old woman passed her dinner to the other he held out his hand and took it and ate if for himself.

"How slow you are kneading that cake," cried the other old woman at last.

"Why, I have given you your dinner, and what more do you want?" replied the second.

"You didn't; at least I never got it," said the other.

"I certainly thought you took it from me, but here is some more." And again the young man stretched out his hand, and the two old women fell

127

to quarreling afresh. But when it happened for the third time the old women suspected some trick, and one of them exclaimed, "I am sure there is a man here. Tell me, are you not my grandson?"

"Yes," answered the young man, who wished to please her, "and in return for your good dinner I will see if I cannot restore your sight; for I was taught the art of healing by the best medicine man in the tribe." And with that he left them, and wandered about till he found the herb which he wanted. Then he hastened back to the old women, and begging them to boil him some water, he threw the herb in. As soon as the pot began to sing he took off the lid, and sprinkled the eyes of the women, and sight came back to them once more.

There was no night in that country, so, instead of going to bed very early, as he would have done in his own hut, the young man took another walk. A splashing noise near by drew him down to a valley through which ran a large river, and up a waterfall some salmon were leaping. How their silver sides glistened in the light, and how he longed to catch some of the great fellows! But how could he do it? He had beheld no one except the old women, and it was not very likely that they would be able to help him. So with a sigh he turned away and went back to them, but, as he walked, a thought struck him. He pulled out one of his hairs which hung nearly to his waist, and it instantly became a strong line, nearly a mile in length.

"Weave me a net that I may catch some salmon," said he. And they wove him the net he asked for, and for many weeks he watched by the river, only going back to the old women when he wanted a fish cooked.

At last, one day, when he was eating his dinner, the old woman who always spoke first, said to him, "We have been very glad to see you, grandson, but now it is time that you went home." And pushing aside a rock, he saw a deep hole, *so* deep that he could not see to the bottom. Then they dragged a basket out of the house, and tied a rope to it. "Get in, and wrap this blanket around your head," said they, "and, whatever happens, don't uncover it till you get to the bottom." Then they bade him farewell, and he curled himself up in the basket.

Down, down, down he went; would he *ever* stop going? But when the basket *did* stop, the young man forgot what he had been told, and put his head out to see what what was the matter. In an instant the basket moved, but, to his horror, instead of going down, he felt himself being drawn upward, and shortly after he beheld the faces of the old women.

"You will never see your wife and son if you will not do as you are bid," said they. "Now get in, and do not stir till you hear a crow calling."

128

This time the young man was wiser, and though the basket often stopped, and strange creatures seemed to rest on him and to pluck at his blanket, he held it tight till he heard the crow calling. Then he flung off the blanket and sprang out, while the basket vanished in the sky.

He walked on quickly down the track that led to the hut, when, before him, he saw his wife with his little son on her back.

"Oh! There is father at last," cried the boy, but the mother bade him cease from idle talking.

"But, mother, it is true, father is coming!" repeated the child. And, to satisfy him, the woman turned around and perceived her husband.

Oh, how glad they all were to be together again! And when the wind whistled through the forest, and the snow stood in great banks round the door, the father used to take the little boy on his knee and tell him how he caught salmon in the Land of the Sun.

The Boy and the Wolves

Once upon a time an Indian hunter built himself a house in the middle of a great forest, far away from all his tribe; for his heart was gentle and kind, and he was weary of the treachery and cruel deeds of those who had been his friends. So he left them, and took his wife and three children, and they journeyed on until they found a spot near to a clear stream, where they began to cut down trees, and to make ready their wigwam. For many years they lived peacefully and happily in this sheltered place, never leaving it except to hunt the wild animals, which served them both for food and clothes. At last, however, the strong man felt sick, and before long he knew he must die.

So he gathered his family around him, and said his last words to them. "You, my wife, the companion of my days, will follow me ere many moons have waned to the island of the blest. But for you, O my children, whose lives are but newly begun, the wickedness, unkindness, and ingratitude from which I fled are before you. Yet I shall go hence in peace, my children, if you will promise always to love each other, and never to forsake your youngest brother."

"Never!" they replied, holding out their hands. And the hunter died content.

Scarcely eight moons had passed when, just as he had said, the wife went forth, and followed her husband; but before leaving her children she bade the two elder ones think of their promise never to forsake the younger, for he was a child, and weak. And while the snow lay thick upon the ground, they tended him and cherished him; but when the earth showed green again, the heart of the young man stirred within him, and he longed to see the wigwams of the village where his father's youth was spent.

Therefore he opened all his heart to his sister, who answered, "My brother, I understand your longing for our fellow men, whom here we cannot see. But remember our father's words. Shall we not seek our own pleasures, and forget the little one?"

But he would not listen, and, making no reply, he took his bow and arrows and left the hut. The snows fell and melted, yet he never returned; and at last the heart of the girl grew cold and hard, and her little boy became a burden in her eyes, till one day she spoke thus to him, "See, there is food for many days to come. Stay here within the shelter of the hut. I go to seek our brother, and when I have found him I shall return hither."

But when, after hard journeying, she reached the village where her brother dwelt, and saw that he had a wife and was happy, and when she, too, was sought by a young brave, then she also forgot the boy alone in the forest and thought only of her husband.

Now, as soon as the little boy had eaten all the food which his sister had left him, he went out into the woods, and gathered berries and dug up roots, and while the sun shone he was contented and had his fill. But when the snows began and the wind howled, then his stomach felt empty and his limbs cold, and he hid in trees all the night, and only crept out to eat what the wolves had left behind. And by and by, having no other friends, he sought their company, and sat by while they devoured their prey, and they grew to know him, and gave him food. And without them he would have died in the snow.

But at last the snows melted, and the ice upon the great lake, and as the wolves went down to the shore, the boy went after them. And it happened one day that his big brother was fishing in his canoe near the shore, and he heard the voice of a child singing in the Indian tone.

"My brother, my brother!
I am becoming a wolf,
I am becoming a wolf!"

And when he had so sung he howled as wolves howl. Then the heart of the elder sunk, and he hastened toward him, crying, "Brother, little brother, come to me", but he, being half a wolf, only continued his song. And the louder the elder called him, "Brother, little brother, come to me," the swifter he fled after his brothers the wolves, and the heavier grew his skin, till, with a long howl, he vanished into the depths of the forest.

So, with shame and anguish in his soul, the elder brother went back to his village, and, with his sister, mourned the little boy and the broken promise till the end of his life.

Sailors' Yarns and Fishy Tales

Captain Ichabod Paddock and the Whale

Once upon a time, and not so very long ago, the main business of many of the fishing ports of New England was whaling. At one time hundreds of ships set out after the whales, and there are many stories and legends from the old whaling industry in Massachusetts. The most famous is *Moby Dick*, a novel by Herman Melville, which tells how Captain Ahab pursued the great white whale. Melville probably got the idea from true accounts of a fierce white whale which is said to have caused the deaths of more than 30 men in the 1840s—not long before he began writing *Moby Dick*.

But the tales of the whalers go back much further than that. Captain Paddock was a famous whaling master in early colonial times. I believe there is still a tavern named after him in Nantucket, for he seems to have been a real person, although this is a fairy story.

For many years Ichabod Paddock had been hunting a great sperm whale which bore the scars of many a battle and, because of some injury he had suffered to his big lower jaw, was known as Crook-Jaw. Captain Paddock had slain many whales, big and small, by throwing his harpoon from a boat, and he had many times thrown his harpoon at Crook-Jaw. But the iron spike bounced off his hide like a dull axe on green pine, or else it broke into a hundred pieces against his tough old hide.

In the end, Captain Paddock came to the conclusion the whale was bewitched, and he swore he would find out what kind of spell lay on the creature if it were the last thing he did.

Not so long afterward, he found Crook-Jaw basking on the surface sound asleep, and snoring like a sinner on a Sunday morning. He dropped anchor about a mile off, got out of his heavy leggings, and dived into the sea. He swam straight up to the whale—and then he waited, treading water. After about half an hour, Crook-Jaw opened his great mouth wide in a yawn. You could have driven a horse and cart into that mouth. Ichabod did not hesitate. He dived straight in, past rows of teeth, and down the whale's gullet.

It was dark inside the whale, and the air was close, but the Captain spied a light glimmering far below and set off toward it. He found it came from a snug little cabin, with a lamp standing on the table, and on either side of the table two people were playing cards. One was a beautiful maiden, with hair the color of ripe corn, skin the color of plum blossom, and eyes as green as the sea. The other was the Devil.

As Ichabod entered the cabin, the Devil flung his cards down on the table and swore. "I lose!" he grunted, got up, kicked over his chair in a temper, and vanished.

"Good day, ma'am," said the Captain, "I'm sorry to have broken up your game."

The maiden laughed, and the sound was like the ripple of water on the bows of a boat. "The game was finished," she said, giving Ichabod an eager kind of look.

"Your friend seemed put out," said Ichabod. "Can a body inquire what stakes you were playing for?"

She raised her deep green eyes at him and said softly, "Captain Paddock, *you* were the stakes."

The gallant Captain gazed deep into her eyes and, strong man though he was, he began to feel a mite weak in the joints.

Time passed, and back on the ship the crew were ready to give the Captain up for lost. But as dawn was breaking, they saw someone swimming toward them, very slowly, as if he were tired. The Captain pulled himself aboard.

He told them nothing of what had happened, but the next evening he shed his heavy leggings again and slipped over the side. His crew saw him no more until he appeared at dawn, slowly swimming back.

This happened for many nights—until the ship was due for re-rigging. And after that had been done, the Captain sailed back to where Crook-Jaw lay dozing and again disappeared each night over the side, to return at first light in the morning. After a few weeks of this, Captain Paddock was in danger of losing his reputation as a great whale master, and his crew were beginning to grumble. The Captain said nothing, and there was talk that he was not right in the head.

The next time he came ashore, his wife, a handsome woman still the right side of 30, gave him a present. It was a harpoon of shining silver. The Captain was very pleased, but he also felt a mite guilty, as it reminded him of his neglected profession. He was not so pleased when his wife said she wanted her father to go with him next time he put to sea.

A few days later they set out, and they were not far beyond the surf when old Crook-Jaw spotted the Captain's ship. Now by this time things were different between them. Crook-Jaw saw the Captain as, if not a close friend, at least an honored guest, and he swam right up to them.

The Captain's father-in-law grew excited. "Look at the size of him!" he shouted, and he could not wait to get the boat lowered. Ichabod could not very well refuse, so they climbed into the small boat and, with his father-in-law urging him on, Ichabod launched his shiny new harpoon right at Crook-Jaw. He was not worried because he'd done it so often before without causing the whale any damage at all. But to his amazement, the harpoon stuck right in. He had old Crook-Jaw fast. Well, the great whale heaved and churned and lashed at the water but, in the end, he died. The Captain's father-in-law could not understand why Ichabod was not more pleased.

When they cut up the whale, all Ichabod found inside, where his cozy cabin had been, was a strand of seaweed bleached the color of ripe corn, a shell the color of plum blossom, and two stones like emeralds, as green as the sea.

Of course, that harpoon his wife gave him was made of silver, and silver is the only thing that will pierce the heart of a witch.

The Sea Serpent

A few years after the first colonists had settled in Massachusetts, a giant sea serpent was seen curled up on a rock off Cape Ann. A gentleman in a passing boat was about to take a shot at it, but he was stopped by an Indian who told him it would bring bad luck.

A couple hundred years later, the serpent turned up again. It was seen in Nahant Bay and around the harbor of Gloucester, Massachusetts. Many people saw it, as it hung about there for about two weeks, and although it did not come out on any rock, it was once seen half on the shore. It caused a great scare, and a reward was offered for its capture, dead or alive.

It was most often seen lolling in the waves, with its back showing like a row of arches. It would swim fast, or it would dawdle along as if it had all the time in the world. One captain who saw it from his ship said it was as long as the mainmast of a 74-gun warship; another said it took him 15 minutes to sail from its head to its tail, although he had a six-knot breeze behind him. It had a smooth skin that was dark brown or black, a long forked tongue and an eye like the eye of an ox.

As word got around, people rushed to the beaches of northern Massachusetts in hopes of catching a sight of it. Some went out in small boats to have a closer look, and a few of the whalers tried to catch it for the reward. A revenue cutter was sent to hunt it but never got in a shot. One man said he fired his bird gun at its head, but it didn't seem to notice. It never took any notice of anything, and it never was heard to make a sound. It was last seen in Long Island Sound.

That was over 150 years ago, and the serpent hasn't been seen since.

The Pirates' Treasure

Once, not long after the United States gained its independence, a young man known as Black Sam was fishing in the waters off Long Island, when he was caught by a sudden storm which drove him off course and forced him to take shelter in a little cove he did not know. He decided to wait in the shelter of the rocky cove, which was also sheltered by the branches of trees growing over it, until the storm stopped. It was already getting dark, and after a while Sam dozed off to sleep.

When he awoke it was about midnight—so far as he could judge by the state of the tide. The storm had stopped, and all was quiet. He prepared for the long row home, but as he was about to cast off, he heard the sound of a boat approaching, and peering out over the dark water he saw the glimmer of a light.

As Sam retreated into the cover of the trees, a boat pulled in to the other side of the cove. There were five men in the boat, one wearing a three-cornered hat, the others woolen caps. They were rough-looking fellows, and heavily armed. After mooring their boat, they made their way up the bank. They seemed to be carrying something large and heavy between them. Sam heard one of them say, "This is the place—look—the iron ring."

As Sam cautiously shifted his position, a branch cracked. "What's that?" came a hoarse cry, and the sound of a pistol being cocked. The men stopped and their leader, who was carrying a lantern, raised it high so the light fell on the leaves below which Sam was hiding. But they did not see him.

The men advanced further into the woods, and pretty soon Sam heard the clink and thunk of digging. In spite of his fear, he carefully climbed the rocks to a place where he could see what was going on. By the time he reached it, the men were filling in a large hole. Suddenly, Sam knew what they had buried. They were murderers, and they had come in secret to this deserted spot to hide the body of their victim!

The startling thought made Sam cry out the word, "Murderers!" Five villainous heads turned toward him, and the moonlight glinted on pistol barrels as the man in the three-cornered hat yelled, "Discovered!"

Sam rolled sideways off the rock toward the cover of the brush, and with the aid of a trailing vine, he swung himself up on to another rock beyond. But for an instant he stood on the top of the rock and, dark as it was, he was outlined against the sky. A shot whistled past his head.

With great presence of mind, Sam let out a cry as though he'd been hit, fell flat, and at the same time kicked a rock over the edge of the cliff. It fell into the sea with a loud splash, and he heard one of the men say, with a cruel laugh, "He'll tell no tales—except to the fish!"

When the men had left in their boat, Sam clambered down to his own little skiff and set off for home.

He did not go back to that cove, and for some time he said nothing of what he had seen. What good was it to report a possible murder by men he did not know of someone he knew not who? But, after some time had passed, Sam did tell someone what he had seen that night, and eventually the story became quite well-known.

One of those who came to hear it was Wolfert Webber, and he was interested in it because it seemed to him there might be a different explanation of what Sam had seen. By the time Webber came around to doing something about it, Sam was an old man, still fit and clear in the head, but white-haired. Without saying what he suspected, Webber asked Sam if he would guide him to the place where he had seen the "body" buried.

After so many years, Sam had lost his fear of the place, and he agreed. But after so many years, could he still find it? The two men walked along the shore, in those days still wild and overgrown, and eventually they found the cove where Sam had taken shelter from the storm. At first he wasn't quite sure that it was the right cove, but what clinched it was his discovery of an iron ring, driven into a rock. Here the men had tied their boat.

Finding the grave was more difficult. Somehow the place seemed to have changed, and Sam wasn't sure where the men had gone or where he had hidden to watch them. He thought it was over there, near the mulberry tree—but no, perhaps it was there, by that mossy rock? Or was it up that way? The light was beginning to fail, so Webber made a few rough plans of the place and they gave up. On their way back they passed near a ruined house, where no one had lived for many years. Walking up the path they saw a man, wearing a red woolen cap the color of blood. He scowled and shook his fist at them, and he looked altogether so frightful that they both fled at top speed and did not stop until they came to a road leading to the city.

Webber soon got over his fright, and he was all the more eager to find the place where *something* had been buried. But how was it to be done, since Sam could no longer remember exactly where it was? He sought help from a mysterious doctor by the name of Knipperhausen, a man expert in many strange crafts, who was said to have been a successful treasure-hunter many years ago.

The three of them, Webber, old Sam, and Dr. Knipperhausen,

returned to the cove, bringing certain things the doctor said would be needed. One of them was a divining rod. When they reached the clearing where Sam thought the object of their search must lie, the doctor padded around with the divining rod held out in front of him. After a long time, the rod suddenly dipped downward, and Knipperhausen exclaimed in great excitement, "This is the spot!"

It was now dark, but the doctor said it was necessary to perform certain rites in the darkness for their search to be successful. He drew a rough circle around the place where the divining rod had dipped, and lit a fire, on which he burned strange herbs. They set up a nasty-smelling smoke, which made the others cough. Then he read a kind of spell from a book in a foreign language. When all these preparations were complete, he told Sam to start digging.

Sam set to work. The ground was not too hard and he soon had a hole two or three feet deep. He thrust in the spade again, and it struck against something hard. A few seconds scraping and scrabbling revealed a squareish piece of wood, bound in brass.

"A chest!" Sam exclaimed.

"A *treasure* chest!" said Webber. "We shall be rich!"

As they gathered around and Sam prepared to break open the lid, something made them all look up. Staring down at them from a rock was the hideous face of a buccaneer with a murderous light in his eyes.

Sam dropped the spade, Webber dropped the lantern, they all yelled in terror. And then they ran. Blindly, in different directions, careless of scratching briars, tangling vines, and bruising rocks—they ran as long as they had breath. Webber felt someone grab his cloak, a pistol went off close behind him, and he heard a terrible curse and the sound of men fighting. Moments later, he fell over the cliff at the edge of the cove and tumbled among the rocks, knocking himself unconscious.

Webber's wife had sent a friend in a boat to keep watch over the treasure hunters, and it was in this boat, as dawn was breaking, that Webber regained consciousness. The others also made their way home somehow, frightened, bleeding, and exhausted.

None of them ventured to that cove again, but when the story got around, others, not frightened of ghostly pirates, set out to look for the treasure chest. A great deal of digging went on, and no more pirates were seen. Neither was the treasure chest. It seems that it was necessary to have the right spell to reveal its hiding place. Dr. Knipperhausen had succeeded, but his days of treasure-hunting were over, and the pirates' treasure—if it is treasure—remains undiscovered to this day.

Captain Santos's Wooden Leg

Not many people now remember Captain Santos. He had his leg bitten off by a shark, but they fixed him up with a wooden one, which he declared was better than the original. How proud he was of that wooden leg! He used to carry around furniture polish in case it got scratched, and he put copper on the bottom to make sure the worms wouldn't get into it, as they do in the hull of a ship.

There's a saying—you've all heard it—that once a shark puts his mark on a man, that man is doomed to be eaten by sharks if he keeps on going to sea. Captain Santos, wooden leg and all, kept on going to sea.

One day his trawler got caught in a bad November gale. It was feared that she had gone under, but the following day she limped in to port minus most of her sails and rigging. And minus three men—two members of the crew and Captain Santos. They had been washed overboard at the height of the gale, and no one had seen them again.

A day or two later the bodies of the two crew men drifted ashore, but not the Captain's. Then, two days after that, Captain Santos's wooden leg was washed up on the beach. The man who found it there took it to the Captain's grieving widow, Mary. They had been married for 30 years. Mary Santos took the leg into the house, petting it and talking to it, as it was the only part of her husband she had left. Later, she stored it in the spice cupboard.

Exactly one year after the night of the gale in which the Captain was lost, something strange happened. Mary was asleep in bed when she woke up, suddenly, and saw the Captain standing there on his one leg. He hopped over to the bed and said, "The barometer's falling, Mary, and the wind's in the north-east. We're in for thick weather, and I'll want my wooden leg to keep me steady when the storm strikes." He lent forward and pinched her cheek, at which Mary gave a yell and shut her eyes. When she opened them again, the Captain was gone.

Next morning, Mary said, she had a little red mark on her cheek, although it soon faded. She took the Captain's wooden leg out of the spice cupboard and left it ready for him in a corner near the fireplace. Just in case.

When she went to bed that night, the wind was already rising, and it was in the north-east. In a couple of hours it had turned into a genuine gale, and the willow tree outside was beating against the wall as if it wanted to come in out of the storm. Then Mary heard a thump, thump, thump across the floor below, and the sound of the door banging shut.

She stayed right where she was, in bed.

Next morning she went to see if the Captain's leg was still there. It was—in the corner where she'd put it—but it was wet.

Well, it had rained enough in the night to come down the chimney. All the same, the sight of that leg, wet through as it was, preyed on Mary's mind until she became sick.

She called in the doctor, but he couldn't find anything wrong. "Come on, now, Mary," said the Doc. "Something's eating you. What is it?"

And she told him the whole story.

The Doc smiled to himself and went over to look at the leg, and examined it closely. "You say you left it by the fireplace all night and rain came down the chimney and wet it?" he said to Mary. He was not smiling now, not even to himself.

"That's right, Doctor," Mary told him.

He came over and sat down beside her. "Mary," he said, "I'm going to ask one of the men to take that leg out to sea and weight it down and sink it. I'm a physician," he said, "and I don't listen to stories. But," he said, "I put my tongue to that wood, Mary, and *it doesn't rain salt water.*"

Old Stormalong

Just as the lumberjacks have Paul Bunyan and the steel workers have Joe Maragac, sailors have their own "superhero", Old Stormalong.

There are different estimates of Stormalong's size, but it is generally agreed that he measured four fathoms from the neck to the bridge of his nose.

He was the first sailor to have "A.B." after his name. You probably thought this stands for "Able-Bodied (seaman)". But it was just old Stormalong's initials. His full name was Alfred Bulltop Stormalong.

One strange thing about Stormalong: He was always loyal to the ship he was sailing in—until he saw a bigger ship. Then he wasn't happy until he had signed on with the bigger one. He always complained that ships weren't built big enough for a full-sized man.

"All I ever knowed about him," said one old Cape Cod skipper, "was that he took his whale soup in a dory (a small boat) and that his favorite meat was shark. He liked ostrich eggs for breakfast, and after he'd eaten them he would lie on the deck and pick his teeth with an oar."

Stormalong was a sailor and a fisherman and a whaler. Once, he was on a ship achored in the middle of the North Atlantic looking for whales. The lookout sighted a shoal of them to the east and Stormalong, as bosun, gave the order to raise anchor. But no matter how many men pulled on it, the anchor would not come up. It would give a little, then stop and sink right back down into the mud. It felt as if giant hands were clutching at it and pulling it out of the seamen's grasp. After a while, though, the sailors succeeded in drawing it up far enough to see what the trouble was. A huge octopus had a-hold of it. He was hanging on to it with half his tentacles while the other half hung on to the seaweed on the bottom.

The mate went to tell the captain, and the captain came to have a look for himself. He was just in time to see Stormalong go overboard, with his sheath knife in his teeth. He disappeared below the surface and a terrific struggle began. The water was churned up so much the ship nearly capsized. Everyone on deck was sure the bosun had been torn apart by the octopus. The struggle went on out of sight for about a quarter of an hour, then Stormie's head came to the surface. Some one called out to throw him a line, but he just climbed up the anchor chain hand over hand till he reached the deck. The water was still churning somewhat, but it moved away from the ship.

"All right," yelled Stormie, "all hands lean on it and bring it home."

So they hauled the anchor in. Then they asked Stormie what he had done to the octopus. "I just tied its arms in knots—double Carrick bends," he said. "It'll take him a month of Sundays to untie them."

——— □ ———

How the Panama Canal was Dug

Now and then Old Stormalong would get tired of sailoring. "When this ship ges to port," he said one time, "I'm going to put an oar over my shoulder and I'm going to start walking away from salt water. I'm going to keep right on walking until someone says to me, 'What's that funny stick you have on your shoulder?' and right there I'm going to settle down and dig potatoes."

When the ship reached Boston, Stormalong signed off. He came on deck with his duffel bag over his shoulder.

"Where are you a-going?" his shipmates asked.

"Farming," he said. And he heaved the bag over the rail and followed it to the wharf. The crew just stood along the rail and gaped.

Several years later, when the same ship was again docked in Boston, a big, tall man was seen coming down the wharf.

"Stormie, or I'm a fool," said one of the sailors.

The big man came over the side and, sure enough it was Alfred Bulltop Stormalong. He looked different, however. He was taller than ever, but his flesh sort of hung on him and in his eyes were the signs of great suffering endured. He looked hungrily at the sea and breathed in deep breaths of the salt air. This seemed to bring back something of his old spirit.

"Stormie, where have you been?"

"Farming," he said.

"How did you like it?"

"Terrible. Nothing but green grass and trees and hills and hot work. Nary a breeze nor a smell of the sea. Nothing but hot winds, hot sun, and pushing on a plow. All my muscles were made for pulling, and on a farm there's nothing to do but push. Sailoring's the best job after all."

So he signed on for his old job of bosun, and the ship set off on a trading voyage to the Caribbean.

Six months later, as she was on her way back to Boston, she came in sight of the biggest ship you've ever seen. Her lines were perfect, her sails pure white and hung on silver masts.

The Fishery, American whaling print published by Currier & Ives, 1852

The Great Steamboat Race between Robert E Lee and the Natchez in 1870, from a painting by H Charles McBarron

That ship was so big that all officers and men on watch were mounted on horses. Her masts went up into the clouds, and her sails were so big that the builders had to take the sailmakers out to the Sahara Desert to find room to sew them. The captain, who gave his orders through a megaphone, had to order all hands aloft six days before a storm, and some who went up her rigging as young men came down as graybeards. Once the captain ordered all hands forrard and it took nearly a week for them all to get there. Some got lost because they had not brought their compasses with them.

Of course, the moment Stormalong saw the *Courser*, he had to sail on her. He didn't wait 'till they reached port. He just swam over to her during the night.

The *Courser* was so big she had to keep to the oceans. Other waterways were too small for her to turn about. But there was never a storm big enough as could cause her any trouble.

But one time she was caught in one of those big gales in the North Atlantic. The storm lasted two weeks, and it was so dark and foggy the sun was never seen. The *Courser* was blown way off her course, and when the storm stopped she was in the North Sea, which is the other side of the British Isles, and heading south.

That meant trouble, for the *Courser* could never get through the English Channel, where it's only 22 miles between England and France. But the North Sea wasn't big enough to turn around in. The skipper decided the only thing to do was to try to ease her through the Channel. Stormie was at the wheel (otherwise it took 32 men to turn her), and all sails were reefed.

"Will she make it?" the skipper yelled to Stormie through his megaphone.

"I think so!" was the answer. "May scrape a bit of paint off our sides, but she'll go through. Better send all hands over and soap the sides. Put an extra heavy coat on the starboard."

The skipper got the whole crew plastering the sides of the ship with soap, and the big ship eased through sweet as honey. It was such a tight fit that the cliffs of Dover scraped off all the soap on the starboard side. That's why those cliffs are white today. And if you are ever in the English Channel, you'll see that it is still a bit foamy from the soap.

The *Courser* kept on going, but the water was a bit shallow, so the crew had to jettison all the ballast. You can still see it. The English call it the Channel Islands.

There was only one other time when the *Courser* met a storm that was big enough to cause her any trouble. It was another September gale—the kind that causes so much damage down in Florida. This hurricane was strong enough to turn the ship about, and although the Captain wasn't afraid of losing the ship, he was afraid of hitting one of the Caribbean islands and knocking all the inhabitants into the sea. She just missed Haiti and headed west like a bronco with the bit between its teeth. Right through the Gulf she went until she came to the Isthmus of Panama. There was a bit of a bump and a few minutes later the *Courser* found herself in the Pacific Ocean. There were two army officers on the land who had been sent down by the United States to make surveys for a canal. Right in front of them the *Courser* dug the canal for them. Of course, they took all the credit afterward, but it was the *Courser*, with Old Stormalong at the wheel, who dug the Panama Canal.

The Weathervane

There was once an old whaling man, long retired from the sea, who lived on Cape Cod in a house with a weathervane on the roof. It was a fine weathervane, but it did not turn easily and the old man never oiled it because he was afraid he might fall off the roof. So when the weathervane got stuck pointing in the wrong direction, what he did was this.

He made himself a giant catapult out of a length of green rawhide and an ash tree bough that was conveniently forked. When the wind shifted, he took a pebble and fired it at the vane to make it point the right way. Sometimes it took him two hours or more, firing pebbles at the vane, until it pointed the way the wind was blowing, but he never gave up until he had got it right. But first, of course, he had to find out which way the wind *was* blowing, and he did that by wetting his finger and holding it up in the breeze.

The Giant Halibut

There was an old fisherman from Provincetown who, like Captain Santos, had a wooden leg from the knee, which was made from the butt of an oar. In his later years, when he looked old enough to have fished in the Flood, he used to enjoy telling how he had lost his leg.

"Twas a halibut took my leg off, though the crittur didn't mean no harm. Used to be a lot of 'em around inshore in those days, big fellers, shaped like a sole or a flounder, broad with both eyes on one side of their heads; spotted light and dark brown on the back and dead white underneath. Only place they get 'em now is well offshore, but in them days they used to run right in to the beach. They get 'em now that run to three or four hundred pound, but there was bigger ones than that when I was young.

"A halibut is a bottom fish, but there's times when they come up. They'll lay almost awash, with their sides and fins curled up like a saucer. Just lay there. What for? The Lord only knows.

"Well, this day I was hauling lobster pots and doing a little handlining. I was running along under sail in my boat, making good time before a light southerly that was blowing, and glad of it too because fog was coming up. I must have been three miles from land when I fetched up solid. Pretty nigh capsized. Figured 'twas a piece of driftwood, and went forrard to look for damage. It looked like I was aground, but the sea bottom didn't look like no bottom I ever seen before, and besides there should have been 40 feet of water there.

"I got clear and put off, wondering about it. I run on clear for maybe 20 minutes, then tacked inshore and—bingo! I was aground again! About six times I hit before took it in that there was *something* between me and home. Then, just as I pushed off the last time, I noticed a flurry some fathoms ahead of me, and I see something big break water, an oval brown thing that opened and shut. It was a head—but what a head! I could see two eyes, and the distance between them was twice the length of a whaleboat oar. Looking around they was.

"By an' by I realized what the eyes belonged to. A halibut! Lying awash. I had been sailing across his saucer-like back for nigh on an hour!

"How to get clear—that was the question. I figured I'd run on to his fin, climb out, stand on it and hang on to my boat, which might be light enough to ride over. I headed for where I knew his side lay, but I miscalculated some and hit it before I expected. Hit it hardish, too.

Then I jumped over the bow to haul the boat over, if I could. I felt something hit my knee, and felt a terrible pain. I got back in the boat and tied a line around to stop the bleeding, then I took an oar and tried to shove the boat over. As she moved ahead and went clear, I saw what had done the damage.

"I had struck that fish solid and knocked up a couple of its scales. There they were, four foot across, sharp as a meat ax, hard as flint, and standing half on edge. I had stumbled on to one, and later, when some of the bunch picked me up, they found that my leg was so nigh cut off that they had to finish the job."

You could hear stories a lot less probable than that in the old Sandwich Tavern after a round or two of rum.

The Friendly Shark

Old Tom told how he had once been given a bottle of rum by the mate of the *Nancy*. As he and the mate didn't get along, he was suspicious the rum might be poisoned, so he tipped it over the side. A shark alongside happened to open his mouth at that moment and received a dose of grog.

Was that shark happy? Why, he followed the *Nancy* like a dog, all the way around the Horn and across the Pacific till they came to the island of Tahiti. There Tom went ashore, and when the shark got no more grog, he took to worrying, and cruised around the shoreline looking for his old friend Tom. By and by he found him, sitting on a cliff, playing his guitar and singing songs to a lady who was dressed in flowers. The shark stuck his snout over the cliff, opened his mouth and bared his teeth, like a long row of white tomb-stones.

That gave Tom a nasty fright and he jammed his guitar down the shark's throat. It went down sideways and stuck in his gullet. Thereafter, whenever the shark swallowed, he made beautiful music.

Another time Tom was swallowed by a whale. It was a killer whale, which came up under the boat and smashed it, throwing Tom into the water, still holding his oar. Once inside the whale, Tom struck a flint and looked around. He tickled its ribs for a while, hoping it would cough him up. That didn't work so he took his knife and stabbed it in the heart. After a while it died, but when Tom came up to take a look, he found he was way up in the Arctic. Icebergs were clinging to the killer's whiskers. So he went back down inside where it was warm, cut a hole in the back of the whale and stuck his oar through it. Then he rowed back to Fairhaven.

Was that before or after the time Tom was caught by cannibals in Africa and they wouldn't boil him because he was too tough? I forget.

How to Get Out of Ireland

An old skipper by the name of Asey said he had once sailed to Ireland and got his bows stuck hard in the wharf at Queenstown harbor.

"How're you a-going to get her out?" his first mate asked.

Asey scratched his head and looked on shore where a whole lot of Irishmen was standing and laughing at him. Then the Captain grinned. He took off his hat and waved it in the air, shouting, "God Save King George! Hooray for Parliament! God Save England!"

The Irish were that mad they pushed the prow so hard out of Queenstown harbor that the ship shot across the Atlantic backward.

Animal
Yarns

The Big Bear of Arkansas

The Big Bear of Arkansas is a classic story of the backwoods, written by T. B. Thorpe and first published in 1841. I have made a few small changes, but I haven't changed the woodsman's dialect.

It is a story within a story. The first story-teller is an ordinary, rather dull and serious man traveling on a Mississippi steamboat. He tells how the variegated company on the boat is joined by Jim Doggett, a backwoodsman from Arkansas, who keeps them amused with tall tales of the woods. It is Jim Doggett himself who is "the big bar (bear) of Arkansaw" and the subject of the main story. An actual bear is the subject of Jim Doggett's story-within-the-story.

A steamboat on the Mississippi frequently, in making her regular trips, carries between places varying from 1,000–2,000 miles apart. And as these boats advertise to land passengers and freight at "all intermediate landings," the variety of the passengers of one of these up-country boats can scarcely be imagined by one who has never seen it with his own eyes. Starting from New Orleans in one of these boats, you will find yourself associated with men from every state in the Union, and from every portion of the globe. Here may be seen jostling together the wealthy southern planter, and the pedlar of tin-ware from New England—the northern merchant, and the southern jockey—a venerable bishop, and a desperate gambler—the land speculator, and the honest farmer—professional men of all creeds and characters—Wolvereens, Suckers, Hoosiers, Buckeyes, and Corn-crackers, beside a plentiful sprinkling of the half-horse and half-alligator species of men, who are peculiar to old Mississippi, and who appear to gain a livelihood simply by going up and down the river. In the pursuit of pleasure or business, I have frequently found myself in such a crowd.

On one occasion, when in New Orleans, I had occasion to take a trip of a few miles up the Mississippi, and I hurried on board the well-known "high-pressure-and-beat-every-thing" steamboat *Invincible*, just as the last note of the last bell was sounding. As my trip was to be of a few hours' duration only, I made no endeavors to become acquainted with my fellow passengers, most of whom would be together many days. Instead of this, I took out of my pocket the latest paper, and more critically than usual examined its contents; my fellow passengers at the same time disposed themselves in little groups.

While I was thus busily employed in reading, and my companions were more busily employed in discussing such subjects as suited them, we were startled most unexpectedly by a loud Indian whoop, uttered in that part of the cabin fitted off for a bar. Then was to be heard a loud crowing, which would not have continued to have interested us—such sounds being quite common in that place of spirits—had not the hero of these windy accomplishments stuck his head into the cabin and hallooed out, "Hurra for the Big Bar of Arkansaw!". And then might be heard a confused hum of voices, unintelligible, save in such broken sentences as "horse," "screamer," "lightning is slow," etc. As might have been expected, this continued interruption attracted the attention of everyone in the cabin. All conversation dropped, and in the midst of this surprise the "Big Bar" walked into the cabin, took a chair, put his feet on the stove, and looking back over his shoulder, passed the general and familiar salute of "Strangers, how are you?" He then expressed himself as much at home as if he had been at "the Forks of Cypress," and "perhaps a little more so." Some of the company at this familiarity looked a little angry, and some astonished; but in a moment every face was wreathed in a smile

There was something about the intruder that won the heart on sight. He appeared to be a man enjoying perfect health and contentment. His eyes were as sparkling as diamonds, and good-natured to simplicity. Then his perfect confidence in himself was irresistibly droll.

"Perhaps," said he, "gentlemen," running on without a person speaking, "perhaps you have been to New Orleans often. I never made *the first visit before*, and I don't intend to make another in a crow's life. I am thrown away in that ar place, and useless, that ar a fact. Some of the gentlemen thar called me *green*—well, perhaps I am, said I, *but I arn't so at home*. And if I ain't off my trail much, the heads of them perlite chaps themselves weren't much the hardest. For according to my notion, they were real *know-nothings*, green as a pumpkin vine—couldn't, in farming, I'll bet, raise a crop of turnips: And as for shooting, they'd miss a barn if the door was swinging, and that, too, with the best rifle in the country. And then they talked to me 'bout hunting, and laughed at my calling the principal game in Arkansaw poker."

" 'Perhaps,' said I, 'you prefer roulette,' at this they laughed harder than ever, and asked me if I lived in the woods, and didn't know what *game* was? At this I rather think I laughed. 'Strangers,' I said, 'if you'd asked me *how we got our meat* in Arkansaw, I'd a-told you at once, and given you a list of varmints that would make a caravan, beginning with the bar, and ending off with the cat; that's *meat* though, not game.'"

"Game, indeed that's what city folks call it. And with them it means chippen-birds and shite-pokes; maybe such trash live in my diggins, but I arn't noticed them yet. A bird anyway is too trifling. I never did shoot at but one, and I'd never forgiven myself for that, had it weighed less than forty pounds. I wouldn't draw a rifle on any thing less than that; and when I meet with another wild turkey of the same weight I will drop him."

"A wild turkey weighing forty pounds!" exclaimed 20 voices in the cabin at once.

"Yes, strangers, and wasn't it a whopper? You see, the thing was so fat that it couldn't fly far."

"Where did that happen?" asked a cynical-looking Hoosier.

"Happen? Happened in Arkansaw! Where else could it have happened, but in the creation state, the finishing-up country—a state where the *sile* [soil] runs down the center of the 'arth, and government gives you a title to every inch of it? Then its airs—just breathe them, and they will make you snort like a horse. It's a state without a fault, it is."

"Excepting mosquitoes," cried the Hoosier.

"Well, stranger, except them; for it ar a fact that they are rather *enormous*, and do push themselves in somewhat troublesome. But, stranger, they never stick twice in the same place; and give them a fair chance for a few months, and you will get as much above noticing them as an alligator. They can't hurt my feelings, for they lay under the skin; and I never knew but one case of injury resulting from them, and that was to a Yankee. And they take worse to foreigners, anyhow, than they do to natives. But the way they used that fellow up! First they punched him until he swelled up and busted. Then he su-per-a-ted, as the doctor called it, until he was as raw as beef; then he took the ague, owing to the warm weather, and finally he took a steamboat and left the country. He was the only man that ever took mosquitoes to heart that I know of. But mosquitoes is natur, and I never find fault with her. If they ar large, Arkansaw is large, her varmints ar large, her trees ar large, her rivers ar large, and a small mosquito would be of no more use in Arkansaw than preaching in a canebrake."

This knock-down argument in favor of big mosquitoes used the Hoosier up, and the logician started on a new track, to explain how numerous bear were in his "diggins," where he represented them to be "about as plenty as blackberries, and a little plentifuler."

Upon the utterance of his assertion, a timid little man near me inquired if the bear in Arkansaw ever attacked the settlers in numbers. "No," said our hero, warming with the subject, "no, stranger, for you see it ain't the natur of bar to go in droves; but the way they squander about in pairs and single ones is edifying. And the way I hunt them the old black rascals know the crack of my gun as well as they know a pig's squealing. They grow thin in our parts, it frightens them so, and they do take the noise dreadfully, poor things. That gun of mine is perfect *epidemic among bar*; if not watched closely, it will go off as quick on a warm scent as my dog bowie-knife will. And then that dog—whew! why the fellow thinks that the world is full of bar, he finds them so easy. It's lucky he don't talk as well as think; for with his natural modesty, if he should suddenly learn how much he is acknowledged to be ahead of all other dogs in the universe, he would be astonished to death in two minutes. Strangers, the dog knows a bar's way as well as a horse-jockey knows a woman's. He always barks at the right times, bites at the exact place, and whips without getting a scratch. I never could tell whether he was made expressly to hunt bar, or whether bar was made expressly for him to hunt. Anyway, I believe they were ordained to go together as naturally as Squire Jones says a man and woman is, when he moralizes in marrying a couple."

"What season of the year do your hunts take place?" inquired a gentlemanly foreigner, who, from some peculiarities of his baggage, I suspected to be an Englishman.

"The season for bar hunting, stranger," said the man of Arkansaw, "is generally all the year round, and the hunts take place about as regular. I read in history that varmints have their fat season, and their lean season. That is not the case in Arkansaw, feeding as they do upon the *spontenacious* productions of the sile, they have one continued fat season the year round. Though in winter things in this way is rather more greasy than in summer, I must admit. For that reason bar with us run in warm weather, but in winter, they only waddle. Fat, fat! it's an enemy to speed; it tames everything that has plenty of it. I have seen wild turkeys, from its influence, as gentle as chickens. Run a bar in this fat condition, and the way it improves the critter for eating is amazing; it sort of mixes the ile [oil] up with the meat, until you can't tell t'other from which. I've done this often. I recollect one perty morning in particular, of putting an old fellow on the stretch, and considering the weight he carried, he run well. But the dogs soon tired him down, and when I came up with him wasn't he in a beautiful sweat—I might say fever; and then to see his tongue sticking out of his mouth a foot, and his sides sinking and opening like a bellows, and his cheeks so fat he couldn't look cross. In this fix I blazed at him, and pitch me naked into a briar patch if the steam didn't come of the bullet-hole ten foot in a straight line. The fellow, I reckon was made on the high-pressure system, and the lead sort of bust his biler [boiler]."

"That column of steam was rather curious, or else the bear must have been *warm*," observed the foreigner, with a laugh.

"Stranger, as you observe, that bar was *warm*, and the blowing off of the steam show'd it, and also how hard the varmint had been run. I have no doubt if he had kept on two miles farther his insides would have been stewed."

"Whereabouts are these bears so abundant?" inquired the foreigner.

"Why, stranger, they inhabit the neighborhood of my settlement, one of the prettiest places on old Mississippi—a perfect location, and no mistake. A place that had some defects until the river made the cut-off at Shirt-tail Bend, and that remedied the evil, as it brought my cabin on the edge of the river—a great advantage in wet weather, I assure you, as you can now roll a barrel of whiskey into my yard in high water from a boat, as easy as falling off a log. It's a great improvement, as toting it by land in a jug, as I used to do, *evaporated* it too fast, and it became expensive. Just stop with me, stranger, a month or two, or a year if you like, and you will appreciate my place. I can give you plenty to eat. For beside hog and hominy, you can have bar ham, and bar sausages, and a mattrass of bar-skins to sleep on, and a wildcat-skin, pulled off hull [whole], stuffed with corn shucks, for a pillow. That bed would put you to sleep if you had the rheumatics in every joint in your body. I call that ar bed a *quietus*.

"Then look at my land—the government ain' got another such a piece to dispose of. Such timber, and such bottom land, why you can't preseve anything natural you plant in it unless you pick it young, things thar will grow out of shape so quick. I once planted in those diggins a few potatoes and beets. They took a fine start, and after that an ox team couldn't have kept them from growing. About that time I went off to old Kentuck on bisiness, and did not hear from them things in three months, when I accidentally stumbled on a fellow who had stopped at my place, with an idea of buying me out.

"'How did you like things?' said I. 'Pretty well,' said he; 'the cabin is convenient, and the timber land is good; but that bottom land ain't worth the first red cent.' 'Why?' said I. ''Cause,' said he. ''Cause what?' said I. ''Cause it's full of cedar stumps and Indian mounds,' said he, '*and it can't be cleared*.' 'Lord,' said I, 'them ar "cedar stumps" is beets, and them ar "Indian mounds" ar tater hills.' As I expected, the crop was overgrown and useless: the sile is too rich.

The questioner, who thus elicited the description of our hero's settlement, seemed to be perfectly satisfied, and said no more; but the "Big Bar of Arkansaw" rambled on from one thing to another with a volubility perfectly astonishing, occasionally disputing with those around him, particularly with a "live Sucker" from Illinois, who had the daring to say that our Arkansaw friend's stories "smelt rather tall."

In this manner the evening was spent; but conscious that my own association with so singular a personage would probably end before morning, I asked him if he would not give me a description of some particular bear hunt; adding that I took great interest in such things, though I was no sportsman. The desire seemed to please him, and he squared himself round toward me, saying, that he could give me an idea of a bar hunt that was never beat in this world, or in any other. His manner was so singular, that half of his story consisted in his excellent way of telling it, the great peculiarity of which was, the happy manner he had of emphasizing the prominent parts of his conversation. As near as I can recollect, I have italicized them, and given the story in his own words

"Stranger," said he, "in bar hunts *I am numerous*, and which particular one, as you say, I shall tell, puzzles me. There was the old she-devil I shot at the Hurricane last fall—then there was the old hog thief I popped over at the Bloody Crossing, and then—Yes, I have it! I will give you an idea of a hunt, in which the greatest bar was killed that ever lived, *none excepted*; about an old fellow that I hunted, more or less, for two or three years; and if that ain't a particular bar hunt, I ain't got one to tell.

"You see when I and some more first settled in our region, we were driven to hunting naturally; we soon liked it, and after that we found it an easy matter to make the thing our business. One old chap who had pioneered afore us, gave us to understand that we had settled in the right place. He dwelt upon its merits until it was affecting, and showed us, to prove his assertions, more marks on the sassafras trees than I ever seen.

" 'Who keeps that ar reckoning?' said I. 'The bar,' said he. 'What for?' said I. 'Can't tell,' said he, 'but so it is: The bar bite the bark and wood too, at the highest point from the ground they can reach, and you can tell, by the marks,' said he, 'the length of the bar to an inch.'

"Well, stranger, just one month from that time I killed a bar, and told its exact length before I measured it, by those very marks; and when I did that, I swelled up considerable—I've been a prouder man ever since. So I went on, larning something every day, until I was allowed to be decidedly the best bar hunter in my district. And that is a reputation as much harder to earn than to be reckoned first man in Congress, as an iron ramrod is harder than a toadstool. When the varmints grow over-cunning by being fooled with greenhorn hunters, and by this means get troublesome, they send for me as a matter of course. And thus I do my own hunting, and most of my neighbors'.

I walk into the varmints though, and it has become about as much the same to me as drinking. It is told in two sentences—a bar is started, and he is killed. The thing is somewhat monotonous now—I know just how much they will run, where they will tire, how much they will growl, and what a thundering time I will have in getting them home. I could give you this history of the chase with all particulars at the commencement, I know the signs so well—*Stranger, I'm certain*. Once I met a match though, and I will tell you about it; for a common hunt would not be worth relating.

"On a fine fall day, long time ago, I was trailing about for bar, and what should I see but fresh marks on the sassafras trees, about eight inches above any in the forests that I knew of. Says I, 'them marks is a hoax, or it indicates the damnedest bar that was ever grown.' In fact, stranger, I couldn't believe it was real, and I went on. Again I saw the same marks, at the same height, and *I knew the thing lived*. That conviction came home to my soul like an earthquake. Says I, 'here is something a-purpose for me, that bar is mine, or I give up the hunting business.' The very next morning what should I see but a number of buzzards hovering over my cornfield. 'The rascal has been there,' said I, 'for that sign is certain,' and, sure enough, on examining, I found the bones of what had been as beautiful a hog the day before, as was ever raised by a Buckeye. Then I tracked the critter out of the field to the woods, and all the marks he left behind, showed me that he was *the bar*.

"Well, stranger, the first fair chase I ever had with that big critter, I saw him no less than three distinct times at a distance: The dogs run him over eighteen miles and broke down, my horse gave out, and I was as nearly used up as a man can be. Before this adventure, such things were unknown to me as possible; but, strange as it was, that bar got me used to it before I was done with him; for he got so at last, that he would leave me on a long chase *quite easy*. How he did it, I never could understand. That a bar runs at all is puzzling; but how this one could tire down and bust up a pack of hounds and a horse, that were used to

The Contested Game, by William de la Montagne Cary, 1879

Hug Me Closer, George!, comic print published by Currier & Ives, 1866

overhauling everthing they started after in no time, was past my understanding. Well, stranger, that bar finally got so sassy, that he used to help himself to a hog off my premises whenever he wanted one; the buzzards followed after what he left, and so between the *bar and buzzard*, I rather think I was *out of pork*.

"Well, missing that bar so often took hold of my vitals, and I wasted away. The thing had been carried too far, and it reduced me in flesh faster than an ague. I would see that bar in everything I did: *He hunted me*, and that, too, like a devil, which I began to think he was. While in this fix, I made preparations to give him a last brush, and be done with it. Having completed everything to my satisfaction, I started at sunrise, and to my great joy, I discovered from the way the dogs run, that they were near him; finding his trail was nothing, for that had become as plain to the pack as a turnpike road. On we went, and coming to an open country, what should I see but the bar very leisurely ascending a hill, and the dogs close at his heels, either a match for him in speed, or else he did not care to get out of their way—I don't know which. But wasn't he a beauty, though? I loved him like a brother.

"On he went, until he came to a tree, the limbs of which formed a crotch about six feet from the ground. Into this crotch he got and seated himself, the dogs yelling all around it; and there he sat eyeing them as quiet as a pond in low water. A green-horn friend of mine, in company, reached shooting distance before me, and blazed away, hitting the critter in the center of his forehead. The bar shook his head as the ball struck it, and then walked down from that tree as gently as a lady would from a carriage. 'Twas a beautiful sight to see him do that—he was in such a rage that he seemed to be as little afraid of the dogs as if they had been sucking pigs. And the dogs warn't slow in making a ring around him at a respectful distance, I tell you; even bowie-knife, himself, stood off. Then the way his eyes flashed—why the fire of them would have singed a cat's hair; in fact that bar was *wrath all over*. Only one pup came near him, and he was brushed out so totally with the bar's left paw, that he entirely disappeared; and that made the old dogs more cautious still.

"In the meantime, I came up, and taking deliberate aim as a man should do, at his side, just back of his foreleg, *if my gun did not snap* [misfire] call me a coward, and I won't take it personal. Yes, stranger, *it snapped*, and I could not find a [percussion] cap about my person. While in this predicament, I turned around to my fool friend—says I, 'Bill,' says I, 'you're an ass—you're a fool—you might as well have tried to kill

161

that bar by barking the tree under his belly, as to have done it by hitting him in the head. Your shot has made a tiger of him, and blast me, if a dog gets killed or wounded when they come to blows, I will stick my knife into your liver, I will—',my wrath was up. I had lost my caps, my gun had snapped, the fellow with me had fired at the bar's head, and I expected every moment to see him close in with the dogs, and kill a dozen of them at least. In this thing I was mistaken, for the bar leaped over the ring formed by the dogs, and giving a fierce growl, was off—the pack, of course, in full cry after him. The run this time was short, for coming to the edge of a lake the varmint jumped in, and swam to a little island in the lake, which it reached just a moment before the dogs. 'I'll have him now,' said I, for I had found my caps in the *lining of my coat*— so, rolling a log into the lake, I paddled myself across to the island, just as the dogs had cornered the bar in a thicket. I rushed up and fired—at the same time the critter leaped over the dogs and came within three feet of me, running like mad; he jumped into the lake, and tried to mount the log I had just deserted, but every time he got half his body on it, it would roll over and send him under. The dogs, too, got around him, and pulled him about, and finally bowie knife clenched with him, and they sunk into the lake together. "Stranger, about this time, I was excited, and I stripped off my coat, drew my knife, and intended to have taken a part with bowie knife myself, when the bar rose to the surface. But the varmint stayed under—bowie knife came up alone, more dead than alive, and with the pack came ashore.

"'Thank God,' said I, 'the old villain has got his deserts at last.' Determined to have the body, I cut a grapevine for a rope, and dove down where I could see the bar in the water, fastened my queer rope to his leg, and fished him, with great difficulty, ashore. Stranger, may I be chawed to death by young alligators, if the thing I looked at wasn't a *she bar, and not the old critter after all*. The way matters got mixed on that island was unaccountably curious, and thinking of it made me more than ever convinced that I was hunting the Devil himself. I went home that night and took to my bed—the thing was killing me. The entire team of Arkansaw in bar-hunting, acknowledged himself used up, and the fact sunk into my feelings like a snagged boat will in the Mississippi. I grew as cross as a bar with two cubs and a sore tail. The thing got out among my neighbors, and I was asked how come on that individu-al that never lost a bar when once started? and if that same individu-al didn't wear telescopes when he turned a she bar, of ordinary size, into an old he one, a little larger than a horse? 'Perhaps,' said I, 'friends', getting wrathy, 'perhaps you want to call somebody a liar.' 'Oh, no,' said they, 'we only heard such things as being *rather common* of late, but we don't believe one word of it; oh, no', and then they would ride off and laugh like so many hyenas. It was too much, and I determined to catch that bar, go to Texas, or die—and I made my preparations accordin'. I had the pack shut up and rested. I took my rifle to pieces and iled it. I put caps in every pocket about my person, *for fear of the lining.* I then told my neighbors, that on Monday morning—naming the day—I would start *that bar*, and bring him home with me, or they might divide my settlement among them, the owner having disappeared. Well, stranger, on the morning previous to the great day of my hunting expedition, I went into the woods near my house, taking my gun and bowie knife along, to relieve myself, and what should I see, getting over my fence, but *the bar!* Yes, the old varmint was within a hundred yards of me, and the way he walked *over that fence*—stranger, he loomed up like *black mist*, he seemed so large, and he walked right toward me. I raised myself, took deliberate aim, and fired. Instantly the varmint wheeled, gave a yell, and *walked through the fence* like a falling tree would through a cobweb. I started after, but was tripped up by my pants, which were about my heels, and before I had really gathered myself up, I heard the old varmint groaning in a thicket nearby, like a thousand sinners, and by the time I reached him he was a corpse. Stranger, it took five Blacks and myself to put that carcase on a mule's back and old long-ears waddled under the load, as if he was foundered in every leg of his body, and with a common whopper of a bar, he would have trotted off, and enjoyed himself. 'Twould astonish you to know how big he was: I made a *bed-spread of his skin*, and the way it used to cover my bar mattress, and leave several feet on each side to tuck up, would have delighted you. It was in fact a creation bar, and if it had lived in Samson's time, and had met him in a fair fight, it would have licked him in the twinkling of a dice-box. But, strangers, I never like the way I hunted, and *missed him.* There is something curious about it, I could never understand—and I never was satisfied at his giving in so easy at last. Perhaps, he had heard of my preparations to hunt him the next day, so he jist come in to save his wind to grunt with in dying; but that ain't likely. My private opinion is, that that bar was an *unhuntable bar, and died when his time come.*"

When the story was ended, our hero sat some minutes with his auditors in a grave silence; I saw there was a mystery connected with the bear whose death he had just related, that had evidently made a strong

163

impression on his mind. It was also evident that there was some superstitious awe connected with the affair—a feeling common with all "children of the wood," when they meet with anything out of their everyday experience. He was the first one, however, to break the silence, and jumping up, he asked all present to "liquor" before going to bed—a thing which he did, with a number of companions, evidently to his heart's content.

Long before day, I was put ashore at my place of destination, and I can only follow with the reader, in my imagination, our Arkansas friend, in his adventures at the "Forks of Cypress" on the Mississippi.

A New Way to Catch a Trout

An old woodsman from northern New England told a tale of how a bear showed him an unusual way to catch trout.

He had spent the day fishing on a lake and returned, feeling tired, to his camp late in the day. As he approached his shack in the woods, he saw that the front door was open. Approaching with caution, he saw a big black bear inside. It had got hold of a jar of molasses and was just pulling the cork out with its teeth. The syrup spilt all over the floor. The bear licked some of it up and patted at it with its paw, making a fair old mess and getting his paw covered with syrup.

The woodsman slunk around to the rear of the shack and shouted through the window. The bear took off like a sprinter and headed for the lake—but he ran on three legs, as he was holding his syrupy paw up in the air. He sat down by the edge of the lake still holding his paw up, and clouds of insects soon gathered around it, attracted by the molasses.

After a while the bear got up and waded into the water. He kept going until the water was about up to his sholders, but he held his paw, with the flies still swarming around it, just above the surface. In a moment or two a good-sized trout leaped out of the water to snatch one of the flies. With his other paw, the bear gave it a thump that sent it clear up the beach. This happened several times, until a pile of fish lay on the sand. Having got enough for supper, the bear waded ashore, licking his paw clean of the syrup—and the flies that were sticking to it.

He had a good meal, eating five or six trout, and then he paused, lifted his head, and looked back toward the woodsman's shack. He placed the remaining trout in a neat row and ambled off in the direction of the woods, looking back over his shoulder now and then.

The woodsman walked down and found half a dozen trout laid out for him. The bear was still in sight, so he waved and yelled out, "Thanks!" The bear waved back before he dove into the trees, and since then, that woodsman has never shot a bear.

The Ladder of Lions

Joel Chandler Harris (1848–1908), born and reared in Atlanta, Georgia, was a white writer who became famous for his adaptations of black folktales, especially the Uncle Remus stories. Uncle Remus is the lovable old black servant who tells the tales to the young son of the white family that employs him. The characters in the stories are animals, who, however, speak and act like humans. Some people today would call Uncle Remus an "Uncle Tom" and others object to stories in which the characters are animals that behave like human beings. They are still good stories, however. The first one comes from another collection by Harris, and was written later than the Uncle Remus stories.

"I told Brother Lion that if he wasn't careful, Mr. Man would catch him and put him in a cage for his children to look at. But he just hooted at it—and now, sure enough, there he is! I mind the first time he began his pursuit of Mr. Man. That was the time he got his hand caught in the split of the log."

"I done hear my daddy tell dat tale," remarked Drusilla.

"Yes," said Mr. Rabbit, "it soon became common talk in the neighborhood. Brother Lion had come a long way to hunt Mr. Man, and as soon as he got his hand out of the split in the log he started to go home again. I went part of the way with him, and then it was that I told him he'd find himself in a cage if he wasn't careful. I made a burdock poultice for his hand the best I could..."

"And it's mighty good for bruises, I tell you now!" exclaimed Mrs. Meadows.

"And then Brother Lion went on home, feeling better, but still very mad. Crippled as he was, he was a quick traveler, and it was not long before he came to his journey's end.

"Well, when his mother saw him she was very sorry. But when he told her what the matter was she was vexed. 'Aha!' said she, 'how often have I told you about meddling with somebody else's business! How often have I told you about sticking your nose into things that don't concern you! I'm not sorry for you one bit, because if you had obeyed me you wouldn't be coming home now with your hand mashed all to flinders. But, no! daddy-like, you've got to go and get yourself into trouble with Mr. Man, and now you see what has come of it. I'm not feeling at all well myself, but now I've got to go to work and make a whole parcel of poultices and tie your hand up and nurse you—and I declare somebody ought to be nursing me this very minute.'

"That was what Brother Lion's mother said," continued Mr. Rabbit, "but Brother Lion didn't say anything. He just lay on the sheepskin pallet she made him and studied how he would be revenged on Mr. Man. After a while his hand got well, but still he said very little about the matter. The more he thought about the way he had been treated, the madder he got. He gnashed his teeth together and waved his long tail about until it looked like a snake. Finally he sent word to all his kin—his uncles and his cousins—to meet him somewhere in the woods and hold a convention to consider how they should catch the great monster, Mr. Man, who had caused a log of wood to mash Brother Lion's hand.

"Well, it wasn't long before the uncles and cousins began to arrive. They came from far and near, and they seemed to be very ferocious. They shook their manes and showed their tushes. They went off in the woods and held their convention, and Brother Lion laid his complaint before them. He told them what kind of treatment he had received from Mr. Man, and asked them if they would help to get his revenge. He made quite a speech, and when he sat down, his uncles and cousins were very much excited. They roared and howled. They said they were ready to tear Mr. Man limb from limb. They declared they were ready to go where he was, and gnaw him and claw him on account of the scandalous way he had treated their blood kin.

"But when Brother Lion's mother heard what they proposed to do she shut her eyes and shook her head from side to side, and told the uncles and the cousins that they had better go back home, all of them. She said that before they got through with Mr. Man they'd wish they had never been born. But go they would and go they did.

"So they started out soon one morning and traveled night and day for nearly a week. They were getting very tired and hungry, and some of the younger blood cousins wanted to stop and rest, and some wanted to turn around and go back home. But one morning while they were going through the woods, feeling a little shaky in head and limb, they suddenly came in sight of Mr. Man. He was cutting down trees and splitting them into timber. He had his coat off, and seemed to be very busy.

"But he was not so busy that he didn't hear Mr. Lion and his uncles and blood cousins sneaking through the woods over the dry leaves, and he wasn't so busy that he couldn't see them moving about among the trees. He was very much astonished. He wondered where so many of the lion family came from, and what they were doing there, but he didn't stop to ask any questions. He dropped his axe and climbed a tree.

"Brother Lion and his uncles and his blood cousins were very much pleased when they saw Mr. Man climb the tree. 'We have him now,' said Brother Lion, and the rest licked their jaws and smiled. Then they gathered around the tree and sat on their haunches and watched Mr. Man. This didn't do any good, for Mr. Man sat on a limb and swung his legs, just as contentedly as if he was sitting on his rocking-chair at home.

"Then Brother Lion and his uncles and his blood cousins showed their teeth and growled. But this didn't do any good. Mr. Man swung his feet and whistled a dance tune. Then Brother Lion and his blood cousins opened their mouths wide and roared as loud as they could. But this didn't do any good. Mr. Man leaned his head against the trunk of the tree and pretended to be nodding.

"This made Brother Lion and his blood kin very mad. They ran around the tree and tore the bark with their claws, and waved their tails back and forth. But this didn't do any good. Mr. Man just sat up there and swung his feet and laughed at them.

"Brother Lion and his blood kin soon found that if they intended to capture Mr. Man they'd have to do something else besides caper around the foot of the tree. So they talked it over, and Brother Lion fixed up a plan. He said that he would stand at the foot of the tree and rear up against the trunk, and one of his blood cousins could climb on his back and rear up, and then another cousin or uncle could climb up, and so on until there was a ladder of bloodthirsty lions high enough to reach Mr. Man.

"Brother Lion, mind you, was to be at the bottom of the Lion ladder," remarked Mr. Rabbit, with a chuckle. "And he had a very good reason for it. He had had dealings with Mr. Man, and he wanted to keep as far away from him as possible.

"But before they made the Lion ladder, Brother Lion looked up at Mr. Man and called out: 'What are you doing up there?'

"'You'll find out a great deal too soon for your comfort,' replied Mr. Man.

"Brother Lion said, 'Come down from there.'

"Mr. Man answered, 'I'll come down much sooner than you want me to.'

"Then Brother Lion, his uncles, and blood cousins began to build their ladder. Brother Lion was the bottom rung of this ladder, as you may say," continued Mr. Rabbit. "He reared up and placed his hands

against the tree, and one of his uncles jumped on his shoulders, and put his hands against the tree. Then a cousin, and then another uncle, and so on until the ladder reached a considerable distance up the tree. It was such a high ladder that it began to wobble, and the last uncle had hard work to make his way to the top. He climbed up very carefully and slowly, for he was not used to this sort of business. He was the oldest and the fiercest of the old company, but his knees shook under him as he climbed up and felt the ladder shaking and wobbling.

"Mr. Man saw that by the time this big lion got to the top of the ladder his teeth and his claws would be too close for comfort, and so he called out in an angry tone 'Just hold on! Just stand right still! Wait! I'm not after any of you except that fellow at the bottom there. I'm not trying to catch any of you but him. He has bothered me before. I let him go once, but I'll not let him get away this time. Just stand right still and hold him there till I climb down the other side of the tree.'

"With that Mr. Man shook the limbs and leaves and dropped some pieces of bark. This was more than Brother Lion could stand. He was so frightened that he jumped from under the ladder, and his uncles and his blood cousins came tumbling to the ground, howling, growling, and fighting.

"They were as sorry-looking a sight as ever you saw when they came to their senses. Those that didn't have their bones broken by the fall were torn and mangled. They had acted so foolishly that out of the whole number, Mr. Man didn't get but three lion-skins that could be called perfect.

"Brother Lion went home to his mother as fast as he could go and remained quiet a long time. And now you tell me he's in a cage."

The Tar Baby

In Uncle Remus's stories, a continual battle is waged between Brer ("Brother") Rabbit and Brer Fox. The fox is always trying to catch the rabbit, and the rabbit is always outsmarting him. The stories were written in dialect—to sound like the way Uncle Remus would have spoken. Because this can be hard to understand today, this story of Brer Rabbit, Brer Fox and the Tar Baby is told in more ordinary language.

"Didn't the fox *ever* catch the rabbit, Uncle Remus?" asked the little boy.

"He came mighty near it, honey, Brer Fox did . . . One day, Brer Fox got hold of some tar, and mixed it with turpentine, and he made what he called a tar baby, a figure modeled out of tar. He put the Tar Baby near the side of the road, then he lay down in the bushes nearby, out of sight. He didn't have to wait for long, for by and by Brer Rabbit came hopping down the road—lippity-clippity, clippity-lipperty—just as sassy as a jay-bird. Brer Fox lay low. Brer Rabbit came prancing along, 'till he saw the Tar Baby.

"'Good morning,' said Brer Rabbit, 'Nice weather we're having.'

"The Tar Baby said nothing, and Brer Fox lay low.

"'And how are you feeling, today?' said Brer Rabbit.

"Brer Fox grinned and lay low; the Tar Baby said nothing.

"'What's the matter with you?' said Brer Rabbit, getting irritated. 'Are you deaf? Because, if you are, I can holler louder, you know.'

"The Tar Baby said nothing, and Brer Fox lay low.

"'You are stuck up, that's what you are,' said Brer Rabbit, 'and I'm going to cure you, that's what I'm going to do.'

"Brer Fox chuckled silently; the Tar Baby said nothing.

"'I'm going to teach you how to talk to respectable folks if it's the last thing I do,' said Brer Rabbit. 'If you don't take off your hat and say Howdy, I'm going to bust you wide open,' he said.

"The Tar Baby said nothing, and Brer Fox lay low.

"Brer Rabbit kept on asking, and the Tar Baby kept on saying nothing, until presently Brer Rabbit drew back his fist and thumped the Tar Baby on the side of the head. And that was his first mistake, because his fist stuck to the tar and he couldn't pull it loose. But the Tar Baby said nothing, and Brer Fox lay low.

"'If you don't let me loose, I'll thump you again,' said Brer Rabbit. He thumped the Tar Baby with the other fist—and that one stuck, too. The Tar baby said nothing, and Brer Fox lay low.

"'Turn me loose before I kick the stuffing out of you!' said Brer Rabbit, but the Tar Baby said nothing, just held on to his hands. So Brer Rabbit used his feet, and they both got stuck the same way his hands were. Brer Fox lay low. Brer Rabbit yelled that if the Tar Baby didn't turn him loose pronto, he would butt him in the tummy. And then he butted, and his head was tuck to the Tar Baby, too.

"Then Brer Fox sauntered forth, looking just as innocent as a mocking-bird in a cage.

"'Howdy, Brer Rabbit,' said Brer Fox. 'You look sort of stuck up this morning,' and he started to laugh. He laughed so much he rolled on the ground."

Here Uncle Remus paused, to give the fire a poke.

"Did the fox eat the rabbit?" asked the little boy.

"That's as far as the tale goes," replied the old man. "He might have, and then again he mightn't—but I hear Miss Sally calling. You'd better run along now."

"Uncle Remus," said the little boy one evening when he found the old man with nothing to do, "did the fox kill and eat the rabbit when he caught him with the Tar Baby?"

"Lord, honey, haven't I told you about that? Well...

"When Brer Fox found Brer Rabbit mixed up with the Tar Baby, he felt mighty good, and he rolled on the ground laughing.

"By and by he got up, and he said, 'Well, I expect I got you this time, Brer Rabbit. Maybe I ain't, but I expect I have. You have been running around sassing me for a long while now, but I reckon you have come to the end of the line. You have been bouncing around in this neighborhood as if you believe you are the boss of the place, and you are always poking your nose in where you have no business. Who asked you to come up and start talking to this Tar Baby? And who stuck you up the way you are now? Nobody in the whole world—you just got yourself stuck up with that Tar Baby all by your self. Well, you are stuck there now, and you can stay there while I make a fire, because I am going to barbecue you for my dinner,' said Brer Fox.

"Then Brer Rabbit began to speak very humbly. 'I don't care what you do to me, Brer fox,' he said, 'as long as you don't fling me in that briar patch. Roast me, Brer Fox,' he said, 'but don't fling me in that briar patch.'

"'It's too much trouble to make a fire,' said Brer Fox, 'so I think I'll have to hang you instead.'

"'Hang me as high as you please, Brer Fox,' said Brer Rabbit, 'but for the good Lord's sake, don't fling me in that briar patch.'

"'I ain't got no string with me,' said Brer Fox, 'so I suppose I'll have to drown you instead.'

"'Drown me as deep as you please, Brer Fox,' said Brer Rabbit, 'but don't—don't fling me in that briar patch.'

"'There's no water around here,' said Brer Fox, 'so I suppose I'll have to skin you.'

"'Skin me, Brer Fox,' said Brer Rabbit, 'snatch out my eyeballs, tear off my ears, and cut off my legs,' he said, 'But don't, please, Brer Fox, don't throw me in that briar patch.'

"Of course, Brer Fox wanted to hurt Brer Rabbit as much as he could, so he caught him by the hind legs and slung him right into the middle of the briar patch.

"There was quite a commotion where Brer Rabbit disappeared into the briar patch, and Brer Fox waited to see what would happen. By and by he heard someone calling him from far up on the hillside. There was Brer Rabbit, sitting on a log, and combing the tar out of his fur with a chip of wood. Then Brer Fox knew he had been fooled, and Brer Rabbit could not resist calling down to him: 'Born and bred in a briar patch, Brer Fox, born and bred in a briar patch!' And with that he scampered off, as lively as a cricket."

The White Stallion

In the days when the west was being settled, a pioneer family were making their slow way along the old wagon trail to the south-west. Besides their wagon, they had an old mare, which followed the wagon carrying two big bags of cornmeal. The family's youngest child, a little girl, liked to ride on the old mare as well. She was tied on to her back with rope, so she couldn't fall off.

Passing through a rocky valley, one of the wheels of the wagon broke, and they had to stop until it was repaired. While the men were working on the wheel, the old mare wandered off, seeking fresh grass away from the trail. The litle girl was asleep on her back, and when she woke up she was out of sight of the trail and the wagon.

No one noticed that the little girl and the old mare had disappeared until the wheel had been repaired and they were ready to set off again. These were city people from somewhere in Europe, and none of them had the skill to follow a track. They struck camp, and started to search, but they couldn't find her.

Meanwhile, the little girl had woken up to find the old mare was trotting along at what was for her an unusually brisk pace. She was following a magnificent white stallion, and there was nothing the little girl could do to stop her, as she had no reins nor bridle. Because she was tied on the mare's back, she couldn't jump off either.

Not long before sundown, they came upon a whole herd of wild mares. The white stallion seemed to be their leader. The mares were interested in the newcomer, and gathered around her, whinnying and nuzzling her. They soon found the bags of cornmeal and started to nibble at them. Without meaning to, they also nibbled at the legs of the little girl, sitting on top of the bags of meal. She cried out, and to her surprise, the white stallion trotted up and, seeming to understand what the trouble was, he chivied the mares away from her, even threatening to kick one or two of the most greedy ones. Then he chewed through the ropes that tied the little girl to the old mare and, taking her gently by the collar of her dress, he set her down on the ground.

By this time it was almost dark. The little girl knew that if you are lost in the wilderness, the best thing to do is to stay in one place and wait for the people who are looking for you. So she made herself a rough bed out of long grass under an oak tree and, though she was frightened, she finally fell asleep.

When she awoke, the sun was up and there was no sign of the

horses—not the white stallion, nor her own old mare, nor any of the herd. She was hungry and frightened. Luckily, there was a water hole nearby, so she was in no danger of dying from thirst, but she was also very hungry. She picked some wild berries, but the thorns pricked her hands and she could not get enough.

All that day no one came, and at night, tired and frightened and hungry, she settled down again under the oak tree and cried herself to sleep.

When she woke up the next morning, the old mare was standing over her. How pleased she was to see a friendly creature! But the old mare was not much help. She could not get on her back because she was too short, and when she tried to lead the horse over to a log which would give her a step up, the stupid animal would not budge. The little girl was in tears again, when she heard the sound of hooves, and galloping up to her she saw the beautiful white stallion. Once again, he seemed to know just what was wanted. Although he was a wild animal, and a mighty big one, somehow she was not at all frightened of him. He picked her up gently by the collar, and put her on the old mare's back. Then he seemed to whisper something into the ear of the old mare, before he trotted away. The old mare got going, at her old slow pace, and later that day she arrived at the place where the wagon had broken down, and restored the little girl to her happy family.

The Celebrated Jumping Frog of Calaveras County

This is the story that made Mark Twain (Samuel Clemens) famous. It was the main story in his first book, published in 1867. He did not invent the story, however. A different form of it had been published about 15 years earlier, and the story had been first told, no doubt, some time before that. The two stories that follow it are also by Mark Twain.

In compliance with the request of a friend of mine, who wrote me from the east, I called on good-natured, garrulous [chatty] old Simon Wheeler, and inquired after my friend's friend, Leonidas W. Smiley, as requested to do, and I hereunto append the result. I have a lurking suspicion that Leonidas W. Smiley is a myth; that my friend never knew such a personage; and that he only conjectured that, if I asked old Wheeler about him, it would remind him of his infamous Jim Smiley, and he would go to work and bore me nearly to death with some infernal reminiscence of him as long and as tedious as it should be useless to me. If that was the design, it certainly succeeded.

I found Simon Wheeler dozing comfortably by the bar room stove of the old, dilapidated tavern in the ancient mining camp of Angel's, and I noticed that he was fat and bald headed, and had an expression of winning gentleness and simplicity upon his tranquil countenance. He roused up, and gave me good-day. I told him a friend of mine had commissioned me to make some inquiries about a cherished companion of his boyhood named Leonidas W. Smiley—Rev. Leonidas W. Smiley—a young minister of the Gospel, who he had heard was at one time a resident of Angel's Camp. I added that, if Mr. Wheeler could tell me anything about this Rev. Leonidas W. Smiley, I would feel under many obligations to him.

Simon Wheeler backed me into a corner and blockaded me there with his chair, and then sat me down and reeled off the monotonous narrative which follows this paragraph. He never smiled, he never frowned, he never changed his voice from the gentle-flowing key to which he turned the initial sentence, he never betrayed the slightest suspicion of enthusiasm; but all through the interminable narrative there ran a vein of impressive earnestness and sincerity, which showed me plainly that, so far from his imagining that there was anythng ridiculous or funny about his story, he regarded it as a really important matter, and admired its two heroes as men of transcendent genius in *finesse*. To me, the spectacle of a man drifting serenely along through

176

such a queer yarn without ever smiling, was exquisitely absurd. As I said before, I asked him to tell me what he knew of Rev. Leonidas W. Smiley, and he replied as follows. I let him go on in his own way, and never interrupted him once.

"There was a feller here once by the name of Jim Smiley, in the winter of '49—or may be it was the spring of '50—I don't recollect exactly, somehow, though what makes me think it was one or the other is because I remember the big flume wasn't finished when he first came to the camp; but anyway, he was the curiousest man about always betting on anything that turned up you ever see, if he could get anybody to bet on the other side; and if he couldn't, he'd change sides. Anyway that suited the other man would suit him—anyway just so's he got a bet, *he* was satisfied. But still he was lucky, uncommon lucky; he most always come out winner. He was always ready and laying for a chance; there couldn't be no solit'ry thing mentioned but that feller'd offer to bet on it, and take any side you please, as I was just telling you. If there was a horserace, you'd find him flush, or you'd find him busted at the end of it; if there was a dog fight, he'd bet on it; if there was a cat fight, he'd bet on it; if there was a chicken fight, he'd bet on it; why, if there was two birds setting on a fence, he would bet you which one would fly first; or if there was a camp-meeting, he would be there reg'lar to bet on Parson Walker, which he judged to be the best exhorter about here, and so he was too, and a good man. If he even seen a straddle bug start to go anywheres, he would bet you how long it would take him to get wherever he was going to, and if you took him up, he would foller that straddle bug to Mexico but what he would find out where he was bound for and how long he was on the road. Lots of the boys here has seen that Smiley, and can tell you about him. Why, it never made no difference to *him*—he would bet on *anything*—the dangdest feller. Parson Walker's wife laid very sick once, for a good while, and it seemed as if they warn't going to save her; but one morning he come in, and Smiley asked how she was, and he said she was considerable better—thank the Lord for his inf'nit mercy—and coming on so smart that with the blessing of Prov'dence she'd get well yet; and Smiley, before he thought, says, 'Well, I'll risk two-and-a-half she don't anyway.'

"Thish-yer Smiley had a mare—the boys called her the fifteen-minute nag, but that was only in fun, you know, because of course she was faster than that—and he used to win money on that horse, for all she was so slow and always had the asthma, or the distemper, or the consumption, or something of that kind. They used to give her two or three hundred yards' start, and then pass her under way; but always at the fag-end of the race she'd get excited and desperate-like, and come cavorting and straddling up, and scattering her legs around limber, sometimes in the air, and sometimes out to one side amongst the fences, and kicking up m-o-r-e dust and raising m-o-r-e racket with her coughing and sneezing and blowing her nose—and always fetch up at the stand just about a neck ahead, as near as you could cipher it down.

"And he had a little small bull pup, that to look at him you'd think he wa'n't worth a cent but to set around and look ornery and lay for a chance to steal something. But as soon as money was up on him he was a different dog; his under-jaw'd begin to stick out like the fo'castle of a steamboat, and his teeth would uncover and shine savage like the furnaces. And a dog might tackle him and bully-rag him, and bite him, and throw him over his shoulder two or three times, and Andrew Jackson—which was the name of the pup—Andrew Jackson would never let on but what he was satisfied, and hadn't expected nothing else—and the bets being doubled and doubled on the other side all the time, till the money was all up; and then all of a sudden he would grab the other dog jest by the j'int of his hind leg and freeze to it—not chaw, you understand, but only jest grip and hang on 'till they threwed up the sponge, if it was a year.

"Smiley always come out winner on that pup, 'till he harnessed a dog once that didn't have no hind legs, because they'd been sawed off by a circular saw, and when the thing had gone along far enough, and the money was all up, and he come to make a snatch for his pet holt, he saw in a minute how he'd been imposed on, and how the other dog had him in the door, so to speak, and he 'peared surprised, and then he looked sorter discouraged-like, and didn't try no more to win the fight, and so he got shucked out bad. He give Smiley a look, as much as to say his heart was broke, and it was his fault, for putting up a dog that hadn't no hind legs for him to take holt of, which was his main dependence in a fight, and then he limped off a piece and laid down and died. It was a good pup, was that Andrew Jackson, and would have made a name for hisself if he'd lived, for the stuff was in him and he had genius—I know it, because he hadn't had no opportunities to speak of, and it don't stand to reason that a dog could make such a fight as he could under them circumstances if he hadn't had no talent. It always makes me feel sorry when I think of that last fight of his'n, and the way it turned out.

"Well, thish-yer Smiley had rat terriers, and chicken cocks, and tom

178

cats and all them kind of things, 'till you couldn't rest, and you couldn't fetch nothing for him to bet on but he'd match you. He ketched a frog one day, and took him home, and said he calk'lated to edercate him; and so he never done nothing for three months but set in his back yard and learn that frog to jump. And you bet you he did learn him, too. He'd give him a little punch behind, and the next minute you'd see that frog whirling in the air like a doughnut—see him turn one summerset, or maybe a couple, if he got a good start, and come down flat-footed and all right, like a cat. He got him up so in the matter of ketching flies, and kept him in practice so constant, that he'd nail a fly every time as far as he could see him. Smiley said all a frog wanted was education, and he could do 'most anything—and I believe him. Why, I've seen him set Dan'l Webster down here on this floor—Dan'l Webster was the name of the frog—and sing out, 'Flies, Dan'l, flies!' and quicker'n you could wink he'd spring straight up and snake a fly off'n the counter there, and flop down on the floor ag'in as solid as a gob of mud, and fall to scratching the side of his head with his hind foot as indifferent as if he hadn't no idea he'd been doin' any more'n any frog might do. You never see a frog so modest and straightfor'ard as he was, for all he was so gifted. And when it come to fair and square jumping on a dead level, he could get

179

over more ground at one straddle than any animal of his breed you ever see. Jumping on a dead level was his strong suit, you understand; and when it come to that, Smiley would ante up money on him as long as he had a red. Smiley was monstrous proud of his frog, and well he might be, for fellers that had traveled and been everywheres, all said he laid over any frog that ever they see.

"Well, Smiley kept the beast in a little lattice box, and he used to fetch him down town sometimes and lay for a bet. One day a feller—a stranger in the camp, he was—come across him with his box, and says:

"'What might it be that you've got in the box?'

"And Smiley says, sorter indifferent-like, 'It might be a parrot, or it might be a canary, maybe, but it ain't—it's only just a frog.'

"And the feller took it, and looked at it careful, and turned it around this way and that, and says, 'H'm—so 'tis. Well, what's he good for?'

"'Well,' Smiley says, easy and careless, 'he's good enough for *one* thing, I should judge—he can outjump any frog in Calaveras county.'

"The feller took the box again, and took another long, particular look, and give it back to Smiley, and says, very deliberate, 'Well,' he says, 'I don't see no p'ints about that frog that's any better'n any other frog.'

"'Maybe you don't,' Smiley says. 'Maybe you understand frogs and maybe you don't understand 'em; maybe you've had experience, and maybe you ain't only a amature, as it were. Anyways, I've got my opinion and I'll risk forty dollars that he can outjump any frog in Calaveras county.'

"And the feller studied a minute, and then says, kinder sad like, 'Well, I'm only a stranger here, and I ain't got no frog; but if I had a frog, I'd bet you.'

"And then Smiley says, 'That's all right—that's all right—if you'll hold my box a minute, I'll go and get you a frog.' And so the feller took the box, and put up his forty dollars along with Smiley's and set down to wait.

"So he set there a good while thinking and thinking to hisself, and then he got the frog out and prized his mouth open and took a teaspoon and filled him full of quail shot—filled him pretty near up to his chin—and set him on the floor. Smiley he went to the swamp and slopped around in the mud for a long time, and finally he ketched a frog, and fetched him in, and give him to this feller and says:

"'Now, if you're ready, set him alongside of Dan'l's, with his forepaws just even with Dan'l's, and I'll give the word.' Then he says, 'One—two—three—jump!' and him and the feller touched up the frogs from behind, and the new frog hopped off, but Dan'l give a heave, and hysted up his shoulders—so—like a Frenchman, but it wa'n't no use—he couldn't budge; he was planted as solid as an anvil, and he couldn't no more stir than if he was anchored out. Smiley was a good deal surprised, and he was disgusted too, but he didn't have no idea what the matter was, of course.

"The feller took the money and started away; and when he was going out at the door, he sorter jerked his thumb over his shoulders—this way—at Dan'l and says again, very deliberate, 'Well I don't see no p'ints about that frog that's any better'n any other frog.'

"Smiley he stood scratching his head and looking down at Dan'l a long time, and at last he says, 'I do wonder what in the nation that frog throw'd off for—I wonder if there ain't something the matter with him— he 'pears to look mighty baggy, somehow.' And he ketched Dan'l by the nap of the neck, and lifted him up, and says, 'Why, blame my cats, if he don't weigh five pound!' and turned him upside down and he belched out a double handful of shot. And then he see how it was, and he was the maddest man—he set the frog down and took out after that feller, but he never ketched him. And—

[Here Simon Wheeler heard his name called from the front yard, and got up to see what was wanted.] And turning to me as he moved away, he said: "Just set where you are, stranger and rest easy—I an't going to be gone a second."

But, by your leave, I did not think that a continuation of the history of the enterprising vagabond Jim Smiley would be likely to afford me much information concerning the Rev. Leonidas W. Smiley, and so I started away.

At the door I met the sociable Wheeler returning, and he button-holed me and re-commenced:

"'Well, thish-yer Smiley had a yaller one-eyed cow that didn't have no tail, only jest a short stump like a bannanner, and—"

"Oh! hang Smiley and his afflicted cow!" I muttered, good-naturedly, and bidding the old gentleman good-day, I departed.

Blue Jays

Animals talk to each other, of course. There can be no question about that; but I suppose there are very few people who can understand them. I never knew but one man who could. I knew he could, however, because he told me so himself. He was a middle-aged, simple-hearted miner, who had lived in a lonely corner of California, among the woods and mountains, a good many years, and had studied the ways of his only neighbors, the beasts and the birds, until he believed he could accurately translate any remark which they made. This was Jim Baker. According to Jim Baker, some animals have only a limited education and use only very simple words, and scarcely ever a comparison or a flowery figure; whereas, certain other animals have a large vocabulary, a fine command of language and a ready and fluent delivery; consequently this latter talk a great deal; they like it; they are conscious of their talent, and they enjoy "showing off." Baker said that, after long and careful observation, he had come to the conclusion that the blue jays were the best talkers he had found among birds and beasts. Said he:

"There's more *to* a blue jay than any other creature. He has got more moods and more different kinds of feelings than other creatures; and, mind you, whatever a blue jay feels, he can put into language. And no mere commonplace language, either, but rattling, out-and-out book talk—and bristling with metaphor too—just bristling! And as for command of language—why, *you* never see a blue jay get stuck for a word. No man ever did. They just boil out of him! And another thing: I've noticed a good deal, and there's no bird, or cow, or anything that uses as good grammar as a blue jay. You may say a cat uses good grammar. Well, a cat does—but you let a cat get excited, once; you let a cat get to pulling fur with another cat on a shed, nights, and you'll hear grammar that will give you the lockjaw. Ignorant people think it's the *noise* which fighting cats make that is so aggravating, but it ain't so; it's the sickening grammar they use. Now I've never heard a jay use bad grammar but very seldom; and when they do, they are as ashamed as a human; they shut right down and leave.

"You may call a jay a bird. Well, so he is, in a measure—because he's got feathers on him, and don't belong to no church, perhaps; but otherwise he is just as much a human as you be. And I'll tell you for why. A jay's gifts, and instincts, and feelings, and interests cover the whole ground. A jay hasn't got any more principle than a Congressman. A jay will lie, a jay will steal, a jay will deceive, a jay will betray; and, four times

182

out of five, a jay will go back on his solemnest promise. The sacredness of an obligation is a thing which you can't cram into no blue jay's head. Now, on top of all this, there's another thing: A jay can out-swear any gentleman in the mines. You think a cat can swear. Well, a cat can; but you give a blue jay a subject that calls for his reserve powers, and where is your cat? Don't talk to *me*—I know too much about this thing. And there's yet another thing: In the one little particular of scolding—just good, clean, out-and-out scolding—a blue jay can lay over anything, human or divine. Yes, sir, a jay is everything that a man is. A jay can cry, a jay can laugh, a jay can feel shame, a jay can reason and plan and discuss, a jay likes gossip and scandal, a jay has got a sense of humor, a jay knows when he is an ass just as well as you do—maybe better. If a jay ain't human, he better take in his sign, that's all. Now I am going to tell you a perfectly true fact about some blue jays.

"When I first begun to understand jay language correctly, there was a little incident happened here. Seven years ago, the last man in this region but me moved away. There stands his house—been empty ever since; a log house, with a plank roof—just one big room, and no more; no ceiling—nothing between the rafters and the floor. Well, one Sunday morning I was sitting out here in front of my cabin with my cat, taking the sun, and looking at the blue hills and listening to the leaves rustling so lonely in the trees, and thinking of the home away yonder in the States, that I hadn't heard from in thirteen years, when a blue jay lit on that house, with an acorn in his mouth, and says, 'Hello, I reckon I've struck something!' When he spoke, the acorn fell out of his mouth and rolled down the roof, of course, but he didn't care; his mind was all on the thing he had struck. It was a knot-hole in the roof. He cocked his head to one side, shut one eye and put the other one to the hole, like a 'possum looking down a jug; then he glanced up with his bright eyes, gave a wink or two with his wings—which signifies gratification, you understand—and says, 'It looks like a hole, it's located like a hole— blamed if I don't believe it *is* a hole!

"Then he cocked his head down and took another look; he glances up perfectly joyful this time; winks his wings and his tail both, and says, 'Oh, no, this ain't no fat thing, I reckon! If I ain't in luck!—why, it's a perfectly elegant hole!' So he flew down and got that acorn, and fetched it up and dropped it in, and was just tilting his head back with the heavenliest smile on his face, when all of a sudden he was paralyzed into a listening attitude, and that smile faded gradually out of his countenance like a breath off'n a razor, and the queerest look of surprise took its place. Then he says, 'Why, I didn't hear it fall!' He cocked his eye at the hole again and took a long look; raised up and shook his head; stepped around to the other side of the hole, and took another look from that side; shook his head again. He studied a while, then he just went into the *de*tails—walked round and round the hole, and spied into it from every point of the compass. No use. Now he took a thinking attitude on the comb of the roof, and scratched the back of his head with his right foot a minute, and finally says, 'Well, it's too many for *me*, that's certain; must be a mighty long hole; however, I ain't got no time to fool around here; I got to 'tend to business; I reckon it's all right—chance it, anyway!'

"So he flew off and fetched another acorn and dropped it in, and tried to flirt his eye to the hole quick enough to see what become of it, but he was too late. He held his eye there as much as a minute; then he raised up and sighed, and says, 'Consound it, I don't seem to understand this thing, no way; however, I'll tackle her again.' He fetched another acorn, and done his level best to see what become of it, but he couldn't. He says, 'Well, *I* never struck no such a hole as this before; I'm of the opinion it's a totally new kind of a hole.' Then he begun to get mad. He held in for a spell, walking up and down the comb of the roof, and

shaking his head and muttering to himself; but his feelings got the upper hand of him presently, and he broke loose and cussed himself black in the face. I never see a bird take on so about a little thing. When he got through, he walks to the hole and looks in again for a half a minute; then he says, 'Well, you're a long hole, and a deep hole, and a mighty singular hole altogether—but I've started to fill you, and I'm d——d if I *don't* fill you, if it takes a hundred years!'

"And with that, away he went. You never see a bird work so since you was born. He laid into his work like a slave, and the way he hove acorns into that hole for about two hours and a half was one of the most exciting and astonishing spectacles I ever struck. He never stopped to take a look any more—he just hove 'em in, and went for more. Well, at last he could hardly flop his wings, he was so tuckered out. He comes a-drooping down, once more, sweating like an ice-pitcher, drops his acorn in and says, '*Now* I guess I've got the bulge on you by this time!' So he bent down for a look. If you'll believe me, when his head come up again he was just pale with rage. He says, 'I've shoveled acorns enough in there to keep the family thirty years, and if I can see a sign of one of 'em, I wish I may land in a museum with a belly full of sawdust in two minutes!'

"He just had strength enough to crawl up on to the comb and lean his back agin the chimbly, and then he collected his impressions and begun to free his mind. I see in a second that what I had mistook for profanity in the mines was only just the rudiments, as you may say.

"Another jay was going by, and heard him doing his devotions, and stops to inquire what was up. The sufferer told him the whole circumstance, and says, 'Now yonder's the hole, and if you don't believe me, go and look for yourself.'

"So this fellow went and looked, and comes back and says, 'How many did you say you put in there?'

"'Not any less than two tonnes,' says the sufferer.

"The other jay went and looked again. He couldn't seem to make it out, so he raised a yell, and three more jays come. They all examined the hole, they all made the sufferer tell it over again, then they all discussed it, and got off as many leather-headed opinions about it as an average crowd of humans could have done.

"They did call in more jays; then more and more, till pretty soon this whole region 'peared to have a blue flush about it. There must have been five thousand of them; and such another jawing and disputing and ripping and cussing, you never heard. Every jay in the whole lot put his eye to the hole, and delivered a more chuckle-headed opinion about the mystery than the jay that went there before him. They examined the house all over too. The door was standing half-open, and at last one old jay happened to go and light on it and look in. Of course, that knocked the mystery galley-west in a second. There lay the acorns, scattered all over the floor. He flopped his wings and raised a whoop.

"'Come here!' he says, 'Come here, everybody; hang'd if this fool hasn't been trying to fill up a house with acorns!'

"They all came a-swooping down like a blue cloud, and as each fellow lit on the door and took a glance, the whole absurdity of the contract that the first jay had tackled hit him home, and he fell over backward suffocating with laughter, and the next jay took his place and done the same.

"Well, sir, they roosted around here on the housetop and the trees for an hour, and guffawed over that thing like human beings. It ain't no use to tell me a blue jay hasn't got a sense of humor, because I know better. And memory, too. They brought jays here from all over the United States to look down that hole, every summer for three years. Other birds too. And they could all see the point, except an owl that came from Nova Scotia to visit the Yo Semite, and he took this thing in on his way back. He said he couldn't see anything funny in it. But then, he was a good deal disappointed about Yo Semite, too."

Razorbacks

An animal that features in many humorous old tales of the south is the razorback, that long-snouted, long-bodied, long-tusked, long-legged and half-wild hog that farmers used to keep in those parts (you won't see them nowadays).

Dave McCullum was a real sharp farmer. He went everywhere, read everything, and knew most things. He would take an old machine, tinker with it a while, and sell it for twice what he paid. He was always buying sick or crippled animals, which he would doctor up and re-sell for a profit.

One summer Dave bought a dozen runty little pigs, and said he would make 200-pounders out of them before frost came. They were thin and scared, and the whole lot couldn't have weighed 500 pounds. He unloaded them in the barn lot, which stood on a hill above a little creek. The creek ran through Dave's bottom land, where he had his garden patch, and though the hill where the barn lot was situated was not a high one, it was a steep drop from there to the bottom land.

Next to the barn lot, Dave had his goober (peanut) patch, which was fenced in, hog-tight, and the next morning Dave told his hired hand to put the pigs in the goober patch. He did that, and made sure the gate was closed, but about midday, the boss's wife came hollering to say that the pigs were in the garden patch. They put them back in the barn lot, and judging by the way them came begging for corn, they hadn't eaten many goobers.

The next day the same thing happened. The pigs all got into the garden patch, and they were all hungry for corn when they were taken back to the barn lot.

Dave was mystified. "I don't believe those pigs like goobers," he said, "but what gets me is: How do they get out?"

By Saturday night he had had the pigs for seven days, and every day the same thing had happened. "It beats me," said Dave to his hired hand. "I've watched those pigs a whole week and I don't know how they get out. I'll give you a dollar if you'll find out."

Next day the hired hand put the pigs in the goober patch early and picked a shady place to sit and watch. He thought it was an easy way to make a dollar. As he watched, he noticed the pigs didn't have much luck rooting up goobers. The ground was too hard. They would root and root, but just couldn't turn up the goobers.

So he sat there, thinking how he would spend that extra dollar, when suddenly he came awake and it was past noon. There wasn't one pig left in the patch!

"It's no use," Dave said, "I'll have to take a day off and find out for myself."

On Monday morning, Dave sent his hired hand to the bottom field to work in the orchard. By about two o'clock he was hot and tired, so he found himself a shady place to rest under the hill. He was about to doze off again, when something came smashing through the branches of the tree above him and hit the ground right in front of him. It was one of the razorbacks. Huh! he thought, there must be a hole in the fence and the pig fell through. But as he sat there watching the pig go limping off, farther down the field he saw another pig come flying through the air to land at the foot of the cliff. He waited no longer but ran for the house.

"Dave!" he shouted, "them pigs *fall out* of that pen!"

"No!"

"Sure as shooting!"

So they both went back to the goober patch. Only four pigs were left rooting for goobers. They walked around the fence, but they couldn't find a hole anywhere. They were standing there by the fence at the edge of the cliff when—Zip!—a pig flew past them about head high, over the fence and into the bushes below. "Dag gum!" said Dave.

They climbed on the rail fence and sat there, watching the pigs that remained. One close to them had a hole rooted up against a goober hill, but he could not root out the goobers. He pushed and pushed, but the dirt didn't move. He backed out of the hole and looked at it in a thoughtful manner, then he backed off a fair distance and took at run at it. He drove his snout in under the goober hill and out it came. He gulped the goobers up greedily, and started on another hill. This time, when he took a run at it, he didn't get his snout in far enough down. It stuck in the hard topsoil, the pig's rear end flew up and—Zip!—he went sailing over the fence!

"Dag gum!" said Dave.

They walked slowly back to the house, and all that evening Dave was silent and thoughtful. Next morning he said to his hired hand, 'I'll take the razorbacks out this morning, while you go and prune those persimmon sprouts."

For two or three weeks, nothing more was heard about the hogs, so on one Sunday morning, the hired hand walked over to the goober patch to see how they were getting on. They were all there, rooting for goobers, and he could see they were fattening up nicely. Dave had seen how those pigs were just too light in the rear to root in that hard dirt, so he had tied a chunk of cast iron to their tails to keep them anchored.

The Tame Trout

There was once an old Indian who had a pet trout by the name of Tommy. He used to keep it in a barrel, but as Tommy grew, the barrel became too small for him and the water had to be changed every day. So the Indian decided he would teach the trout how to live out of water.

To begin with, he took Tommy out of the barrel for a few minutes at a time. Each day he kept him out a little longer, and after a while Tommy could stay out for some hours, providing he was put in wet grass. Pretty soon, the Indian found he could keep him out all night in wet grass, and then Tommy got used to staying out even if the grass was dry, as long as he kept in the shade.

Of course, Tommy grew tamer, and he used to follow the Indian about. When his owner went to dig worms for him, Tommy would follow him, and he would gulp down the worms as the Indian dug them up.

The time came when Tommy didn't need water at all. He lived outside all the time. You could see him following the Indian along the dusty road into town, just like a dog, although he didn't walk like a dog, more like a snake.

The Indian thought the world of that trout, and it was a sad day when he lost him. It happened like this.

He started for town one day, with Tommy coming along behind as he always did. There was a bridge over a creek which they had to cross, and there was a plank missing in it. The Indian stepped over it without thinking, but a little later, when he looked round for Tommy, he couldn't see him following. Then he remembered the missing plank in the bridge. He ran back to it, and got down on his knees to look through the hole at the water below. Sure enough, there was Tommy. He was floating on the water upside-down. He'd fallen through the hole into the creek and drowned.

The Wolf Pack

This account of a wolf pack, in bad times and good, comes from *White Fang*, a novel by Jack London, published in 1906.

It tells the story of a wild dog (son of the she-wolf in this extract) which is tamed, after a life of horrible cruelty, and eventually dies while saving his master's home from attack by a criminal. Jack London wrote this book partly because of the great success of *The Call of the Wild*, in which the hero is a dog that goes through the opposite process, from family pet to leader of a wolf pack.

Probably, life in a wolf pack is a little less violent than it appears here—male wolves do not often kill each other fighting over a female. Still, no other writer is better at getting inside a wolf's skin.

It was the she-wolf who had first caught the sound of men's voices and the whining of the sled dogs, and it was the she-wolf who was first to spring away from the cornered man in his circle of dying flame. The pack had been loathe to forego the kill it had hunted down, and it lingered for several minutes, making sure of the sounds, and then it, too, sprang away on the trail made by the she-wolf.

Running at the forefront of the pack was a large gray wolf—one of its several leaders. It was he who directed the pack's course on the heels of the she-wolf. It was he who snarled warningly at the younger members of the pack or slashed at them with his fangs when they ambitiously tried to pass him. And it was he who increased the pace when he sighted the she-wolf, now trotting slowly across the snow.

She dropped in alongside by him, as though it were her appointed position, and took the pace of the pack. He did not snarl at her, nor show his teeth, when any leap of hers chanced to put her in advance of him. On the contrary, he seemed kindly disposed toward her—too kindly to suit her, for he was prone to run near to her, and when he ran too near it was she who snarled and showed her teeth. Nor was she above slashing his shoulder sharply on occasion. At such times he betrayed no anger. He merely sprang to the side and ran stiffly ahead for several awkward leaps, in carriage and conduct resembling an abashed country swain.

This was his one trouble in the running of the pack; but she had other troubles. On her other side ran a gaunt old wolf, grizzled and marked with the scars of many battles. He ran always on her right side. The fact that he had but one eye, and that the left eye, might account for this.

He, also, was addicted to crowding her, to veering toward her till his scarred muzzle touched her body, or shoulder, or neck. As with the running mate to the left, she repelled these attentions with her teeth; but when both bestowed their attentions at the same time, she was roughly jostled, being compelled, with quick snaps to either side, to drive both lovers away, and at the same time to maintain her forward leap with the pack and see the way of her feet before her. At such times her running mates flashed their teeth and growled threateningly across at each other. They might have fought, but even wooing and its rivalry waited upon the more pressing hunger-need of the pack.

After each repulse, when the old wolf sheered abruptly away from the sharp-toothed object of his desire, he shouldered against a young three-year old that ran on his blind right side. This young wolf had attained his full size; and, considering the weak and famished condition of the pack, he possessed more than the average vigor and spirit. Nevertheless, he ran with his head even with the shoulder of his one-eyed elder. When he ventured to run abreast of the older wolf (which was seldom), a snarl and a snap sent him back even with the shoulder again. Sometimes, however, he dropped cautiously and slowly behind and edged in between the old leader and the she-wolf. This was doubly resented, even triply resented. When she snarled her displeasure, the old leader would whirl on the three-year-old. Sometimes she whirled with him. And sometimes the young leader on the left whirled too.

At such times, confronted by three sets of savage teeth, the young wolf stopped precipitately, throwing himself back on his haunches, with fore-legs stiff, mouth menacing, and mane bristling. This confusion in the front of the moving pack always caused confusion in the rear. The wolves behind collided with the young wolf, and expressed their displeasure by administering sharp nips on his hind legs and flanks. He was laying up trouble for himself, for lack of food and short tempers went together; but with the boundless faith of youth he persisted in repeating the manœuvre every little while, though it never succeeded in gaining anything for him but discomfiture.

Had there been food, love-making and fighting would have gone on apace, and the pack formation would have been broken up. But the situation of the pack was desperate. It was lean with long-standing hunger. It ran below its ordinary speed. At the rear limped the weak members—the very young and the very old. At the front were the strongest. Yet all were more like skeletons than full-bodied wolves. Nevertheless, with the exception of the ones that limped, the movements of the animals were effortless and tireless. Their stringy muscles seemed founts of inexhaustible energy. Behind every steel-like contraction of a muscle lay another steel-like contraction, and another, and another, apparently without end.

They ran many miles that day. They ran through the night. And the next day found them still running. They were running over the surface of a world frozen and dead. No life stirred. They alone moved through the vast inertness. They alone were alive, and they sought for other things that were alive in order that they might devour them and continue to live.

They crossed low divides and ranged a dozen small streams in a lower-lying country before their quest was rewarded. Then they came upon moose. It was a big bull they first found. Here was meat and life, and it was guarded by no mysterious fires nor flying missiles of flame. Splay hoofs and palmated antlers they knew, and they flung their customary patience and caution to the wind. It was a brief fight and fierce. The big bull was beset on every side. He ripped them open or split their skulls with shrewdly-driven blows of his great hoofs. He crushed them and broke them on his large horns. He stamped them into the snow under him in the wallowing struggle. But he was foredoomed, and he went down with the she-wolf tearing savagely at his throat, and with other teeth fixed everywhere upon him, devouring him alive, before ever his last struggles ceased or his last damage had been wrought.

There was food in plenty. The bull weighed over 800 pounds—fully 20 pounds of meat per mouth for the 40-odd wolves of the pack. But if they could fast prodigiously, they could feed prodigiously, and soon a few scattered bones were all that remained of the splendid live brute that had faced the pack a few hours before.

There was now much resting and sleeping. With full stomachs, bickering and quarreling began among the younger males, and this continued through the few days that followed before the breaking-up of the pack. The famine was over. The wolves were now in the country of game, and though they still hunted in pack, they hunted more cautiously, cutting out heavy cows or crippled old bulls from the small moose-herds they ran across.

There came a day, in this land of plenty, when the wolf pack split in half and went in different directions. The she-wolf, the young leader on her left, and the one-eyed elder on her right, led their half of the pack down to the Mackenzie River and across into the lake country to the east. Each day this remnant of the pack dwindled. Two by two, male and

192

female, the wolves were deserting. Occasionally a solitary male was driven out by the sharp teeth of his rivals. In the end there remained only four—the she-wolf, the young leader, the one-eyed one, and the ambitious three-year-old.

The she-wolf had by now developed a ferocious temper. Her three suitors all bore the marks of her teeth. Yet they never replied in kind, never defended themselves against her. They turned their shoulders to her most savage slashes, and with wagging tails and mincing steps strove to placate her wrath. But if they were all mildness toward her, they were all fierceness toward one another. The three-year-old grew too ambitious in his fierceness. He caught the one-eyed elder on his blind side and ripped his ear into ribbons. Though the grizzled old fellow could see only on one side, against the youth and vigor of the other he brought into play the wisdom of long years of experience. His lost eye and his scarred muzzle bore evidence to the nature of his experience. He had survived too many battles to be in doubt for a moment about what to do.

The battle began fairly, but it did not end fairly. There was no telling what the outcome would have been, for the third wolf joined the elder, and together, old leader and young leader, they attacked the ambitious three-year-old and proceeded to destroy him. He was beset on either side by the merciless fangs of his erstwhile comrades. Forgotten were the days they had hunted together, the game they had pulled down, the famine they had suffered. That business was a thing of the past. The business of love was at hand—ever a sterner and crueller business than that of getting food.

And, in the meanwhile, the she-wolf, the cause of it all, sat down contentedly on her haunches and watched. She was even pleased. This was her day—and it came not often—when manes bristled, and fang smote fang or ripped and tore the yielding flesh, all for the possession of her.

And in the business of love the three-year-old, who had made this his first adventure upon it, yielded up his life. On either side of his body stood his two rivals. They were gazing at the she-wolf, who sat smiling in the snow. But the elder leader was wise, very wise, in love even as in battle. The younger leader turned his head to lick a wound on his shoulder. The curve of his neck was turned toward his rival. With his one eye the elder saw the opportunity. He darted in low and closed with his fangs. It was a long, ripping slash, and deep as well. His teeth, in passing, burst the wall of the great vein of the throat. Then he leaped clear.

The young leader snarled terribly, but his snarl broke midmost into a tickling cough. Bleeding and coughing, already stricken, he sprang at the elder and fought while life faded from him, his legs going weak beneath him, the light of day dulling on his eyes, his blows and springs falling shorter and shorter.

And all the while the she-wolf sat on her haunches and smiled. She was made glad in vague ways by the battle, for this was the love-making of the Wild, the sex tragedy of the natural world that was tragedy only to those that died. To those that survived it was not tragedy, but realization and achievement.

When the young leader lay in the snow and moved no more, One Eye stalked over to the she-wolf. His carriage was one of mingled triumph and caution. He was plainly expectant of a rebuff, and he was just as plainly surprised when her teeth did not flash out at him in anger. For the first time she met him with a kindly manner. She sniffed noses with him, and even condescended to leap about and frisk and play with him in quite puppyish fashion. And he, for all his gray years and sage experience, behaved quite as puppyishly and even a little more foolishly.

Forgotten already were the vanquished rivals and the love tale, red-

written on the snow. Forgotten, save once, when old One Eye stopped for a moment to lick his stiffening wounds. Then it was that his lips half writhed into a snarl, and the hair of his neck and shoulders involuntarily bristled, while he half crouched for a spring, his claws spasmodically clutching into the snow surface for firmer footing. But it was all forgotten the next moment as he sprang after the she-wolf, who was coyly leading him a chase through the woods.

After that they ran side by side, like good friends who have come to an understanding. The days passed by, and they kept together, hunting their meat and killing and eating it in common. After a time the she-wolf began to grow restless. She seemed to be searching for something that she could not find. The hollows under fallen trees seemed to attract her, and she spent much time nosing about among the larger snow-piled crevices in the rocks and in the caves of overhanging banks. Old One Eye was not interested at all, but he followed her good-naturedly in her quest, and when her investigations in particular places were unusually protracted, he would lie down and wait until she was ready to go on.

They did not remain in one place, but traveled across country until they regained the Mackenzie River, down which they slowly went, leaving it often to hunt game along the small streams that entered it, but always returning to it again. Sometimes they chanced upon other wolves, usually in pairs; but there was no friendliness of intercourse displayed on either side, no gladness at meeting, no desire to return to the pack formation. Several times they encountered solitary wolves. These were always males, and they were pressingly insistent on joining with One Eye and his mate. This he resented, and when she stood shoulder to shoulder with him, bristling and showing her teeth, the aspiring solitary ones would back off, turn tail, and continue on their lonely way.

One moonlight night, running through the quiet forest, One Eye suddenly halted. His muzzle went up, his tail stiffened, and his nostrils dilated as he scented the air. One foot also he held up, after the manner of a dog. He was not satisfied, and he continued to smell the air, striving to understand the message borne upon it to him. One careless sniff had satisfied his mate, and she trotted on to reassure him. Though he followed her, he was still dubious, and he could not forbear an occasional halt in order more carefully to study the warning.

She crept out cautiously on the edge of a large open space in the midst of the trees. For some time she stood alone. Then One Eye, creeping and crawling, every sense on the alert, every hair radiating infinite suspicion, joined her. They stood side by side, watching and listening and smelling.

To their ears came the sounds of dogs wrangling and scuffling, the guttural cries of men, the sharper voices of scolding women, and once the shrill and plaintive cry of a child. With the exception of the huge bulks of the skin lodges, little could be seen save the flames of the fire, broken by the movements of intervening bodies, and the smoke rising slowly on the quiet air. But to their nostrils came the myriad smells of an Indian camp, carrying a story that was largely incomprehensible to One Eye, but every detail of which the she-wolf knew.

She was strangely stirred, and sniffed and sniffed with an increasing delight. But old One Eye was doubtful. He betrayed his apprehension, and started tentatively to go. She turned and touched his neck with her muzzle in a reassuring way, then regarded the camp again. A new wistfulness was in her face, but it was not the wistfulness of hunger. She was thrilling to a desire that urged her to go forward, to be in closer to that fire, to be squabbling with the dogs, and to be avoiding and dodging the stumbling feet of men.

One Eye moved impatiently beside her; her unrest came back upon her, and she knew again her pressing need to find the thing for which she searched. She turned and trotted back into the forest, to the great relief of One Eye, who trotted a little to the fore until they were well within the shelter of the trees.

As they slid along, noiseless as shadows, in the moonlight, they came upon a runway. Both noses went down to the footprints in the snow. These footprints were very fresh. One Eye ran ahead cautiously, his mate at his heels. The broad pads of their feet were spread wide, and in contact with the snow were like velvet. One Eye caught sight of a dim movement of white in the midst of the white. His sliding gait had been deceptively swift, but it was as nothing to the speed at which he now ran. Before him was bounding the faint patch of white he had discovered.

They were running along a narrow alley flanked on either side by a growth of young spruce. Through the trees the mouth of the alley could be seen, opening out on a moonlit glade. Old One Eye was rapidly overhauling the fleeing shape of white. Bound by bound he gained. Now he was upon it. One leap more and his teeth would be sinking into it. But that leap was never made. High in the air, and straight up, soared the shape of white, now a struggling snowshoe rabbit that leaped and bounded, executing a fantastic dance there above him in the air and never once returning to earth.

One Eye sprang back with a snort of sudden fright, then shrank down to the snow and crouched, snarling threats at this thing of fear he did not understand. But the she-wolf coolly thrust past him. She poised for a moment, then sprang for the dancing rabbit. She, too, soared high, but not so high as the quarry, and her teeth clipped emptily together with a metallic snap. She made another leap, and another.

Her mate had slowly relaxed from his crouch and was watching her. He now evinced displeasure at her repeated failures, and himself made a mighty spring upward. His teeth closed upon the rabbit, and he bore it back to earth with him. But at the same time there was a suspicious crackling movement beside him, and his astonished eye saw a young spruce sapling bending down above him to strike him. His jaws let go their grip, and he leaped backward to escape this strange danger, his lips drawn back from his fangs, his throat snarling, every hair bristling with rage and fright. And in that moment the sapling reared its slender length upright, and the rabbit soared dancing in the air again.

The she-wolf was angry. She sank her fangs into her mate's shoulder in reproof; and he, frightened, unaware of what constituted this new onslaught, struck back furiously and in still greater fright, ripping down the side of the she-wolf's muzzle. For him to resent such reproof was equally unexpected to her, and she sprang upon him in snarling indignation. Then he discovered his mistake and tried to placate her; but she proceeded to punish him roundly, until he gave over all attempts at placation, and whirled in a circle, his head away from her, his shoulders receiving the punishment of her teeth.

In the meantime, the rabbit danced above them in the air. The she-wolf sat down in the snow, and old One Eye, now more in fear of his mate than of the mysterious sapling, again sprang for the rabbit. As he sank back with it between his teeth, he kept his eye on the sapling. As before, it followed him back to earth. He crouched down under the impending blow, his hair bristling, but his teeth still keeping tight hold of the rabbit. But the blow did not fall. The sapling remained bent above him. When he moved it moved, and he growled at it through his clenched jaws; when he remained still, it remained still, and he concluded it was safer to continue remaining still. Yet the warm blood of the rabbit tasted good in his mouth.

It was his mate who relieved him from the quandary in which he found himself. She took the rabbit from him, and while the sapling swayed and teetered threateningly above her, she calmly gnawed off the rabbit's head. At once the sapling shot up, and after that gave no more trouble, remaining in the decorous and perpendicular position in which nature had intended it to grow. Then, between them, the she-wolf and One-Eye devoured the game which the mysterious sapling had caught for them.

There were other runways and alleys where rabbits were hanging in the air and the wolf-pair prospected them all, the she-wolf leading the way, old One Eye following and observant, learning the method of robbing snares—a knowledge destined to stand him in good stead in the days to come.

The Boll Weevil

This song of the black workers in the cotton fields tells of the insect that could ruin the crop with such ease. (It is said that a pair of boll weevils, arriving in the cotton field in early spring would have 12 million descendants by the end of the season!) This version of the song is the one published by Carl Sandburg in 1927.

Oh, de boll weevil am a little black bug,
Come from Mexico, dey say,
Come all de way to Texas, jus' a-looking foh a place to stay,
Jus' a-lookin' foh a home, jus' a-lookin' foh a home.

De first time I seen de boll weevil,
He was a-setting on de square,
De next time I seen de boll weevil, he had all of his family dere.
Jus' a-lookin' foh a home, jus' a-lookin' foh a home.

De farmer say to de weevil,
"What make yo' head so red?"
De weevil say to de farmer, "it's a wondah I ain't dead,
A-lookin' foh a home, jus' a-lookin' foh a home."

De farmer take de boll weevil,
"An' he put him in de hot san."
De weevil say: "Dis is mighty hot, but I'll stan' it like a man,
Dis'll be my home, it'll be my home."

De farmer take de boll weevil,
An' he put him in a lump of ice;
De boll weevil say to de farmer: "Dis is mighty cool and nice,
It'll be my home, dis'll be my home."

De farmer take de boll weevil,
An' he put him in de fire.
De boll weevil say to de farmer: "Here I are, here I are,
Dis'll be my home, dis'll be my home."

De boll weevil say to de farmer:
"You better leave me alone;
I done eat all your cotton, now I'm goin' to start on yo' corn,
I'll have a home, I'll have a home."

De merchant got half de cotton,
De boll weevil got de res'.
Didn't leave de farmer's wife but one old cotton dress,
An' it's full of holes, it's full of holes.

De farmer say to de merchant:
"We's in an awful fix;
De boll weevil et all de cotton up an' lef' us only sticks,
We's got no home, we's got no home."

De farmer say to de merchant:
"We ain't made but only one bale,
And befoh we'll give yo' dat one we'll fight and go to jail,
We'll have a home, we'll have a home."

De cap'n say to de missus:
"What d'you t'ink o' dat?
De boll weevil done make a nes' in my bes' Sunday hat,
Goin' to have a home, goin' to have a home."

Paul Bunyan's Natural History

As you can imagine, there were a great many unusual animals around in the forests, swamps and lakes where Paul Bunyan and his men worked. Some were quite harmless, but others were extremely deadly in one way or another. Of course, many of them are now extinct, and the rest are extremely rare. Here are a few of the creatures, all based on the most unreliable and out-of-date information.

The Axehandle Hound. In general appearance, it looked like a dachshund, with a head like a hatchet, a handle-shaped body, and short, stumpy legs. It used to prowl around the lumber camps at night looking for axe handles to eat, and was not known to eat any other kind of food. These troublesome wild hounds were accustomed to eat whole stacks of axe handles.

The Argopelter. This hoary beast lived in hollow tree trunks. From its refuge it would hurl chunks of wood at anything that moved. A number of lumberjacks were maimed, for it seldom missed its aim. Otherwise, little is known of the life history of this creature.

Camp Chipmunks. To begin with, these were small animals, but as a result of eating tons of prune stones discarded from Paul Bunyan's cook shanty, they grew so big that they killed all the bears and cougars in the neighborhood.

The Gumberoo. A very ferocious creature, it lived in burned-over forests and was therefore, fortunately, easy to avoid meeting. It was larger than a bear and had a leathery skin so tough that bullets bounced off it, sometimes rebounding and killing the man who fired them. The only thing that could kill a Gumberoo was fire. When, at night, the lumberjacks were awoken by a loud explosion, they knew this was a Gumberoo going off.

The Stone-Eating Gyascutus. This sordid beast, about the size of a white-tailed deer, had ears like a rabbit and teeth like a mountain lion. It fed on rocks and lichen, the rocks helping it digest the tough and stringy lichen. It was never seen except after a case of snake bite.

The Hidebehind. This very dangerous animal was undoubtedly the cause of the unexplained disappearance of many a lumberjack. It was always hiding behind something, such as a tree. From this position it sprang upon its unsuspecting prey and dragged it back to its lair. Because of its habit of concealment, no one has actually seen one.

The Luferlang. This curious animal had a dark blue stripe down its back and a bushy tail which came out somewhere about the middle of the stripe. It had triple jointed legs, on which it could run just as fast backward or sideways as forward. It only bit once a year, so if you met one that had already bitten somebody in the previous 12 months, you were in no danger.

The Roperite. A very active animal, as large as a pony, it had a beak like a rope, and lassoed even the swiftest rabbits. Sometimes it got a tenderfoot logger.

The Sidehill Dodger. This animal lived only on the sides of hills. It had the legs on one side shorter than the legs on the other, which allowed it to maintain a level position on the slope. Occasionally, it forgot on which side its legs were shorter and tried to stand on the hillside with its longer legs on the uphill side. This often proved disastrous and may explain why it is now extinct.

The Silver Cat. A fierce hunter of the pines, a huge cat with tassels on is ears, it had fierce red eyes, one above the other. Its long tail was fitted with a hard knob at the one end and spikes on one side. It would perch in a tree, and when a lumberjack walked underneath, it knocked him down with the knob and picked him up with the spikes.

Teakettler. This small animal is named after the noise it made, like a boiling kettle. Clouds of steam also issued from its nose, and it preferred to walk backward, when practical.

Goofus Bird. This bird liked to fly backward. The reason for this seems to be that the Goofus bird was more interested in where it had been than where it was going.

Gillygaloo Bird. A kind of plover that nested on hillsides. Because of the nature of its habitat, it used to lay square eggs that did not roll downhill—or not so easily anyhow. The loggers used to hard-boil them and use them as dice.

The Pinnacle Grouse. This bird only had one wing and therefore flew constantly in a circle around the top of a hill. The color of its plumage varied greatly according to the condition of the observer.

The Phillyloo Bird. This bird had a long beak like a stork, long legs, and was rather meanly supplied with feathers. It flew upside down so as to keep its feet warm in the sunshine.

Mosquitoes. Paul Bunyan's men regarded these as birds because of their great size.

Giddy Fish. These were small and very elastic fish, like India rubber. They were caught during winter through holes in the ice. What you did was to hit one on the head with a paddle. This made it bounce up and down. The other fish would copy it, until the shoal was all bouncing. Pretty soon, they bounced themselves right up on the ice, where they could be easily gathered.

Log Gar. This big fish had such powerful saw teeth that it could saw right through a log to get at a lumberjack. Once it had him in the water, it quickly converted him to mincemeat.

The Wild West

The Wild West

Most people's idea of the Wild West is the one shown by Hollywood, in which history and legend are mixed, but with more legend than history.

To say that it was a lawless society is only part of the story, but that was the root of the violence of life in the old cattle and mining towns. Cattle rustlers, horse thieves, stagecoach robbers and other outlaws were much more numerous than law officers, although sometimes you couldn't easily tell the difference. Banks and trains were there to be robbed. Crime was common. There were very few courts, and those that did exist were often run by judges like Roy Bean, whose idea of justice left a lot to be desired.

Men took the law into their own hands, and justice was usually administered by a quick bullet. A type of revolver in common use was called the "Peacemaker," not entirely as a joke.

Books, and later films, made the bad men into heroes of a kind, but most of them were really bad men right enough. There was little to admire in the character of Jesse James, or Doc Holliday, or the Dalton boys, although the legends may say otherwise. The truth about a famous incident, like the Gun Fight at the OK Corral for example, is hard to discover now, but the legend is well established. Was Wild Bill Hickok (you can read his story on pages 210-212) a man of honor and a pillar of law and order, or was he just a more deadly gunslinger than most? Perhaps it is no longer important, and the legend is greater than the man.

Pecos Bill

The Texan cowboy hero, Pecos Bill, is a cousin of Old Stormalong and Paul Bunyan. Sitting around the campfire at night, cowboys loved to tell tall tales, especially if there was a greenhorn present who could be kidded. How long Pecos Bill featured in those stories it's hard to say, but 60 or so years ago some of the tales about him were written down by Edward O'Reilly.

Pecos Bill invented most of the things connected with the cow business. It was Bill who taught the bronco how to buck. He dug the Rio Grande one year when he grew tired of carrying water from the Gulf of Mexico.

Bill was born about the time Sam Houston discovered Texas. His mother was a sturdy pioneer woman who once killed 45 Indians with a broom handle, and his earliest playmates were the bears and mountain lions of east Texas.

When Bill was about a year old, another family moved into the country about 50 miles down the river. His father decided the place was getting too crowded and packed his family in a wagon and headed west.

The day after they crossed the Pecos River, Bill fell out of the wagon. Because there were 16 or 17 other children in the family, his parents didn't miss him for some time, and then it was too late to go back for him.

That was how Bill came to grow up with the coyotes along the Pecos. He used to hunt with them and sit on the hills and howl at night. That was when he learnt to kill deer by running them to death.

Pecos Bill invented the six-shooter and train-robbing, and most of the crimes popular in the old west. He didn't invent cattle-rustling, but he improved on it.

Bill was on his way to join a new outfit when his horse stubbed his toe on a mountain and broke his leg, leaving Bill to go on foot. He slung his saddle over his shoulder and set off hiking. When he'd gone 100 miles or so, a big 10-foot rattlesnake reared up in his path and allowed he'd like a fight. Bill laid down his saddle and, just to be fair about it, he gave the rattlesnake the first three bites. Then he waded into that reptile until it yelled for mercy and admitted that when it came to fighting, Bill started where he let off. So Bill picked up his saddle and went on, carrying the rattlesnake in his hand and snapping it at the Gila monsters.

Fifty miles further on, a big old mountain lion jumped off a cliff and landed on Bill's neck. This was no ordinary lion. It weighed more than three steers and a yearling. Bill laid down his saddle and his snake and went into action. In a minute the fur was flying down the canyon, and the lion hollered, "I give up, Bill. Can't you take a joke?"

So Bill put his saddle on the lion and went down the canyon whooping and yelling, riding the lion and using the rattlesnake as a whip.

It was soon after this that Bill staked out New Mexico and used Arizona as a calf pasture, and about then that he found his famous horse, Widow-maker. He raised him from a colt, and Bill was the only man who could ride him. There wasn't anything Bill couldn't ride. He even rode a cyclone once. It was the worst cyclone ever known, but Bill pulled it down and climbed on its back. It went all across Texas, knocking down mountains and making holes in the ground. The plains used to be well-timbered then, but that big wind swiped the trees off the prairies. Bill rode it through three states, rolling a cigarette in one hand but over in Arizona it got him.

When it saw it couldn't throw him, it rained out from under him. Bill came down in California. The place where he landed is now known as Death Valley, Bill hit it so hard he knocked it more than a 100 feet below sea level.

The Grand Canyon was dug by Bill when he went prospecting. He invented the tarantula and the centipede as a joke on his friends.

Once, Bill took a contract to supply the Southern Pacific Railroad with wood. He hired a few hundred Mexicans to chop the wood and haul it to where they were building the railroad line. As pay for the job, Bill gave each man one-fourth of the wood he hauled. But when they received their share of the wood, the Mexicans did not know what to do with it. So Bill took it off their hands for nothing.

Another job Bill took when the cow business was dull was building the fence along the border from El Paso to the Pacific Ocean. For this job he rounded up a herd of prairie dogs. A prairie dog likes to dig holes by nature, but whenever one of them finished a nice hole and settled down to live in it, Bill drove him out and stuck a fence post in the hole. Everybody admired his foresight, except the prairie dogs, and who cares what a prairie dog thinks?

Bill went hunting with a bunch of Kiowa Indians once. He had his famous hound with him, which was named Norther. The buffalo were getting scarce then, but Bill caught a few. Norther would run down the buffalo and grab hold of its ear, until Bill came up and skinned it alive. Then he would turn it loose to grow a new hide. The scheme worked all right in the summer, but in the winter they caught colds and died.

There's more than one account of the way Pecos Bill met his end. Some say it was the drink. Bill was a fierce drinker, and he got to complaining that liquor didn't have any kick in it any more. So he took to livening it up with strychnine, and putting fish-hooks and barbed wire in it. It was the barbed wire that finally killed him. It rusted away in his interior and gave him indigestion. He wasted away until he didn't weigh more than two tons, then he died and went to his infernal reward.

Others say different. They say that Bill met a man from Boston one day who was wearing a cowboy outfit that he had bought by mail order and was asking fool questions about the west. Poor old Bill laughed so much he died.

AMERICAN FOLK TALES AND LEGENDS

Wild Bill Hickok

James Butler ("Wild Bill") Hickok was born in Illinois. As a youth, he used to shoot wolves for the bounty that was paid for each wolfskin. Many tales are told of his fights, with fists or gun. "I always shoot well," he said, "but I came to be perfect in the mountains by shooting at a dime for a mark, at best of half a dollar a shot."

Hickok was hired by the town of Abilene, a town much troubled by Texas cowboys letting off steam after the long cattle drive, to keep the peace. He is said to have already killed 70 men by the time he took that job. "As to killing men," he said, "I never thought much about it. With most of the men I have killed it was one or t'other of us, and at such times you don't stop to think—and what's the use after it's all over?" He was renowned for his speed with a revolver, but he used to say, "Whenever you get into a row, be sure and not shoot too quick. Take time. I've known many a feller slip up for shooting in a hurry."

Hickok was willing to admit he'd killed many men, but always in self-defence, or in the performance of official duty. "I never in my life took any mean advantage of an enemy. Yet, understand, I never allow a man to get the drop on me."

Sometimes, though, it was impossible to prevent this. Once Hickok found himself facing an outlaw who had a gun in each hand. He raised his own hand and called out, "Don't shoot him, Frank, he's only playing." The outlaw turned around, expecting to see a deputy coming up behind him, and in that instant Wild Bill drew his revolver and shot him dead.

Then there's the tale of how he shot two men who had entered the room at opposite doors. He was facing the man at the front door. He drew his guns (he always carried two), shot the man at the front door, and with his other hand shot the man at the back door over his shoulder. He could see him in a mirror hanging above the front door.

Others tell a different tale of Wild Bill Hickok. They say he was a cold-blooded killer who picked his enemies carefully and made himself scarce when he ran into a real fighting man.

One time, they say, Wild Bill was in a Kansas town and had taken a few drinks. He saw a quiet-looking man standing nearby and thought he would do a little showing-off. "By God," he swore, "I could cut a fellow's hair without touching his head." He put a bullet dead in the center of a small tree about 50 yards off. The quiet man said nothing, but drew his pistols and planted a ball from each of them one inch on

210

each side of Wild Bill's mark. "You can open your barber shop any time you like," he said. Wild Bill said nothing. He left town pretty soon afterward.

Of course, stories like that would get spread by Bill's enemies. The story of the Deadwood stage hold-up is the kind of story that was repeated by his friends.

Wild Bill happened to meet the Deadwood stage one day a few miles out, so he hitched his famous horse, Black Nell, to the stage and took a seat alongside the driver. As they drove along, he took pot shots at squirrels to amuse the passengers, and shot eight of the varmints. Being so near to town and not expecting any trouble, Bill neglected to reload his pistols.

The word had got around that the stage was carrying a Wells Fargo strongbox, and suddenly five armed men swooped down on it. Each man was masked and armed, and as the coach pulled up, one of them shouted to Bill and the driver, "Put your hands up!"

Wild Bill's hands came up all right, but his pistols were in them and they were firing. He dropped four of the outlaws before anyone got off a shot, but remember he had only four shots left after his show with the squirrels. The fifth man leveled a shotgun at him and told him to get down from the coach. Bill recognized his voice as that of Mickey Rose, who had been a barkeeper in Cheyenne. "So it's you, is it, Mickey?" he said, and he flung one of his empty pistols so hard and so straight it broke the man's skull.

"Well," said Wild Bill, "I have saved the marshal a little job."

By the time Wild Bill went to Deadwood he was a famous character, who attracted crowds in any town he entered. But he was also a target. To other gunfighters, he was a figure to envy, and like the champion heavyweight boxer whom everyone wants to beat, Wild Bill was the man who would make anyone who beat him famous.

Not long after he came to Deadwood, six Montana gunfighters were talking in the saloon. They were criticizing Wild Bill and saying they would get rid of him. This talk was reported to Wild Bill, who buckled on his guns, walked over to the saloon, and went straight up to the group who had been muttering about him.

"I hear you cheap Montana gunfighters have been making remarks about me," he said coolly. "If it goes on, I want to tell you there are going to be a number of cheap funerals in Deadwood. I am not looking for trouble, but I am not going to stand for insults either."

Then he lined up those six men against the wall and told them to hand over their guns—which they did. There was no more talk of getting rid of Wild Bill Hickok after that.

There are several different stories of the way Wild Bill Hickok met his death. It seems Wild Bill knew it was coming. When they first came to Deadwood Gulch, Wild Bill said to his friend "Colorado" Charlie Utter, "I have a hunch that I am in my last camp and will never leave this gulch alive."

Colorado Charlie paid him no mind. "Quit dreaming," he said.

A few days later Bill was playing poker, his favorite game, in the saloon. Someone else was sitting in his usual seat against the wall, and Wild Bill had his back to the open door, a position he generally avoided. A man named Jack McCall entered the saloon, moved easily and innocently around behind Wild Bill, drew a revolver and shot him through the head from behind. The doctor said he was the prettiest corpse he had ever seen. Wild Bill was 39 years old.

Some years later they had to put a steel cage around Wild Bill's grave because so many people were chipping bits off his tombstone as souvenirs.

Calamity Jane

Martha Jane Canarray was born in Missouri about 1848. She moved west with her family when she was about 15 and carved out a famous name for herself as Calamity Jane.

No doubt Jane should have been a man. But, as one old Montana hand said of her years later, "She swore, she drank, she wore men's clothing. Where can you find a woman today who doesn't do such things? She was just 50 years ahead of her time."

She was a crack shot, a good rider, and she could handle a mule team with ease. She was a very hard drinker, and she swore like a mule skinner. By the time she turned up in Cheyenne, Wild Bill Hickok's town, she was dressing in men's clothes and chewing tobacco. She had been a drifter, working at one time as a laborer on the Union Pacific Railroad, and some say she joined the army, saving a young officer's life in a desperate battle against the Indians. But she was always a drifter. How she came by her nickname isn't certain, but it was the kind of name that went down well in the saloons of the frontier towns and mining camps. She would swagger into the saloon demanding liquor and maybe firing a shot at the mirror to speed up the service. The bar owners didn't mind. Calamity Jane was good for business.

She was a scout with General Crook's expedition against the Sioux, the General having assumed she was a man. But she made the mistake of going for a dip in the river with the mule-skinners and all was revealed. The General got rid of her right away.

In the 1870s Calamity was roaming around in the Black Hills, and it was there she ran into Wild Bill Hickok. No one can say just what was the link between those two colorful characters. Wild Bill had a wife of whom he was fond, although she never came to Deadwood. Calamity Jane herself had been married once, it was said, and maybe more than once. At that time Wild Bill had a lot of admirers. When he rode down the street in his cream-colored Stetson and his tailored buckskin, with his shiny boots and the silver mounts on his harness all agleam, quite a crowd would tag along. Calamity Jane was one of them. Whether she was more than a friend and a follower, not even legend dares to tell.

But when Wild Bill was shot dead a few months later, Calamity Jane was hit hard. She always acted as if Wild Bill had been the great love of her life. She wept salt tears into her beer in those days.

But maybe it wasn't just the loss of Wild Bill that made her so sad. She was still young, but the life she had led had made her older than her years. Maybe Calamity Jane looked ahead and saw the road going downhill from thereon.

Not long after that the smallpox hit Deadwood, and that showed another side of Calamity Jane, one some people would regard as more suiting to women's estate. At the risk of her own life, she tended the sick and dying miners. Her nursing was kind of rough and ready, it was true, but what else woud you expect. One of her patients was a little boy of the name Robinson. "Drink this, you little bastard," Jane would say, and, "Hold still, damn you, while I wash your face." When that little boy grew up, he became a minister, and he repaid an old debt when he ministered to Calamity Jane at her funeral.

There are many other tales of Calamity Jane in Deadwood—winning a $50 bet by shooting a hole in a top hat on the far side of the saloon, watching a play and getting annoyed at the heroine and letting fly a stream of tobacco juice just as accurately as she had shot a hole in the hat.

A stranger rode up to the saloon one day and offered to trade his horse for Calamity Jane's horse, Jim. He said his was the better animal and challenged her to a race for a $100 stake. Calamity Jane said OK, but she dictated the rules of the race. "We'll start 20 feet back of the platform where the horses are now standing, jump the horses up on the platform, ride into the saloon, take a drink, ride out through the back door, enter the next saloon by the back door, have a drink there, and out the front, enter the next saloon, and so on all the way down the street until all eleven saloons and dance halls on that side of the street are visited in turn. First horse at the bar of the last saloon gets the money."

The stranger agreed to this, which was foolish of him, because Calamity Jane's horse had been trained to do this trick and had been doing it for years. He could even take a bottle in his teeth, tip it up, and drink like a man.

Calamity Jane won the race by three saloons and four drinks.

Like Wild Bill Hickok, Calamity Jane became a legend in her own time. People were writing books about her long before she died, and she wrote a book herself, about her adventures. It contained a lot of lies, but no more than the books other folk were writing. The west went on echoing off and on with explosions set off by Calamity Jane, although she was ageing fast. Someone who met her in 1902, when she would have been in her early 50s, said she looked at least 70. The same year she was thrown out of Billings, Montana, after shooting up a bar.

Not long after that she died, on the same day of the year as Wild Bill Hickok had been shot. Her last words were, "Bury me next to Bill."

Doc Holliday and Big-Nose Kate

Doc Holliday was a dentist with a taste for gambling—and a tendency to kill anyone he suspected of cheating. He also suffered from the lung disease known as consumption. When he was living in Fort Griffin, Texas (this was long before he took part in the Gunfight at the OK Corral with the Earp brothers), he took up with a woman in the town named Kate Fisher. She did have kind of a big nose, although she was a handsome woman overall.

One night Doc was playing poker with a fellow named Ed Bailey. This Bailey was a crooked card man, and he was always playing with the discarded cards. Doc told him to lay off more than once.

After a while a pretty big pot came along. Doc called, and Bailey laid down three kings. Doc threw away his own cards without showing them and claimed the pot. Bailey made a big protest, as you'd expect. "I won that pot!" he yelled.

"I seen you palming a king off the discards," said Doc.

"Give me that money!" said Bailey, and he made a move as if he was going for his gun. Before he could draw, Doc whipped out a knife he had hidden under his coat and gave him a death wound.

Doc was arrested and held in the hotel office by the sheriff and a couple of deputies. Bailey had a lot of friends in town, and soon they gathered outside the hotel, grumbling and talking of getting a rope to hang Doc right away.

When Big-Nose Kate got to hear what was going on at the hotel she hurried on over. The sheriff let her in to have a talk with Doc.

Kate then hired a couple of horses, saddled them up and hitched them out of sight around the corner from the hotel. She changed her clothes for a man's, and lit a fire in a small building at the back of the hotel.

"Fire!" someone hollered, and the crowd in front of the hotel ran around to the back, just as Kate planned. She walked into the hotel office and pulled two revolvers from a bag she was carrying. She threw one of them to Doc, and the two of them took the guns of the sheriff and his deputies and backed out of the door.

By the time the crowd came running back with the fire put out, Doc and Kate were well on their way to Dodge City.

Jesse James

Jesse James and his brother Frank were desperadoes who, like many others, had their lives disrupted as youngsters by the Civil War. Jesse was only 15 when he and his elder brother left home to join the Confederate Bushwackers, led by William Quantrill. After the war had ended unsatisfactorily as far as they were concerned, it was the natural thing to continue a life of banditry.

Jesse James lasted longer than most. In a period of about 16 years his gang robbed 11 banks, seven trains, and several stage-coaches, among other crimes. In legend, of course, the number becomes much greater.

Like other outlaws, Jesse James had a reputation as something of a Robin Hood. He certainly took the cause of revenge very seriously, but he had a good deal of provocation. In bombing his home, Pinkerton detectives wounded his mother and killed his younger brother.

The James brothers led a famous raid on a bank in Northfield, Minnesota, in 1876, when they ran into strong resistance, although the brothers escaped. After that, their luck began to run out.

In 1882, Jesse went into hiding under the name Howard in St. Joseph, Missouri. There he was treacherously shot by a member of his own gang, Robert Ford, who wanted the reward for Jesse James's death.

The death of Jesse James is commemorated in a famous western ballad. No one knows who wrote it, although this version gives the credit to a man named Billy Gashade.

—— □ ——

The Ballad of Jesse James

Jesse James was a lad who killed many a man,
He robbed the Glendale train.
He stole from the rich and he gave to the poor,
He'd a hand and a heart and a brain.
Chorus

Now Jesse had a wife to mourn for his life,
Three children—they were brave.
But that dirty little coward who shot Mister Howard,
Has laid Jesse James in his grave.

Yes it was Robert Ford, that dirty little coward,
I wonder how he does feel,
For he ate of Jesse's bread and he slept in Jesse's bed,
Then he laid Jesse James in his grave.
Chorus

Jesse was a man, a friend to the poor,
He'd never see a man suffer pain,
And with his brother Frank he robbed the Chicago bank
And stopped the Glendale train.
Chorus

It was on a Wednesday night and the moon was shining bright,
He stopped the Glendale train,
And the people all did say, from many miles away,
It was robbed by Frank and Jesse James.
Chorus

It was on a Saturday night, and Jesse was at home,
Talking to his family so brave,
Robert Ford came along like a thief in the night,
And laid Jesse James in his grave.
Chorus

All the people held their breath when they heard of Jesse's death,
And wondered how he ever came to die,
It was one of the gang, called little Robert Ford,
That shot Jesse James on the sly.
Chorus

Jesse went to rest with his hand on his breast,
The devil will be upon his knee,
He was born one day in the county of Shea
And he came of a solitary race.
Chorus

This song was made by Billy Gashade,
As soon as the news did arrive,
He said there was no man with the law in his hand
Could take Jesse James when alive.
Chorus

— □ —

Jesse James Helps a Poor Widow

One day Frank and Jesse James and some of their gang were traveling through northern Missouri. It was about noon and they were hungry. They pulled off the road and found a small farmhouse with a lone woman there. They asked her if she could give them something to eat.

At first the woman hesitated. The men showed her money and assured her they would gladly pay for what they ate. She then proceeded to prepare such food as she had. As she was making coffee and cooking eggs, the James crowd sat around the room. They noticed that she was weeping. Tears were rolling down her cheeks.

Jesse James was always tender-hearted—couldn't stand a woman's tears. He asked her why she was crying. She tried to smile it off, and said that seeing the men around the house reminded her of the happy time when her husband was living and had other men now and then helping him do the farm work. She was just thinking how sadly things had changed since his death, and that was what made her cry.

Jesse kept on asking questions. The woman said she had several children at school, some miles down the road. There was a mortgage on the farm, she said, for $1,400. It was overdue, and this was the last day to pay it.

"So that's what really makes you cry," said Jesse "you're afraid you're going to lose your home?"

She admitted that was it. That very afternoon, she said, the man who held the mortgage was coming out from town to demand his money. He was a hard-hearted old miser, and she didn't have a dollar to put toward the debt. The man would be sure to turn her and her helpless little ones out.

"Huh!" said Jesse "It that so?," his eyes blinking fast and furiously. "Well now, ma'am, I don't know about that. I—well, I think you may not lose your farm after all."

The widow looked puzzled. She put the food on the table and all of them sat down and turned to. After they had finished eating, Jesse produced a sack and counted out on the table $1,400.

"Here, lady," said he, "you take this money and pay off your mortgage."

The lady was amazed. "I can't ever pay you back," she said, "and so I won't borrrow it."

"It's no loan," said Jesse. "It's a gift."

The widow said she couldn't believe it was anything but a dream, but Jesse assured her it was real. The money was good money, and it was for her. He then sat down and wrote out a receipt, which he had the woman copy in her own hand writing so his writing wouldn't get into the wrong hands. He told the woman to pay the man the $1,400 and get him to sign the receipt. He also gave her some cash for her immediate needs.

Jesse asked the grateful widow to describe the man who held the mortgage. She did so, telling the kind of rig he drove and about what hour she expected him, and the road by which he would come out from town. The gang then bade her good day and mounted their horses. The widow was still weeping, but now she was weeping for joy.

They rode some distance from the house and hid in the bushes beside the rocky road along which the mortgage man was to come in his buggy. Presently they saw him driving toward the widow's house, and pretty soon driving back, looking prosperous. He was humming "Old Dan Tucker was a fine old feller" as he came opposite the gang's hiding place. They stepped out into the road, held him up, and recovered the $1,400.

The Law West of the Pecos

Roy Bean was appointed justice of the peace after a career in which he had little experience of law studies, but plenty of experience of the rougher side of frontier life. He had once nearly been hanged himself after killing a man over a woman. He held court in his saloon, the Jersey Lily saloon, in the town of Langtry. Both were named after the English actress Lily Langtry, for whom he had a great passion. He never met her, although she visited the town soon after he died.

Judge Roy Bean may have been a little unusual in his rulings, and in his manner of conducting a trial, but he did enforce a certain respect for the law "west of the Pecos."

Here is a typical judgment: "It is the judgment of this court that you are hereby tried and convicted of illegally and unlawfully committing certain grave offences against the peace and dignity of the State of Texas, particularly in my bailiwick, to wit: Drunk and disorderly. And being the Law West of the Pecos, I fine you $2, and now get the hell out of here and never show yourself in this court again."

And here is the judge passing a more severe sentence: "Time will pass and seasons will come and go. Spring with its waving green grass and heaps of sweet-smelling flowers on every hill and in every dale. Then will come sultry summer, with her shimmering heat waves on the baked horizon, and fall, with her yellow harvest moon and the hills growing brown and golden under a sinking sun. And finally winter, with its biting, whining wind, and all the land will be mantled with snow. But you won't be here to see any of 'em, not by a damn sight, because it's the order of this court that you be took to the nearest tree and hanged by the neck 'till you're dead, you son-of-a-billy-goat."

That tale is also told of another famous frontier judge, Judge Isaac Parker of Arkansas, who was known as "the Hanging Judge." But Roy Bean was often merciful, in his own way. Once, a young fellow of about 19 or 20 was brought before him accused of horse-stealing.

"Hear ye, hear ye! This honorable court is now in session, and if any galoot wants a snort afore we start, let him step up to the bar and name his poison." The Judge saw nothing wrong in combining business with profit.

He appointed six men as jury. Twelve is the usual number, of course, but only six were available at the time. The judge did not want any non-drinkers on the jury.

"The honorable court is in session. This here prisoner is charged with stealing a horse and, Oscar, where are the witnesses?"

"We caught him in the act," said one of the ranch hands who had brought him in. "He admitted it."

"Is that right, young feller?" asked the Judge.

"Yes, your Honor," he mumbled.

"Gentlemen of the jury," said the Judge, "the accused pleads guilty to horse theft, and you know as well as I do the penalty. I'm ready for your verdict."

Well, there wasn't much doubt about that, and when the verdict had been given and the Judge had passed sentence, the prisoner asked if he might write a last note to his mother back in Pennsylvania.

"Oscar, fetch the prisoner a piece of wrapping paper and a pencil. I think we've got a pencil back there behind them bottles." The Judge rose in order to allow the lad to sit down at the table where he had been presiding in order to write his note. While he did so, Bean looked over his shoulder.

The young fellow about to be hung wrote about how he was sorry for causing his mother so much grief and trouble. Then he wrote, "Perhaps I can at least repay you the money it cost you keeping me out of trouble by sending you what I have saved, which is $400..."

The Judge's eyes opened wide, and he cleared his throat. "By God," he exclaimed, "damned if there hasn't been a miscarriage of justice! I hearby declare the case reopened."

He sat back down on the beer barrel by the table and the prisoner, who didn't understand what was going on, stood in front of the bar as he had before. "Now then," said the Judge, "that wasn't much of a horse the lad tried to steal. And he didn't actually steal it anyhow. So I rule it's a finable case, and I hereby fine the accused three hundred dollars and get the hell out of this country afore I change my mind."

An Irishman was once brought before Judge Bean charged with killing a Chinese cook. The Judge released him, saying he had looked through his law books and he couldn't find any law against killing a Chinese.

One time Roy Bean went into partnership with a fellow raising hogs. The business went well enough for two years, but Roy never got any of his money back. His partner said expenditure was so high there was no profit. Roy put up with this for a little longer, but in the end he decided to sue his partner. There was no court to sue him in, so he sued him in his own court. No one was very surprised when the Judge awarded damages to the Plaintiff.

221

Roy Bean kept a pet bear whose name was Bruno. The chief purpose of the bear was to help Roy sell more liquor. He got a taste for beer, and if somebody loosend the cork for him, he could open the bottle himself and poured it down his throat. Naturally, people were often willing to buy a bottle of beer just to see Bruno perform this trick.

The Judge also used Bruno to help sober up drunks. He had them chained to the same post, the man on a slightly longer chain than the bear, and Bruno would start in slapping at the drunk. After half an hour dodging and sweating, trying to keep out of reach of Bruno, the drunk would have sweated all the alcohol out of his system.

But Bruno came to a sad end. Someone said this was the only time Judge Bean got angry enough to kill someone.

A whiskey salesman called at the Jersey Lily saloon one day. As usual, he had to buy a lot of drinks, including drinks for Bruno. And as usual, he had to keep quiet while Judge Bean cheated him by slipping in a few empties among the bottles he was supposed to have bought. When it came time to pay, the salesman found he only had a $20 bill. The Judge's eyes popped when he saw it, and he tucked it away with a faraway look in his eyes.

"Hey!" said the salesman, "don't I get no change?"

"Change?" said the Judge. "The only change you got coming is a change of heart, and by God you need it."

Just then the train whistled, and the salesman had to leave, shaking his fist.

A few weeks after that, the salesman happened to run into the Judge in San Anonio, having a quiet drink in the hotel. The Judge asked him where he'd been, and the salesman told him he'd come from El Paso. "Did you pass through my town?" the Judge inquired. The salesman acknowledged as he had. "Everything OK?" asked the Judge. The salesman said everything was just fine and they had another drink.

After a while the salesman said, "Oh, I forgot. Bruno died."

"The hell he did!" said the Judge. He was shocked, and went silent. The salesman said, "Judge, you once promised me I could have the hide of that bear. Is your word good on that?"

Roy Bean prided himself on always keeping his word, so he sent a wire to his son Sam in Langtry, telling him to skin Bruno and send the hide to the whiskey salesman in San Antonio.

When the Judge got home a few days after that, the first thing he asked was how had Bruno died.

"Why, buckshot, naturally," said Sam.

"You mean you shot him?"

"Sure."

"What in hell for?"

"I couldn't skin him alive, could I?"

The Judge didn't see that salesman again for a long time, which was just as well.

Stackalee

Among bad-men heroes, Stackalee is, unlike characters like Jesse James or Roy Bean, purely legendary. He may have been based on a real person—perhaps the Stacker Lee who was founder of a steamship line on the Ohio and Mississippi Rivers—but no one can say for sure.

His legend belongs to black American folklore, and is best know in the form of a ballad, which goes on and on and on. It tells how Stackalee sold his soul to the Devil in return for a magic Stetson hat which enabled him to assume different shapes and to perform extraordinary feats like eating fire. Finally, Stackalee got too ornery even for the Devil who was responsible for involving him in a fight with Billy Lyon, whom Stackalee believed had stolen the magic Stetson. Here are a few verses.

It was on one cold and frosty night
When Stackalee and Billy Lyons had one awful fight
All about an old Stetson hat.
Chorus: Everybodys' talking about Stackalee,
        That bad man Stackalee,
        Oh, tough man Stackalee,
        Oh, Lord, Oh Lordy-lord,
        All about an old Stetson hat.

Stackalee got his gun. Boy, he got it fast!
He shot poor Billy through and through, the bullet broke a looking glass.
Chorus

Stackalee shot Billy once, his body fell to the floor,
He cried out, "Oh please, Stack, please don't shoot, me no more."
Chorus

The White Elephant Barrel House was wrecked that night,
Gutters full of beer and whiskey, it was an awful sight.
Chorus

"Have mercy," Billy groaned, "Oh, please spare my life,
I've got two little babies and an innocent wife."
Chorus

A Cotton Plantation on the Mississippi, by W A Walker in 1883

Indians Attacking the Grizzly Bear, from a painting by George Catlin

Stack says, "God bless your children, damn your wife!
You stole my magic Stetson, I'm gonna steal your life."
Chorus

He shot poor Billy once, he shot him twice,
And the third time Billy pleaded, "Please go tell my wife."
Chorus

Yes, Stackalee the gambler, everybody knowed his name,
Made his living hollering high low, jack and the game.
Chorus

Meantime, the sergeant strapped on his big forty-five,
Says, "Now we'll bring in this bad man, dead or alive."
Chorus

Sent for the wagon and it hurried and come,
Loaded with pistols and a big gatling gun [*a machine gun*]
Chorus

"Jailer, jailer," says Stack, "I can't sleep.
For around my bedside poor Billy Lyons still creeps."
Chorus

Stackalee went to sleep that night by the city clock bell,
Dreaming the Devil had come all the way up from hell.
Chorus

Red devil was saying, "You better hunt your hole,
I've hurried here from hell just to get your soul."
Chorus

Stackalee told him, "Yes, maybe you're right,
But I'll give even you one hell of a fight."
Chorus

When they got into the scuffle, I heard the Devil shout,
"Come and get this bad man before he puts my fire out."
Chorus

Then here come Stack's woman running, says, "Daddy, I love you true,
See what beer, whiskey, and smoking hop has done to you."
Chorus

Crowds jammed the sidewalk, far as you could see,
Trying to get a good look at tough Stackalee.
Chorus

The judge says, "Stackalee, I would spare your life,
But I know you're a bad man, I can see it in your red eyes."
Chorus

The jury came to agreement, the clerk he wrote it down,
And everybody was whispering, "He's penitentiary bound."
Chorus

Judge looked over his glasses, says, "Mr. Bad Man Stackalee,
The jury finds you guilty of murder in the first degree."
Chorus

Now the trial's come to an end, how the folks gave cheers,
Bad Stackalee was sent down to Jefferson pen for seventy-five years.
Chorus

On the Range

The true hero of the American west is not the glamorous outlaw, but the lonesome cowboy. His life was extremely hard and dangerous, and the cowboy had to be tough, loyal and persevering. Generally a silent character, the cowboy had to be prepared to put up with a lot of his own company, often alone except for his horse and several hundred head of cattle for days on end. Around the camp fire he might become more talkative, but he reserved all pleasure and enjoyment for those brief periods of sometimes rather rough entertainment in town at the end of the drive.

"A cowboy," someone once defined him, "is a man with guts and a horse." One old cowpoke said to another as they turned their horses out in the night pasture after 10 hours in the saddle, "You know, by God, I love that damn horse so much I like him."

— □ —

Argument

The cowboy was a man of few words (and many of them curse words).

Two cowboys who had been punching cattle together for years were out on a long drive. Each day they'd ride off in different directions to corral the herd, and at the end of the day's trek they'd meet to cook a meal and go to sleep. Every day was the same, for week after week.

One night as they were going off to sleep, they heard a bellow coming from somewhere in the herd.

"Bull," said the first cowboy.

"Sounds like a steer to me," said the other.

All was quiet and they went off to sleep. They reached the end of the drive next day, and the first cowboy saddled up his horse to leave.

"Leaving?" asked the second cowboy.

"Yep," he replied, "too much damn argument."

— □ —

The Slickest Thing I Ever Saw

Apart from cattle rustlers, hostile Indians, rattlesnakes and so on, the most dangerous thing that could happen was a stampede. Someone once described how he had seen a lone cowboy stop a stampede of about 700 cattle.

"The herd was going straight for a high bluff, where they would certainly tumble into the canyon and be killed. I wouldn't have given a dollar for the whole herd at that moment, but the cowboy spurred up his mustang, came in front of the herd, cut across their path at a right angle, and then galloped leisurely to the edge of the bluff. There he halted and looked around at the wild mass of beef coming right toward him. He was as cool as a cucumber, though I expected to see him killed.

"When the leaders had got within about a quarter of a mile of him, I saw them try to slack up, although they could not do it very quickly. But the whole herd wanted to stop, and when the cows and steers in the rear got about where the cowboy had cut across their path I was surprised to see them stop and commence to nibble at the grass. Then the whole herd stopped, wheeled, straggled back and went to fighting for a chance to eat where the rear guard was.

"You see, that cowboy had opened a big bag of salt he had brought out from the ranch to give the cattle, galloped across the herd's course, and emptied the bag. Every crittur sniffed that line of salt, and of course that broke up the stampede. But I tell you it was a strange sight to see that man out there on the edge of the bluff quietly rolling a cigarette when it seemed as if he'd be lying under two-hundred tons of beef in about a minute and a half. Yes, sir, it was the slickest thing I ever saw."

———— □ ————

A Nice, New Rope

Almost the most serious crime in the west was horse stealing—one reason why it was so serious being that it was so common. One man explained how he'd come by a particularly fine horse.

"I was walking along one day when I see a nice new rope in the road, and I says to myself 'I'd better pick that up and take it along or some son-of-a-goat might steal it.'

"Well, sir, believe it or not, when I got back home there was a horse at the other end of it. Now I knowed them ornery neighbors of mine wouldn't believe that was an accident, so I stepped up on the horse and come out to New Mexico."

No Change

An English visitor went into a saloon in Dodge City and got to talking to a cowboy there. He offered him a drink, and when he put his hand in his pocket to pay, he brought out some English coins. He showed one of them to the cowboy, and pointing to the king's head on the coin, he said, "You see this likeness?"

"Yep."

"That, my good fellow, is His Majesty the King. He made my grandfather an Earl."

The cowboy looked at the coin, then took out one of his own. He pointed to the Indian's face on the coin and said, "You see this likeness?"

"I do, sir."

"That, partner, is a Red Indian and he made my grandpappy an angel."

—— □ ——

Squirrel's Brains

Cowboys spent a lot of their leisure time, what there was of it, trying to get a rise out of each other. A tenderfoot was always the butt of jokes—there are hundreds of them. A man's birthplace, or religious beliefs, could also be the basis of a skilfully thought-out insult. Here is a man, who had taken a lot of jokes about being a Mormon, getting his own back on some Texan cowboys.

"There's one thing you'll never find around a Mormon town," said Bishop, "and that's Texans. Of course, a Mormon has to work hard, and that bars most of 'em for a start. But I don't know, it seems like the first Mormon settlers took a prejudice against them. I remember my old man telling how it come that way. The Mormons think a Texan ain't got no sense—of course they must be mistaken.

"My grandpa was one of the first settlers. One day, when he was getting kind of old and feeble-like, he got a notion into his head that he wanted a squirrel skin, and so he called in my father and said, 'Son, take your rifle up on the peaks and get me a gray tree squirrel. And be careful not to shoot him in the head, because I want the brains to tan the skin with.'

"So my father he went up in the pines and hunted around, but the only gray squirrel he could find was sticking his head over a branch, and rather than not get nothing, he shot him anyhow. He brought it back, and said to the old man, 'I'm mighty sorry, Dad. The squirrels was awful scarce and, rather than not get any, I had to shoot this one right through the head.'

"'Oh that's all right,' the old man says, 'you got a nice skin anyway, and I reckon we can fix it somehow. I tell you what to do. There's a bunch of Texans camped down on the lower water. You go down and kill one of them, and maybe we can use *his* brains.'

"The speaker paused, and looked around with squinched-up, twinkling eyes. At last one of them broke the silence. 'Well,' he asked, 'what's the joke?'

"'Well, sir,' Bishop went on, 'you wouldn't hardly believe it, but my old man told me he had to kill six of them Texans to get brains enough to tan that squirrel skin.'"

— □ —

Texas Weather

There's an old saying that in Texas, nobody prophesies about the weather except newcomers and damn fools.

One evening when things were slow in the saloon, a fresh-looking fellow with a Derby hat and store-bought clothes breezed into the place, walked up to the bar and ordered a drink. The loafers looked on disapprovingly but said nothing. In a leisurely way, the easterner finished his drink, wiped his mouth with a new silk handkerchief, and said, "Well, I believe it's going to rain."

Nothing could have pleased the idle crowd more. One old fellow, who was the leader in the local war of wits, said, very fatherly-like, "My friend, did you know that there are only two kinds of people who prophesy about Texas weather?'

"Two kinds of people who prophesy about Texas weather? No, I can't say I ever heard that."

Then the old fellow, with all the contempt he could, sneered, "Newcomers and damn fools."

And the whole crowd started to laugh. "Haw-haw! That's a good one! He got you that time! Set 'em up! You owe drinks to the house!"

The easterner stood at the bar smiling. He wasn't at all troubled, and when the row had died down, he said very slowly. "So there are only two kinds of people who prophesy about Texas weather—newcomers and damn fools. You are right. Those are the only two kinds in Texas."

——— □ ———

How a Cowboy Gets Dressed

A cowboy who had made a lot of money in a poker game went to Chicago to have a good time. He spent most of his money in a week, and just as he was thinking of going home, he fell in with a friendly fellow with whom he got very drunk. He didn't remember much till he woke up next morning.

"The first thing I do is to look at the windows. There's no bars on 'em, and I feel easier. I'm in a small room with two bunks. The one opposite me holds a feller that's smoking a cigarette and sizing me up between the whiffs while I'm dressing. I'm lacing up my shoes when the stranger speaks.

"'Neighbor, you're a long way from your range.'

"It beats me how he figures where I came from, I tells him.

"'It's your ways, while I'm laying here, watching you get into your garments. Now, humans dress up and cowpunchers dress down. When you raised, the first thing you put on is your hat. Another thing that shows you up is you don't shed your shirt when you bed down. So next comes your vest and coat, keeping your hindquarters covered till you slide into your pants, and now you're lacing your shoes. I notice you done all of it without quitting the blankets, like the ground's cold. I don't know what state or territory you hail from, but you've smelt sagebrush and drank alkali. You've slept a whole lot with nothing but sky over your head, and there's time when that old roof leaks, but judging from appearances, you wouldn't mind a little open air right now.'"

——— □ ———

Rattlesnake Soup

Have you ever tasted rattlesnake soup? No? Well, nor had Jack, a greenhorn in a cowboys' camp in Montana 100 or so years ago.

One of them started the game by asking innocently, "Does your Ma make her rattlesnake soup good and rich?"

At first Jack thought this was a bit of nonsense, but the others chimed in seriously, "I like that kind of soup better than any other," and "Shucks, all western folk hankers for it, but they can't often get it because it's hard to make just right."

Another said, "Cuttle, your old woman contrives it nicer than anybody in this region, but she ain't got time to make none now, for it's an awful complicated job."

Now Jack was hooked. "Cuttle," he begged, "won't you tell me how you do it?"

So Cuttle set off. "First, you get yourself a couple of tin pails, one big and t'other smaller, so's you won't get 'em mixed. Them pails must naturally be sort of rusty on the inside, else the soup won't turn out good, but be sure the tin ain't ate all the way through, otherwise the best part of the soup'll leak out. The rust puts iron into your blood and tonics up your system. Any shape of pail will do, because you don't coil the snakes into the pails, you put 'em in in pieces.

"Of course, you must also get some sugar and salt and pepper and, if you like high seasoning, some mustard and a big patch of young leaves from the sagebrush. Red or black pepper? I usually mixes 'em, about one-third red, two-thirds black. Some folks think adding a touch of prickly pear tones it up, along with a few drops of vinegar. I never uses cinnamon nor nutmeg.

"Now, Jack, you've learned all the necessary fixings and flavorings, and the snakes is the next thing. Some folks insist on assorted sizes, but I don't necessarily hold with them. Of course if it's all little snakes, it lacks body, and all big snakes tends to make it tough. Folks mostly disagrees whether the snakes should be skinned or left with the skins on. For me myself, I absolutely likes the skins kept on.

"The next step? Well, you lay the snakes out flat, cut off the heads right behind the ears, put all the heads into the little pail and pour in water just to cover them. Then set that carefully to one side. Take off all the rattles and lay 'em near the little pail so you can easy find 'em when you need 'em for decoration. And now, with a sharp knife you slice the snakes crosswise into pieces three inches long. It's contrary to reason to slice 'em lengthwise—it'll make the soup stringy."

There followed a short discussion as to which region produces the best snakes for soup, then Cuttle resumed.

"You take the big pail, cover the bottom with the sagebrush leaves, and start to stack up the pieces of snake in it, the first layer lengthwise, the next crosswise and so on till all the snakes is in. Then you reaches for your flavorings. That's all."

Cuttle stopped talking and started stuffing tobacco into his mouth. Jack exclaimed, "Tell me honest, what happens next?"

Cuttle spat carefully and after a moment's pretence of deep thought, he announced solemnly, "I said that's all, and it is. The only other thing you do is put on your hat and, in a respectful and dignified way, ride off and quit the stinking mess."

— □ —

The Cowboy's Lament

As I walked out on the streets of Laredo,
As I walked out in Laredo one day,
I spied a poor cowboy wrapped up in white linen,
Wrapped up in white linen as cold as the clay.

"Oh, beat the drum slowly and play the fife lowly,
Play the dead march as you carry me along,
Take me to the green valley, there lay the sod o'er me,
For I'm a young cowboy and I know I've done wrong.

"I see by your outfit that you are a cowboy—"
These words he did say as I boldly stepped by.
"Come and sit down beside me and hear my sad story,
I am shot in the breast and I know I must die.

"Let sixteen gamblers come handle my coffin,
Let sixteen cowboys come sing me a song.
Take me to the graveyard and lay the sod o'er me,
For I'm a poor cowboy and I know I've done wrong.

"My friends and relations they live in the Nation,
They know not where their boy has gone.
He first came to Texas and hired to a ranchman,
Oh, I'm a young cowboy and I know I've done wrong.

"It was once in the saddle I used to go dashing,
It was once in the saddle I used to go gay,
First to the dram-house and then to the card-house,
Got shot in the breast and I am dying today.

"Get six jolly cowboys to carry my coffin,
Get six pretty maidens to bear up my pall,
Put bunches of roses all over my coffin,
Put roses to deaden the sods as they fall.

"Then swing your rope slowly and clap your spurs lowly,
And give a wild whoop as you carry me along,
And in the grave throw me and roll the sod o'er me,
For I'm a young cowboy and I know I've done wrong.

"Oh bury beside me my knife and six-shooter,
My spurs on my heel and my rifle by my side,
And over my coffin a bottle of brandy
That the cowboys may drink as they carry me along.

"Go bring me a cup, a cup of cold water,
To cool my parched lips," the cowboy then said,
Before I had brought it his soul had departed,
And gone to the round-up—the cowboy was dead.

We beat the drum slowly and played the fife lowly,
And bitterly wept as we bore him along,
For we all loved our comrade, so brave, young, and handsome,
We all loved our comrade although he'd done wrong.

How Santa Claus Came to Simpson's Bar

This story was written by Bret Harte (1836-1902), who was for a short time a miner himself in the Gold Rush Days and spent most of the rest of his life writing stories about prospectors and other inhabitants of the mining settlements. The story here is as he wrote it except for a few small changes and one or two omitted passages.

It had been raining in the valley of the Sacramento. The North Fork had overflowed its banks, and Rattlesnake Creek was impassable. The few boulders that had marked the summer ford at Simpson's Crossing were obliterated by a vast sheet of water stretching to the foothills. The up-stage was stopped at Granger's; the last mail had been abandoned in the *tules*, the rider swimming for his life. "An area," remarked the *Sierra Avalanche*, with pensive local pride, "as large as the State of Massachusetts is now under water."

Nor was the weather any better in the foothills. The mud lay deep on the mountain road; wagons that could not move from the evil ways into which they had fallen encumbered the track, and the way to Simpson's Bar was indicated by broken-down teams and hard swearing. And further on, cut off and inaccessible, rained upon and bedraggled, smitten by high winds and threatened by high water, Simpson's Bar, on the eve of Christmas Day, 1862, clung like a swallow's nest to the rocky sides of Table Mountain, and shook in the blast.

As night shut down on the settlement, a few lights gleamed through the mist from the windows of cabins on either side of the highway, now crossed and gullied by lawless streams and swept by marauding winds. Happily most of the population were gathered at Thompson's store, clustered around a redhot stove, at which they silently spat in some accepted sense of social communion that perhaps rendered conversation unnecessary. Indeed, most methods of diversion had long since been exhausted on Simpson's Bar; high water had suspended the regular occupations on gulch and on river, and a consequent lack of money and whiskey had taken the zest from most illegitimate recreation.

The occupants of Thompson's store sat that evening in the listless apathy begotten of idleness and lack of excitement. Even the sudden splashing of hoofs before the door did not arouse them. Dick Bullen alone paused in the act of scraping out his pipe, and lifted his head, but no other one of the group indicated any interest in, or recognition of, the man who entered.

It was a figure familiar enough to the company, and known in Simpson's Bar as "The Old Man." A man of perhaps 50 years; grizzled and scant of hair, but still fresh and youthful of complexion. A face full of ready but not very powerful sympathy, with a chameleon-like aptitude for taking on the shade and color of contiguous moods and feelings. He had evidently just left some hilarious companions, and did not at first notice the gravity of the group, but clapped the shoulder of the nearest man jocularly, and threw himself into a vacant chair.

"Jest heard the best thing out, boys! Ye know Smiley, over yar— Jim Smiley—funniest man in the Bar? Well, Jim was jest telling the richest yarn about—"

"Smiley's a—fool," interrupted a gloomy voice.

"A particular—skunk," added another in sepulchral accents.

A silence followed these positive statements. The Old Man glanced quickly around the group. Then his face slowly changed. "That's so," he said reflectively, after a pause, "certainly a sort of a skunk and suthin' [something] of a fool. In course." He was silent for a moment, as in painful contemplation of the unsavoriness and folly of the unpopular Smiley. "Dismal weather, ain't it?" he added, now fully embarked on the current of prevailing sentiment. "Mighty rough on the boys, and no show for money this season. And tomorrow's Christmas."

There was a movement among the men at this announcement, but whether of satisfaction or disgust was not plain. "Yes," continued the Old Man in the lugubrious tone he had, within the last few moments, unconsciously adopted, "yes, Christmas, and tonight's Christmas Eve. Ye see, boys, I kinder thought—that is, I sorter had an idee, jest passin' like, you know—that maybe ye'd all like to come over to my house tonight and have a sort of tear around. But I suppose, now, you wouldn't? Don't feel like, it, maybe?" he added with anxious sympathy, peering into the faces of his companions.

"Well, I don't know," responded Tom Flynn with some cheerfulness. "P'r'aps we may. But how about your wife, Old Man? What does *she* say to it?"

The Old Man hesitated. His experience of marriage had not been a happy one, and the fact was known to Simpson's Bar. His first wife, a delicate, pretty little woman, had run off with another man leaving a boy of three years to comfort her bereaved husband. The Old Man's present wife had been his cook. She was large, loyal, and aggressive.

Before he could reply, Joe Dimmick suggested with great directness that it was the "Old Man's house," and that, by God, if the case were his own, he would invite whom he pleased.

"In course. Certainly. Thet's it," said the Old Man with a sympathetic frown. "Thar's no trouble about thet. It's my own house, built every stick on it myself. Don't you be afeard o' her, boys, She *may* cut up a trifle rough—these wimmin do—but she'll come round." Secretly the Old Man trusted to the exaltation of liquor and the power of courageous example to sustain him in such an emergency.

As yet, Dick Bullen, the oracle and leader of Simpson's Bar, had not spoken. He now took his pipe from his lips. "Old Man, how's that yer Johnny gettin on? Seems to me he didn't look so peart last time I seed him. Maybe now, we'd be in the way ef he wus sick?"

The father hastened to assure him that Johnny was better, and that a "little fun might liven him up." Whereupon Dick arose, shook himself, and saying, "I'm ready. Lead the way, Old Man: Here goes," himself led the way with a leap, a characteristic howl, and darted out into the night. As he passed through the outer room he caught up a blazing brand from the hearth. The action was repeated by the rest of the party, closely following and elbowing each other, and before the astonished proprietor of Thompson's grocery was aware of the intention of his guests, the room was deserted,

The night was pitchy dark. In the first gust of wind their temporary torches were extinguished, and only the red brands dancing and flitting in the gloom like drunken will-o'-the-wisps indicated their where-abouts. Their way led up Pine-Tree Canyon at the head of which a broad, low, bark-thatched cabin burrowed in the mountain side. It was the home of the Old Man, and the entrance to the tunnel in which he worked when he worked at all. Here the crowd paused for a moment, out of delicate deference to their host, who came up panting in the rear.

"P'r'aps ye'd better hold on a second out yer, whilst I go in and see that things is all right," said the Old Man, with an indifference he was far from feeling. The suggestion was graciously accepted, the door opened and closed on the host, and the crowd, leaning their backs against the wall and cowering under the eaves, waited and listened.

For a few moments there was no sound but the dripping of water from the eaves, and the stir and rustle of wrestling boughs above them. Then the men became uneasy, and whispered suggestion and suspicion passed from the one to the other. "Reckon she's caved in his head the first lick!" "Decoyed him inter the tunnel and barred him up, likely." "Got him down and sittin on him." "Prob'ly boilin suthin to heave on us: Stand clear the door, boys!" For just then the latch clicked, the door slowly opened, and a voice said, "Come in out o' the wet."

The voice was neither that of the Old Man nor of his wife. It was the voice of a small boy, its weak treble broken by that preternatural hoarseness which only vagabondage and the habit of premature self-assertion can give. It was the face of a small boy that looked up at theirs a face that might have been pretty, and even refined, but that it was darkened by evil knowledge from within, and dirt and hard experience from without. He had a blanket around his shoulders, and had evidently just risen from his bed. "Come in," he repeated, "and don't make no noise. The Old Man's in there talking to Ma," he continued, pointing to an adjacent room which seemed to be a kitchen from which the Old Man's voice came in deprecating accents. "Let me be," he added querulously to Dick Bullen, who had caught him up, blanket and all, and was affecting to toss him into the fire, "let go o' me, you damned old fool, d' ye hear?"

Thus adjured, Dick Bullen lowered Johnny to the ground with a smothered laugh, while the men, entering quietly, ranged themselves around a long table of rough boards which occupied the center of the room. Johnny then gravely proceeded to a cupboard and brought out several articles, which he deposited on the table. "Thar's whiskey. And crackers. And cheese." He took a bite of the latter on his way to the table. "And sugar." He scooped up a mouthful *en route* with a small and very dirty hand. "And terbacker. Thar's dried appils too on the shelf, but I don't admire 'em. Appils is swellin. Thar," he concluded, "now wade in, and don't be afeard. *I* don't mind the old woman. She don't b'long to *me*. S'long."

He had stepped to the threshold of a small room, scarcely larger than a closet, partitioned off from the main apartment, and holding in its dim recess a small bed. He stood there a moment looking at the company, his bare feet peeping from the blanket, and nodded.

"Hello, Johnny! You ain't goin' to turn in agin, are ye?" said Dick.

"Yes, I are," responded Johnny decidedly.

"Why, wot's up, old fellow?"

"I'm sick."

"How sick?"

"I've got a fever. And childblains. And roomatiz," returned Johnny, and vanished within. After a moment's pause, he added in the dark, apparently from under the bedclothes,—"And boils!"

There was an embarrassing silence. The men looked at each other and at the fire. Even with the appetizing banquet before them, it seemed as if they might again fall into the despondency of Thompson's grocery, when the voice of the Old Man, incautiously lifted, came deprecatingly from the kitchen.

"Certainly! Thet's so. In course they is. A gang o' lazy, drunken loafers, and that ar Dick Bullen's the ornariest of all. Didn't hev no more savvy that to come round yar with sickness in the house and no provision. Thet's what I said: 'Bullen,' sez I, 'it's crazy drunk you are, or a fool,' sez I, 'to think o' such a thing.' 'Staples,' I sez, 'be you a man, Staples, and spect to raise hell under my roof and invalids lyin round?' But they would come, they would. Thet's wot you must spect o' such trash as lays around the Bar."

A burst of laughter from the men followed this unfortunate exposure. Whether it was overhead in the kitchen, or whether the Old Man's irate companion had just then exhausted all other modes of expressing her contemptuous indignation, I cannot say, but a back door was suddenly slammed with great violence. A moment later and the Old Man reappeared, haply unconscious of the cause of the late hilarious outburst, and smiled blandly.

"The old woman thought she'd jest run over to Mrs MacFadden's for a sociable call," he explained with jaunty indifference, as he took a seat at the board.

Oddly enough it needed this untoward incident to relieve the embarrassment that was beginning to be felt by the party, and their natural audacity returned with their host. I do not propose to record the convivialities of that evening. The inquisitive reader will accept the statement that the conversation was characterized by the same intellectual exaltation, the same cautious reverence, the same fastidious delicacy, the same rhetorical precision, and the same logical and coherent discourse somewhat later in the evening, which distinguish similar gatherings of the masculine sex in more civilized localities and under more favorable auspices. No glasses were broken in the absence of any; no liquor was uselessly split on the floor or table in the scarcity of that article.

It was nearly midnight when the festivities were interrupted. "Hush," said Dick Bullen, holding up his hand. It was the querulous voice of Johnny from his adjacent closet: "O Dad!"

The old Man arose hurriedly and disappeared in the closet. Presently he reappeared. "His rheumatiz is coming on agin bad," he explained, "and he wants rubbin'." He lifted the demijohn of whiskey from the table and shook it. It was empty. Dick Bullen put down his tin cup with an embarrassed laugh. So did the others. The Old Man examined their contents and said hopefully, "I reckon that's enough: He don't need much. You hold on all o' you for a spell, and I'll be back;" and vanished in the closet with an old flannel shirt and the whiskey. The door closed but imperfectly, and the following dialogue was distinctly audible:

"Now, sonny, whar does she ache worst?"

"Sometimes over yar and sometimes under yer; but it's most powerful from yer to yer. Rub yer, Dad."

A silence seemed to indicate a brisk rubbing. Then Johnny:

"Hevin' a good time out yer, Dad?"

"Yes, sonny."

"Tomorrer's Chrismiss, aint' it?"

"Yes, sonny. How does she feel now?"

"Better. Rub a little furder down. Wot's Chrismiss, anyway? Wot's it all about?"

"Oh, it's a day."

This exhaustive definition was apparently satisfactory, for there was a silent interval of rubbing. Presently Johnny again:

"Ma sez that everywhere else but yer everybody gives things to everybody Chrismiss. She sez thar's a man they call Sandy Claws, not a white man, you know, but a kind o' Chinaman, comes down the chimbley night afore Chrismiss and gives things to chillern—boys like me. Puts 'em in their boots! Thet's what she tried to play upon me. Easy now, Pop, whar are you rubbin' to—thet's a mile from the place. She jest made that up, didn't she, jest to aggrewate me and you? Don't rub thar...Why, Dad!"

In the great quiet that seemed to have fallen upon the house the sigh of the near pines and the drip of leaves without was very distinct. Johnny's voice, too, was lowered as he went on, "Don't you take on now, for I'm gettin' all right fast. Wot's the boys doin' out thar?"

The Old Man partly opened the door and peered through. His guests were sitting there sociably enough, and there were a few silver coins and a lean buckskin purse on the table. "Bettin on suthin—some little game or other. They're all right," he replied to Johnny, and recommenced his rubbing.

"I'd like to take a hand and win some money," said Johnny reflectively after a pause.

The Old Man glibly repeated what was evidently a familiar formula, that if Johnny would wait until he struck it rich in the tunnel he'd have lots of money, etc., etc.

California Gold Rush, 1849: Panning for Gold

Life of the Prairie: The Trapper's Defence, Fire Fight Fire, from a print published by Currier & Ives, 1862

"Yes," said Johnny, "but you don't. And whether you strike it or I win it, it's about the same. It's all luck. But it's mighty curious about Chrismiss, ain't it? Why do they call it Chrismiss?"

Perhaps for some instinctive deference to the overhearing of his guests, or from some vague sense of incongruity, the Old Man's reply was so low as to be inaudible beyond the room.

"Yes," said Johnny, with some slight abatement of interest, "I've heard o' *him* before. Thar, that'll do, Dad. I don't ache near so bad as I did. Now wrap me tight in this yer blanket. So. Now," he added in a muffled whisper, "sit down yer by me till I go asleep." To assure himself of obedience, he disengaged one hand from the blanket, and, grasping his father's sleeve, again composed himself to rest.

For some moments the Old Man waited patiently. Then the unwonted stillness of the house excited his curiosity, and without moving from the bed he cautiously opened the door with his disengaged hand, and looked into the main room. To his infinite surprise it was dark and deserted. But even then a smouldering log on the hearth broke, and by the upspringing blaze he saw the figure of Dick Bullen sitting by the dying embers.

"Hello!"

Dick started, rose, and came somewhat unsteadily toward him.

"Whar's the boys?" said the Old Man.

"Gone up the canyon a little. They're coming back for me in a minit. I'm waiting round for 'em. What are you starin' at, Old Man?" he added, with a forced laugh, "do you think I'm drunk?"

The Old Man might have been pardoned the supposition, for Dick's eyes were humid and his face flushed. He loitered and lounged back to the chimney, yawned, shook himself, buttoned up his coat and laughed. "Liquor ain't so plenty as that, Old Man. Now don't you get up," he continued, as the Old Man made a movement to release his sleeve from Johnny's hand. "Don't you mind manners. Sit jest whar you be; I'm goin' in a jiffy. Thar, that's them now."

There was a low tap at the door. Dick Bullen opened it quickly, nodded "Goodnight" to his host, and disappeared. The Old Man would have followed him but for the hand that still unconsciously grasped his sleeve. He could have easily disengaged it—it was small, weak, and emaciated. But perhaps because it *was* small, weak, and emaciated he changed his mind, and, drawing his chair closer to the bed, rested his head upon it. The room flickered and faded before his eyes, reappeared, faded again, went out, and left him—asleep.

Meantime Dick Bullen, closing the door, confronted his companions. "Are you ready?" said Staples. "Ready," said Dick. "What's the time?" "Past twelve," was the reply, "can you make it? It's nigh on fifty miles, the round trip hither and yon." "I reckon," returned Dick shortly. "Whar's the mare?" "Bill and Jack's holdin' her at the crossin'." "Let 'em hold on a minit longer," said Dick.

He turned and re-entered the house softly. By the light of the guttering candle and dying fire he saw that the door of the little room was open. He stepped toward it on tip-toe and looked in. The Old Man had fallen back in his chair, snoring, his helpless feet thrust out in a line with his collapsed shoulders, and his hat pulled over his eyes. Beside him, on a narrow wooden bedstead, lay Johnny, muffled tightly in a blanket that hid all save of forehead and a few curls damp with perspiration. Dick Bullen made a step forwards, hesitated, and glanced over his shoulder into the deserted room. Everything was quiet. With a sudden resolution he parted his huge mustaches with both hands and stooped over the sleeping boy. But even as he did so a mischievous blast, lying in wait swooped down the chimney, rekindled the hearth, and lit up the room with a shameless glow from which Dick fled in bashful terror.

His companions were already waiting for him at the crossing. Two of them were struggling in the darkness with some strange misshapen bulk, which as Dick came nearer took the semblance of a great yellow horse.

It was the mare. She was not a pretty picture. From her Roman nose to her rising haunches, from her arched spine hidden by the stiff Mexican saddle, to her thick, straight bony legs, there was not a line of equine grace. In her half-blind but wholly vicious white eyes, in her protruding under-lip, in her monstrous color, there was nothing but ugliness and vice.

"Now then," said Staples, "stand clear of her heels, boys, and up with you. Don't miss your first holt of her mane, and mind ye get your off stirrup *quick*. Ready?"

There was a leap, a scrambling struggle, a bound, a wild retreat of the crowd, a circle of flying hoofs, two springless leaps that jarred the earth, a rapid play and jingle of spurs, a plunge, and then the voice of Dick somewhere in the darkness. "All right!"

"Don't take the lower road back onless you're hard pushed for time! Don't hold her in down hill. We'll be at the ford at five. G'lang! Hoopa! Mula! *Go!*"

A splash, a spark struck from the ledge in the road, a clatter in the rocky cut beyond, and Dick was gone.

O what a ride Dick Bullen had! By one o'clock he had only gained Rattlesnake Hill. For in that time Jovita had rehearsed to him all her imperfections and practiced all her vices. Thrice had she stumbled. Twice had she thrown up her Roman nose in a straight line with the reins, and, resisting bit and spur, struck out madly across country. Twice had she reared, and, rearing, fallen backward; and twice had the agile Dick, unharmed, regained his seat before she found her vicious legs again. And a mile beyond them, at the foot of a long hill, was Rattlesnake Creek. Dick knew that here was the crucial test of his ability to perform his enterprise, set his teeth grimly, put his knees well into her flanks, and changed his defensive tactics to brisk aggression. Bullied and maddened, Jovita began the descent of the hill. Here the artful Dick pretended to hold her in with well-feigned cries of alarm. It is unnecessary to add that Jovita instantly ran away. Nor need I state the time in the descent; it is written in the chronicles of Simpson's Bar. Enough that in another moment, as it seemed to Dick, she was splashing on the overflowed banks of Rattlesnake Creek. As Dick expected, the momentum she had acquired carried her beyond the point of balking, and, holding her well together for a mighty leap, they dashed into the middle of the swiftly flowing current. A few moments of kicking, wading, and swimming, and Dick drew a long breath on the opposite bank.

The road from Rattlesnake Creek to Red Mountain was tolerably level. Either the plunge in Rattlesnake Creek had dampened her baleful fire, or the art which led to it had shown her the superior wickedness of her rider, for Jovita no longer wasted her surplus energy in wanton conceits. Once she bucked, but it was from force of habit; once she shied, but it was from a new, freshly painted meeting-house at the crossing of the country road. Hollows, ditches, gravelly deposits, patches of freshly springing grasses, flew from beneath her rattling hoofs. She began to smell unpleasantly, once or twice she coughed slightly, but there was no abatement of her strength or speed. By two o'clock he had passed Red Mountain and begun the descent to the plain. At half past two Dick rose in his stirrups with a great shout. Stars were glittering through the rifted clouds, and beyond him, out of the plain, rose two spires, a flagstaff, and a straggling line of black objects. Dick jingled his spurs, Jovita bounded forward, and in another moment they swept into Tuttleville, and drew up before the wooden piazza of The Hotel of All Nations.

What transpired that night at Tuttleville is not strictly a part of this record. Briefly I may state, however, that after Jovita had been handed over to a sleepy ostler, whom she at once kicked into unpleasant consciousness, Dick sallied out with the barkeeper for a tour of the sleeping town. Lights still gleamed from a few salons and gambling-houses; but, avoiding these, they stopped before several closed shops, and by persistent tapping and judicious outcry roused the proprietors from their beds, and made them unbar their doors and expose their wares. Sometimes they were met by curses, but oftener by interest and some concern in their needs, and the interview was invariably concluded by a drink. It was three o'clock before this pleasantry was given over, and with a small waterproof bag strapped on his shoulders, Dick returned to the hotel. And then he sprang to the saddle and dashed down the lonely street and out into the lonelier plain, where presently the lights, the black line of houses, the spires, and the flagstaff sank into the earth behind him again and were lost in the distance. The storm had cleared away, the air was brisk and cold, the outlines of adjacent landmarks were distinct, but it was half-past four before Dick reached the meeting house and the crossing of the country road. To avoid the rising grade he had taken a longer and more circuitous road, in whose liquid mud Jovita sank fetlock deep at every bound. It was a poor preparation for a steady ascent of five miles more; but Jovita, gathering her legs under her, took it with her usual blind, unreasoning fury, and a half-hour later reached the long level that led to Rattlesnake Creek. Another half-hour would bring him to the creek. He threw the reins lightly upon the neck of the mare, chirruped to her, and began to sing.

Suddenly Jovita shied with a bound that would have unseated a less practiced rider. Hanging to her rein was a figure that had leaped from the bank, and at the same time from the road before her arose a shadowy horse and rider. "Throw up your hands," commanded this second apparition, with an oath.

Dick felt the mare tremble, quiver, and apparently sink under him. He knew what it meant and was prepared.

"Stand aside, Jack Simpson. I know you, you damned thief! Let me pass, or—"

He did not finish the sentence. Jovita rose straight in the air with a terrific bound, breaking away from the man holding her rein with a

244

single shake of her vicious head, and charged with deadly malevolence down on the rider obstructing her. An oath, a pistol-shot, and horse and highwayman rolled over in the road. The next moment Jovita was a 100 yards away. But the good right arm of her rider, shattered by a bullet, dropped helplessly at his side.

Without slacking his speed he shifted the reins to his left hand. But a few moments later he was obliged to halt and tighten the saddle-girths that had slipped in the onset. This in his crippled condition took some time. He had no fear of pursuit, but looking up he saw that the eastern stars were already paling, and that the distant peaks had lost their ghostly whiteness, and now stood out blackly against a lighter sky. Day was upon him. Then completely absorbed in a single idea, he forgot the pain of his wound, and mounting again dashed on towards Rattlesnake Creek. But now Jovita's breath came broken by gasps, Dick reeled in his saddle and brighter and brighter grew the sky.

Ride, Richard; run, Jovita; linger, O day! For the last few rods there was roaring in his ears. Was it exhaustion from loss of blood? He was dazed and giddy as he swept down the hill, and did not recognize his surroundings. Had he taken the wrong road or was this Rattlesnake Creek?

It was. But the brawling creek he had swum a few hours before had risen, more than doubled its volume, and now a swift and resistless river rolled between him and Rattlesnake Hill. For the first time that night Richard's heart sank within him. The river, the mountain, the quickening east, swam before his eyes. He shut them to recover his self-control. In that brief interval, by some fantastic mental process, the little room at Simpson's Bar and the figures of the sleeping father and son rose upon him. He opened his eyes wildly, cast off his coat, pistol, boots, and saddle, bound his precious pack tightly to his shoulders, grasped the bare flanks of Jovita with his bared knees, and with a shout dashed into the yellow water. A cry rose from those who waited on the opposite bank as the head of a man and horse struggled for a few moments against the battling current, and then were swept away amidst uprooted trees and whirling driftwood.

The Old Man started and woke. The fire on the hearth was dead, the candle in the outer room flickering in its socket, and somebody was rapping at the door. He opened it but fell back with a cry before the dripping, half-naked figure that reeled against the doorpost. "Dick?"

"Hush! Is he awake yet?"

"No, but, Dick—"

"Dry up, you old fool! Get me some whiskey, *quick!*" The Old Man flew and returned with—an empty bottle! Dick would have sworn, but his strength was not equal to the occasion. He staggered, caught at the handle of the door, and motioned to the Old Man.

"Thar's suthin' in my pack yer for Jonny. Take it off. I can't"

The Old Man unstrapped the pack, and laid it before the exhausted man. "Open it, quick." He did so with trembling fingers. It contained only a few poor toys, cheap and barbaric enough, goodness knows, but bright with paint and tinsel. One of them was broken; another, I fear, was irretrievably ruined by water, and on the third—ah me! there was a cruel spot.

"It don't look like much, that's a fact," said Dick ruefully"

"...But it's the best we could do...Take 'em, Old Man, and put 'em in his stocking, and tell him—tell him, you know—hold me, Old Man." The Old Man caught at his sinking figure. "Tell him" said Dick, with a weak little laugh, "tell him Sandy Claus has come."

And even so, bedraggled, ragged, unshaven and unshorn, with one arm hanging helplessly at his side, Santa Claus came to Simpson's Bar and fell fainting on the first threshold. The Christmas dawn came slowly after, touching the remoter peaks with the rosy warmth of ineffable love. And it looked so tenderly on Simpson's Bar that the whole mountain, as if caught in a generous action, blushed to the skies.

A Ballad of the Gold Rush

The discovery of gold in California in 1848 turned California from a quiet ranching country into a roaring, crowded, hell-raising land of opportunity, and began that good old American idea of getting as rich as possible as quickly as possible.

By May 1849, someone on the Missouri had counted about 12,000 wagons on the westward trail and the population of California leapt from 12,000 to 100,000 in less than two years. Besides those who followed the overland trail, thousands more took the long sea route, around Cape Horn. But of those who set out, a much smaller number arrived, and of those who arrived, only a few actually got rich.

Folk tales and folk songs are often about "losers" rather than "winners," about hardship more than success. This song tells of the grimmer side of the Gold Rush. (A scow, in the first line, is a flat-bottomed boat; here it means a ship that is not seaworthy.)

> The poor, the old and rotten scows were advertised to sail
> From New Orleans with passengers, but they must pump and bale;
> The ships were crowded more than full, and some hung on behind,
> And others dived off from the wharf and swam till they were blind.
> > *Chorus*:
> > Then they thought of what they had been told
> > When they started after gold,
> > That they never in the world would make a pile.
>
> With rusty port and stinking beef, and rotten, wormy bread,
> And captains too that never were up as high as the main-mast head,
> The steerage passengers would rave and swear that they'd paid
> > their passage,
> And wanted something more to eat than stale Bologna sausage.
> > *Chorus*
>
> Then they began to cross the plains, with oxen, hollering "Haw!"
> And steamers they began to run as far as Panama,
> And there for months the people stayed that started after gold,
> And some returned disgusted with the lies that had been told.
> > *Chorus*

The people died on every route, they sickened and died like sheep,
And those at sea, before they died, were launched into the deep;
And those that died while crossing the Plains fared not so well as that,
For a hole was dug and them thrown in, along the miserable Platte.
  Chorus

Of course, that was not the kind of song that the folks on the wagons sang as they rolled and bumped along. They preferred something more cheerful, like *Sweet Betsy from Pike*.

Oh, don't you remember Sweet Betsy from Pike
Who crossed the big mountains with her lover Ike,
With two yoke of cattle, a large yellow dog,
A tall Shanghai rooster, and one spotted hog.
    Saying goodbye, Pike County,
    Farewell for a while,
    We'll come back again
    When we've panned our pile.

Strange Tales

Rip Van Winkle

This story of the Dutch-American who went to sleep for 20 years was written by Washington Irving. It is based on an old European legend, transferred to the banks of the Hudson River.

Whoever has made a voyage up the Hudson, must remember the Kaatskill Mountains. They are a dismembered branch of the great Appalachian family, and are seen away to the west of the river, swelling up to a noble height, and lording it over the surrounding country. Every change of season, every change of weather, indeed every hour of the day, produces some change in the magical hues and shapes of these mountains, and they are regarded by all the good wives, far and near, as perfect barometers. When the weather is fair and settled, they are clothed in blue and purple, and print their bold outlines on the clear evening sky; but sometimes, when the rest of the landscape is cloudless, they will gather a hood of gray vapors about their summits, which, in the last rays of the setting sun, will glow and light up like a crown of glory.

At the foot of these fairy mountains, the voyager may have described the light smoke curling up from a village, whose shingle roofs gleam among the trees, just where the blue tints of upland melt away into the fresh green of the nearer landscape. It is a little village of great antiquity, having been founded by some of the Dutch colonists, in the early times of the province, just about the beginning of the government of the good Peter Stuyvesant (may he rest in peace!), and there were some of the houses of the original settlers standing within a few years, built of small yellow bricks brought from Holland, having latticed windows and gable fronts, surmounted with weathercocks.

In that same village, and in one of these very houses (which, to tell the precise truth, was sadly time-worn and weather-beaten), there lived many years since; while the country was yet a province of Great Britain, a simple good-natured fellow, of the name of Rip Van Winkle. He was a descendant of the Van Winkles who figured so gallantly in the chivalrous days of Peter Stuyvesant, and accompanied him to the siege of Fort Christina. He inherited, however, but little of the martial character of his ancestors. I have observed that he was a simple, good-natured man; he was moreover, a kind neighbor, and an obedient henpecked husband. Indeed, to the latter circumstance might be owing that meekness of spirit which gained him such universal popularity; for those men are most apt to be obsequious and conciliating abroad, who are under the discipline of shrews at home. Their tempers, doubtless, are rendered pliant and malleable in the fiery furnace of domestic tribulation, and a curtain lecture is worth all the sermons in the world for teaching the virtues of patience and long-suffering. A termagant wife may therefore, in some respects, be considered a tolerable blessing; and if so, Rip Van Winkle was thrice blessed.

Certain it is, that he was a great favorite among all the good wives of the village, who, as usual with the amiable sex, took his part in all family squabbles; and never failed, whenever they talked those matters over in their evening gossipings, to lay all the blame on Dame Van Winkle. The children of the village, too, would shout with joy whenever he approached. He assisted at their sports, made their playthings, taught them to fly kites and shoot marbles, and told them long stories of ghosts, witches, and Indians. Whenever he went dodging about the village, he was surrounded by a troop of them, hanging on his skirts, clambering on his back and playing a thousand tricks on him with impunity; and not a dog would bark at him throughout the neighborhood.

The great error in Rip's composition was an insuperable aversion to all kinds of profitable labor. It could not be from the want of assiduity or perseverance; for he would sit on a wet rock, with a rod as long and heavy as a Tartar's lance, and fish all day without a murmur, even though he should not be encouraged by a single nibble. He would carry a fowling piece on his shoulder, for hours together, trudging through woods and swamps, and up hill and down dale, to shoot a few squirrels or wild pigeons. He would never refuse to assist a neighbor even in the roughest toil, and was a foremost man at all country frolics for husking Indian corn, or building stone fences; the women of the village, too, used to employ him to run their errands, and to do such little odd jobs as their less obliging husbands would not do for them. In a word, Rip was ready to attend to anybody's business but his own; but as to doing family duty, and keeping his farm in order, he found it impossible.

In fact, he decleared it was of no use to work on his farm; it was the most pestilent little piece of ground in the whole country; everything about it went wrong, and would go wrong, in spite of him. His fences were continually falling to pieces; his cow would either go astray, or get among the cabbages; weeds were sure to grow quicker in his fields than anywhere else; the rain always made a point of setting in just as he had some outdoor work to do; so that although his patrimonial estate had dwindled away under his management, acre by acre, until there was little more left than a mere patch of Indian corn and potatoes, yet it was the worst conditioned farm in the neighborhood.

His children, too, were as ragged and wild as if they belonged to nobody. His son Rip, an urchin begotten in his own likeness, promised to inherit the habits, with the old clothes of his father. He was generally seen trooping like a colt, at his mother's heels, equipped in a pair of his father's cast-off galligaskins, which he had much ado to hold up with one hand, as a fine lady does her train in bad weather.

Rip Van Winkle, however, was one of those happy mortals, of foolish, well-oiled dispositions, who take the world easy, eat white bread or brown, whichever can be got with least thought or trouble, and would rather starve on a cent than work for a dollar. If left to himself, he would have whistled life away, in perfect contentment; but his wife kept continually dinning in his ears about his idleness, his carelessness, and the ruin he was bringing on his family. Morning, noon, and night, her tongue was incessantly going, and everything he said or did was sure to produce a torrent of house-hold eloquence. Rip had but one way of replying to all lectures of the kind, and that, by frequent use, had grown into a habit. He shrugged his shoulders, shook his head, cast up his eyes, but said nothing. This, however, always provoked a fresh volley from his wife; so that he was fain to draw off his forces, and take to the outside of the house—the only side which, in truth, belongs to a henpecked husband.

Rip's sole domestic adherent was his dog Wolf, who was as much henpecked as his master; for Dame Van Winkle regarded them as companions in idleness, and even looked upon Wolf with an evil eye, as the cause of his master's going so often astray. True it is, in all points of spirit befitting an honorable dog, he was as courageous an animal as ever scoured the woods—but what courage can withstand the ever-during and all-besetting terrors of a woman's tongue? The moment Wolf entered the house his crest fell, his tail drooped to the ground or curled between his legs, he sneaked about with a gallows air, casting many a sidelong glance at Dame Van Winkle, and at the least flourish of a broomstick or ladle, he would fly to the door with yelping precipitation.

Times grew worse and worse with Rip Van Winkle as years of matrimony rolled on; a tart temper never mellows with age, and a sharp tongue is the only edge tool that grows keener with constant use. For a long while he used to console himself, when driven from home, by frequenting a kind of perpetual club of the sages, philosophers, and

other idle personages of the village; which held its sessions on a bench before a small inn, designated by a rubicund portrait of his majesty George the Third. Here they used to sit in the shade, of a long lazy summer's day, talk listlessly over village gossip, or tell endless sleepy stories about nothing. But it would have been worth any statesman's money to have heard the profound discussions that sometimes took place, when by chance an old newspaper fell into their hands from some passing traveler. How solemnly they would listen to the contents as drawled out by Derrick Van Bummel, the schoolmaster, a dapper learned little man, who was not to be daunted by the most gigantic word in the dictionary; and how sagely they would deliberate upon public events some months after they had taken place.

The opinions of this junto were completely controlled by Nicholas Vedder, a patriarch of the village, and landlord of the inn, at the door of which he took his seat from morning till night, just moving sufficiently to avoid the sun, and keep in the shade of a large tree; so that the neighbors could tell the hour by his movements as accurately as by a sundial. It is true, he was rarely heard to speak, but smoked his pipe incessantly. His adherents, however (for every great man has his adherents), perfectly understood him, and knew how to gather his opinions. When anything that was read or related displeased him, he was observed to smoke his pipe vehemently, and send forth short, frequent, and angry puffs; but when pleased, he would inhale the smoke slowly and tranquily, and emit it in light and placid clouds, and sometimes taking the pipe from his mouth, and letting the fragrant vapor curl about his nose, would gravely nod his head in token of perfect approbation.

From even this stronghold the unlucky Rip was at length routed by his termagant wife, who would suddenly break in upon the tranquility of the assemblage and call the members all to naught; nor was that august personage, Nicholas Vedder himself, sacred from the daring tongue of this terrible virago, who charged him outright with encouraging her husband in habits of idleness.

Poor Rip was at last reduced almost to despair; and his only alternative to escape from the labor of the farm and the clamor of his wife, was to take gun in hand, and stroll away into the woods. Here he would sometimes seat himself at the foot of a tree, and share the contents of his wallet with Wolf, with whom he sympathized as a fellow-sufferer in persecution. "Poor Wolf," he would say, "thy mistress leads thee a dog's life of it; but never mind, my lad, whilst I live thou shalt never want a friend to stand by thee!" Wolf would wag his tail, look wistfully in his master's face, and if dogs can feel pity, I verily believe he reciprocated the sentiment with all his heart.

In a long ramble of the kind on a fine autumnal day, Rip had unconsciously scrambled to one of the highest parts of the Kaatskill Mountains. He was after his favorite sport of squirrel shooting, and the still solitudes had echoed and re-echoed with the reports of his gun. Panting and fatigued, he threw himself, late in the afternoon, on a green knoll, covered with mountain herbage, that crowned the brow of a precipice. From an opening between the trees he could overlook all the lower country for many a mile of rich woodland. He saw at a distance the lordly Hudson, far, far below him, moving on its silent but majestic course, with the reflection of a purple cloud, or the sail of a lagging bark, here and there sleeping on its glassy bosom, and at last losing itself in the blue highlands.

On the other side he looked down into a deep mountain glen, wild, lonely, and shagged, the bottom filled with fragments from the impending cliffs, and scarcely lighted by the reflected rays of the setting sun. For some time Rip lay musing on this scene; evening was gradually advancing; the mountains began to throw their long blue shadows over the valleys; he saw that it would be dark long before he could reach the village, and he heaved a heavy sigh when he thought of encountering the terrors of Dame Van Winkle.

As he was about to descend, he heard a voice from a distance, hallooing, "Rip Van Winkle! Rip Van Winkle!" He looked around, but could see nothing but a crow winging its solitary flight across the mountain. He thought his fancy must have deceived him and turned again to descend, when he heard the same cry ring through the still evening air: "Rip Van Winkle! Rip Van Winkle!"—at the same time Wolf bristled up his back, and giving a low growl, skulked to his master's side, looking fearfully down into the glen. Rip now felt a vague apprehension stealing over him; he looked anxiously in the same direction, and perceived a strange figure slowly toiling up the rocks, and bending under the weight of something he carried on his back. He was surprised to see any human being in this lonely and unfrequented place, but supposing it to be someone of the neighborhood in need of his assistance he hastened down down to yield it.

On nearer approach, he was still more surprised at the singularity of the stranger's appearance. He was a short, square-built old fellow, with thick bushy hair, and a grizzled beard. His dress was of the antique Dutch fashion—a cloth jerkin strapped around the waist—several pairs of breeches, the outer one of ample volume, decorated with rows of buttons down the sides, and bunches at the knees. He bore on his shoulder a stout keg, that seemed full of liquor, and made signs for Rip to approach and assist him with the load. Though rather shy and distrustful of this new acquaintance, Rip complied with his usual alacrity, and mutually relieving each other, they clambered up a narrow gully, apparently the dry bed of a mountain torrent. As they ascended, Rip every now and then heard long rolling peals, like distant thunder, that seemed to issue out of a deep ravine, or rather cleft between lofty rocks, toward which their rugged path conducted. He paused for an instant, but supposing it to be the muttering of one of those transient thunder showers which often take place in mountain heights, he proceeded. Passing through the ravine, they came to a hollow, like a small amphitheater, surrounded by perpendicular precipices over the brinks of which impending trees shot their branches, so that you only caught glimpses of the azure sky, and the bright evening cloud. During the whole time Rip and his companion had labored on in silence, for though the former marveled greatly what could be the object of carrying a keg of liquor up this wild mountain, yet there was something strange and incomprehensible about the unknown, that inspired awe and checked familiarity.

On entering the amphitheater, new objects of wonder presented themselves. On a level spot in the center was a company of odd-looking personages playing at nine-pins. They were dressed in a quaint, outlandish fashion: Some wore short doublets, others jerkins, with long knives in their belts, and most of them had enormous breeches, of similar style with that of the guide's. Their visages, too, were peculiar: One had a large head, broad face, and small piggish eyes; the face of another seemed to consist entirely of nose, and was surmounted by a white sugarloaf hat, set off with a little red cock's tail. They all had beards, of various shapes and colors. There was one who seemed to be the commander. He was a stout old gentleman, with a weather-beaten countenance; he wore a laced doublet, broad belt and hanger, high-crowned hat and feather, red stockings, and high-heeled shoes, with roses in them. The whole group reminded Rip of the figures in an old Flemish painting, in the parlor of Dominie Van Schaick, the village parson, and which had been brought over from Holland at the time of the settlement.

What seemed particularly odd to Rip was, that although these folks

were evidently amusing themselves, yet they maintained the gravest faces, the most mysterious silence, and were, withal, the most melancholy party of pleasure he had ever witnessed. Nothing interrupted the stillness of the scene, but the noise of the balls, which, whenever they were rolled, echoed along the mountains like rumbling peals of thunder.

As Rip and his companion approached them, they suddenly desisted from their play, and stared at him with such fixed statue-like gaze, and such strange, uncouth, lack-luster countenances, that his heart turned within him, and his knees smote together. His companion now emptied the contents of the keg into large flagons and made signs to him to wait upon the company. He obeyed with fear and trembling; they quaffed the liquor in profound silence, and then returned to their game.

By degrees, Rip's awe and apprehension subsided. He even ventured, when no eye was fixed upon him, to taste the beverage, which he found had much of the flavor of excellent Hollands. He was naturally a thirsty soul, and was soon tempted to repeat the draught. One taste provoked another, and he reiterated his visits to the flagon so often, that at length his senses were overpowered, his eyes swam in his head, his head gradually declined, and he fell into a deep sleep.

On waking, he found himself on the green knoll from whence he had first seen the old man of the glen. He rubbed his eyes—it was a bright sunny morning. The birds were hopping and twittering among the bushes, and the eagle was wheeling aloft, and breasting the pure mountain breeze. "Surely," thought Rip, "I have not slept here all night." He recalled the occurrences before he fell asleep. The strange man with a keg of liquor, the mountain ravine, the wild retreat among the rocks, the wo-begone party at nine-pins, the flagon—"Oh! that flagon! That wicked flagon!" thought Rip, "What excuse shall I make to Dame Van Winkle?"

He looked around for his gun, but in place of the clean, well-oiled fowling piece, he found an old firelock lying by him, the barrel encrusted with rust, and lock falling off, and the stock worm eaten. He now suspected that the grave roysters of the mountain had put a trick upon him, and having dosed him with liquor, had robbed him of his gun. Wolf, too, had disappeared, but he might have strayed away after a squirrel or partridge. He whistled after him and shouted his name, but all in vain; the echoes repeated his whistle and shout, but no dog was to be seen. He determined to revisit the scene of the last evening's gambol, and if he met with any of the party, to demand his dog and gun. As he rose to walk he found himself stiff in the joints, and wanting in his usual activity. "These mountain beds do not agree with me," thought Rip, "and if this frolic should lay me up with a fit of the rheumatism, I shall have a blessed time with Dame Van Winkle." With some difficulty he got down into the glen: He found the gully up which he and his companion had ascended the preceding evening; but to his astonishment a mountain stream was now foaming down it, leaping from rock to rock, and filling the glen with babbling murmurs. He, however, made shift to scramble up its sides, working his toilsome way through thickets of birch, sassafras, and witch hazel, and sometimes tripped up or entangled by the wild grapevines that twisted their coils and tendrils from tree to tree, and spread a kind of network in his path.

At length he reached to where the ravine had opened through the cliffs, to the amphitheater; but no traces of such opening remained. The rocks presented a high impenetrable wall, over which the torrent came tumbling in a sheet of feathery foam, and fell into a broad deep basin, black from the shadows of the surrounding forest. Here, then, poor Rip was brought to a stand. He again called and whistled after his dog; he was only answered by the cawing of a flock of idle crows, sporting high in air about a dry tree that overhung a sunny precipice; and who, secure in their elevation, seemed to look down and scoff at the poor man's perplexities. What was to be done? The morning was passing away, and Rip felt famished for want of his breakfast. He grieved to give up his dog and gun; he dreaded to meet his wife; but it would not do to starve among the mountains. He shook his head, shouldered the rusty firelock, and, with a heart full of trouble and anxiety, turned his steps homeward.

As he approached the village he met a number of people, but none whom he knew, which somewhat surprised him, for he had thought himself acquainted with everyone in the country round. Their dress, too, was of a different fashion from that to which he was accustomed. They all stared at him with equal marks of surprise, and whenever they cast eyes upon him, invariably stroked their chins. The constant recurrence of this gesture induced Rip, involuntarily, to do the same, when, to his astonishment, he found his beard had grown a foot long!

He had now entered the skirts of the village. A troop of strange children ran at his heels, hooting after him, and pointing at his gray beard. The dogs, too, not one of which he recognized for an old acquaintance, barked at him as he passed. The very village was altered: It was larger and more populous. There were rows of houses which he had never seen before, and those which had been his familiar haunts

had disappeared. Strange names were over the doors—strange faces at the windows—everything was strange. His mind now misgave him; he began to doubt whether both he and the world around him were not bewitched. Surely this was his native village, which he had left but the day before. There stood the Kaatskill mountains, there ran the silver Hudson at a distance, there was every hill and dale precisely as it had always been. Rip was sorely perplexed—"That flagon last night," thought he, "has addled my poor head sadly!"

It was with some difficulty that he found the way to his own house, which he approached with silent awe, expecting every moment to hear the shrill voice of Dame Van Winkle. He found the house gone to decay—the roof fallen in, the windows shattered, and the doors off the hinges. A half-starved dog, that looked like Wolf, was skulking about it. Rip called him by name, but the cur snarled, showed his teeth, and passed on. This was an unkind cut indeed. "My very dog," sighed poor Rip, "has forgotten me!"

He entered the house, which, to tell the truth, Dame Van Winkle had always kept in neat order. It was empty, forlorn, and apparently abandoned. This desolateness overcame all his connubial fears—he called loudly for his wife and children—the lonely chambers rung for a moment with his voice, and then all again was silence.

He now hurried forth, and hastened to his old resort, the village inn—but it too was gone. A large rickety wooden building stood in its place, with great gaping windows, some of them broken, and mended with old hats and petticoats, and over the door was painted, "The Union Hotel, by Jonathan Doolittle." Instead of the great tree that used to shelter the quiet little Dutch inn of yore, there now was reared a tall naked pole, with something on the top that looked like a red nightcap, and from it was fluttering a flag, on which was a singular assemblage of stars and stripes—all this was strange and incomprehensible. He recognized on the sign, however, the ruby face of King George, under which he had smoked so many a peaceful pipe, but even this was singularly metamorphosed. The red coat was changed for one of blue and buff, a sword was held in the hand instead of a sceptre, the head was decorated with a cocked hat, and underneath was painted in large characters, "General Washington".

There was, as usual, a crowd of folk about the door, but none that Rip recollected. The very character of the people seemed changed. There was a busy, bustling, disputatious tone about it, instead of the accustomed phlegm and drowsy tranquility. He looked in vain for the sage Nicholas Vedder, with his broad face, double chin, and fair long pipe, uttering clouds of tobacco smoke instead of idle speeches; or Van Bummel, the schoolmaster, doling forth the contents of an ancient newspaper. In place of these, a lean, bilious-looking fellow, with his pockets full of handbills, was haranguing vehemently about rights of citizens, election, members of Congress, liberty, Bunker's Hill, heroes of '76, and other words, that were a perfect Babylonish jargon to the bewildered Van Winkle.

The appearance of Rip, with his long grizzled beard, his rusty fowling piece, his uncouth dress, and the army of women and children that had gathered at his heels, soon attracted the attention of the tavern politicians. They crowded around him, eyeing him from head to foot, with great curiosity. The orator bustled up to him, and drawing him partly aside, inquired "on which side he voted." Rip stared in vacant stupidity. Another short but busy little fellow pulled him by the arm, and rising on top-toe, inquired in his ear, "whether he was Federal or Democrat." Rip was equally at a loss to comprehend the question; when a knowing, self-important old gentleman, in a sharp cocked hat, made his way through the crowd, putting them to the right and left with his elbows as he passed, and planting himself before Van Winkle, with one arm akimbo, the other resting on his cane, his keen eyes and sharp hat penetrating, as it were, into his very soul, demanded, in an austere tone, "what brought him to the election with a gun on his shoulder, and a mob at his heels, and whether he meant to breed a riot in the village?" "Alas! gentlemen," cried Rip, somewhat dismayed, "I am a poor quiet man, a native of the place, and a loyal subject of the King, God bless him!"

Here a general shout burst from the bystanders—"A tory! A tory! A spy! A refugee! Hustle him! Away with him!" It was with great difficulty that the self-important man in the cocked hat restored order; and having assumed a tenfold austerity of brow, demanded again of the unknown culprit what he came there for, and whom he was seeking. The poor man humbly assured him that he meant no harm, but merely came there in search of some of his neighbors, who used to keep about the tavern.

"Well—who are they? Name them."

Rip bethought himself a moment, and inquired, "Where's Nicholas Vedder?"

There was silence for a little while, when an old man replied, in a thin piping voice, "Nicholas Vedder? Why he is dead and gone these eighteen years! There was a wooden tombstone in the churchyard that used to tell all about him, but that's rotted and gone too."

"Where's Brom Dutcher?"

"Oh, he went off to the army in the beginning of the war; some say he was killed at the storming of Stoney-Point—others say he was drowned in a squall at the foot of Antony's Nose. I don't know, he never came back again."

"Where's Van Bummel, the schoolmaster?"

"He went off to the wars, too, was great militia general, and is now in Congress."

Rip's heart died away, at hearing of these sad changes in his home and friends, and finding himself thus alone in the world. Every answer puzzled him, too, by treating of such enormous lapses of time, and of matters which he could not understand: war, Congress, Stoney-Point; he had no courage to ask after any more friends, but cried out in despair, "Does nobody here know Rip Van Winkle?"

"Oh, Rip Van Winkle!" exclaimed two or three, "Oh, to be sure! That's Rip Van Winkle yonder, leaning against the tree."

Rip looked, and beheld a precise counterpart of himself, as he went up the mountain: Apparently as lazy, and certainly as ragged. The poor fellow was now completely confounded. He doubted his own identity, and whether he was himself or another man. In the mist of his bewilderment, the man in the cocked hat demanded who he was, and what was his name?

"God knows," exclaimed he, at his wit's end, "I'm not myself—I'm somebody else—that's me yonder—no—that's somebody else, got into my shoes—I was myself last night, but I fell asleep on the mountain, and they've changed my gun, and everything's changed, and I'm changed, and I can't tell what's my name, or who I am!"

The bystanders began now to look at each other, nod, wink significantly, and tap their fingers against their foreheads. There was a whisper also, about securing the gun, and keeping the old fellow from doing mischief, at the very suggestion of which the self-important man in the cocked hat retired with some precipitation. At this critical moment a fresh likely-looking woman pressed through the throng to get a peep at the gray-bearded man. She had a chubby child in her arms, which, frightened at his looks, began to cry. "Hush, Rip," cried she, "hush, you little fool, the old man won't hurt you." The name of the child, the air of the mother, the tone of her voice, all awakened a train of recollection in his mind. "What is your name, my good woman?" asked he.

"Judith Gardenier."

"And your father's name?"

"Ah, poor man, his name was Rip Van Winkle; it's twenty years since he went away from home with his gun, and never has been heard of since—his dog came home without him; but whether he shot himself, or was carried away by the Indians, nobody can tell. I was then but a little girl."

Rip had but one question more to ask; but he put it with a faltering sort of voice:

"Where's your mother?"

"Oh, she too had died but a short time since; she broke a blood vessel in a fit of passion at a New England pedlar."

There was a drop of comfort, at least, in this intelligence. The honest man could contain himself no longer. He caught his daughter and her child in his arms. "I am your father!" cried he "Young Rip Van Winkle once—old Rip Van Winkle now!—Does nobody know poor Rip Van Winkle!"

All stood amazed, until an old woman, tottering out from among the crowd, put her hand to her brow, and peering under it in his face for a moment, exclaimed, "Sure enough! It is Rip Van Winkle—it is himself!

Welcome home again, old neighbor—Why, where have you been these twenty long years?"

Rip's story was soon told, for the whole 20 years had been to him as one night. The neighbors stared when they heard it; some were seen to wink at each other, and put their tongues in their cheeks: And the self-important man in the cocked hat, who, when the alarm was over, had retrned to the field, screwed down the corners of his mouth, and shook his head—upon which there was a general shaking of the head throughout the assemblage.

It was determined, however, to take the opinion of old Peter Vander-donk, who was seen slowly advancing up the road. He was a descendant of the historian of that name, who wrote one of the earliest accounts of the province. Peter was the most ancient inhabitant of the village, and well versed in all the wonderful events and traditions of the neighbor-hood. He recollected Rip at once, and corroborated his story in the most satisfactory manner. He assured the company that it was a fact, handed down from his ancestor the historian, that the Kaatskill Mountains had always been haunted by strange beings. That it was affirmed that the great Hendrick Hudson, the first discoverer of the river and country, kept a kind of vigil there every 20 years, with his crew of the *Half-moon*, being permitted in this way to revisit the scenes of his enterprise, and keep a guardian eye upon the river, and that great city called by his name. That his father had once seen them in their old Dutch dresses playing at nine-pins in a hollow of the mountain; and that he himself had heard, one summer afternoon, the sound of their balls like distant peals of thunder.

To make a long story short the company broke up, and returned to the more important concerns of the election. Rip's daughter took him home to live with her: She had a snug, well-furnished house, and a stout cheery farmer for a husband, whom Rip recollected for one of the urchins that used to climb upon his back. As to Rip's son and heir, who was the ditto of himself, seen leaning against the tree, he was employed to work on the farm; but evinced an hereditary disposition to attend to anything else but his business.

Rip now resumed his old walks and habits: He soon found many of his former cronies, although all rather the worse for the wear and tear of time; and preferred making friends among the rising generation, with whom he soon grew into great favor.

Having nothing to do at home, and being arrived at that happy age when a man can do nothing with impunity, he took his place once more on the bench, at the inn door, and was reverenced as one of the patriarchs of the village, and a chronicle of the old times "before the war." It was some time before he could get into the regular track of gossip, or could be made to comprehend the strange events that had taken place during his torpor. How that there had been a revolutionary war, that the country had thrown off the yoke of old England, and that, instead of being a subject of his Majesty George the Third, he was now a free citizen of the United States. Rip, in fact, was no politician; the changes of states and empires made but little impression on him; but there was one species of despotism under which he had long groaned, and that was—petticoat government. Happily, that was at an end; he had got his neck out of the yoke of matrimony, and could go in and out whenever he pleased, without dreading the tyranny of Dame Van Winkle. Whenever her name was mentioned, however, he shook his head, shrugged his shoulders, and cast up his eyes; which might pass either for an expression of resignation to his fate, or joy at his deliverance.

He used to tell his story to every stranger that arrived at Mr. Doolittle's hotel. He was observed, at first, to vary on some points every time he told it, which was, doubtless, owing to his having so recently awaked. It at last settled down precisely to the tale I have related, and not a man, woman, or child in the neighborhood, but knew it by heart. Some always pretended to doubt the reality of it, and insisted that Rip had been out of his head, and that this was one point on which he always remained flighty. The old Dutch inhabitants, however, almost universally gave it full credit. Even to this day they never hear a thunder storm of a summer afternoon, about the Kaatskill, but they say Hendrick Hudson and his crew are at their game of nine-pins; and it is a common wish of all henpecked husbands in the neighborhood, when life hangs heavy on their hands, that they might have a quieting draft out of Rip Van Winkle's flagon.

The Wolf Woman

There are stories of human babies brought up by wolves in many countries. Perhaps the most famous is the story of Romulus, the founder of ancient Rome, and his brother Remus. This story comes from Texas.

In the early 1830s John Dent and his partner were trapping in Georgia. John Dent was in love with a mountaineer girl named Mollie, and she seems to have been the reason for the quarrel between Dent and his partner, which ended with a fight in which Dent's partner was killed with a knife.

Dent fled from justice to the west, but before he went he got a message to Mollie telling her he was going to look for a place where they could live together.

Time went by, and the murder was almost forgotten. Then, Mollie went to milk the cows one evening—and disappeared. When her parents went to look for her, they found a bowie knife, which they recognized as Dent's, and, down by the river, signs that a canoe had recently been tied up there. They never saw Mollie again, but about six months later they had a letter from her. The letter didn't say much, and what it did say, Mollie's parents didn't understand. "The Devil," she wrote, "has a river in Texas that is all his own." They supposed this meant that Dent had found some river in Texas where he was trapping. They were a little surprised that Mollie should call her lover "the Devil," but that was how *they* thought of him at any rate.

They had never heard of Devil's River, which runs into the Rio Grande in south-west Texas. In those days it was Comanche country. There were no white settlers—Dent must have come to an arrangement with the Comanches—but a few isolated Mexican farms, rearing goats.

It was at one of these little Mexican goat ranches that, about noon one day a year or two later, a man arrived on a horse that looked as if it was about ready to drop. He told the *ranchero* where he lived, many miles to the east, and said his wife was having a baby and needed help. The Mexican couple agreed to come with him, but as they were preparing to leave, one of those sudden electrical storms that you get in that part of Texas broke. A bolt of lightning struck the stranger and killed him.

The Mexican *ranchero* knew how to get to the stranger's camp, and he and his wife were not the kind of folk to leave a woman in distress. They set off as soon as they could, and reached Devil's River about nightfall. It wasn't until the following day they found the camp, and the woman lay there, under a brush shelter, as dead as her man. It was obvious that she had died while giving birth, but there was no sign of the child. There were, however, fresh tracks of lobos (timber wolves) around the camp, and they concluded that the baby had been killed and eaten by the wolves.

About 10 years later, a boy living at San Felipe Springs told how he had seen a pack of lobos attacking a herd of goats. With the wolves, he said, was a girl. She had long hair and she was dirty and naked, but he was pretty sure she was an ordinary human girl. Nobody believed the story, but it got repeated around the settlements.

A year or so later came another report. This time the girl had been seen along with two big lobos eating a freshly killed goat. When disturbed they had run off, the girl at first running on all fours, then rising to run on two legs to keep up with the wolves.

This time the witness was an adult woman, and she was certain of what she had seen. Someone remembered the disappearance of the baby from the camp near Devil's River some 12 years before. There were no more sightings, but Indians reported human footprints among the tracks of the wolves along the river.

A hunt was organized to capture the wolf-girl, and after two or three days she was cornered in a box canyon. She cowered away from the hunters like a rabbit, but when they moved in on her she fought like a wildcat. She had a big lobo with her, but one of the hunters shot it dead. At that the girl fainted, and they were able to tie her up.

Although she was very muscular for a young girl, and very wild and unkempt, she seemed to be otherwise normal. She was taken to a nearby ranch and put in a room for the night. The people showed her by gestures they meant her no harm, brought her food and clothing, and tried to reassure her. But she would have none of them. She showed only terror and distrust, backing away into the corner of the room when anyone advanced toward her. As night fell, they left her alone. The door was locked, and the window barred with a plank nailed across it.

There were four or five men at the place, and they did not get any sleep. From the room next door came the most terrible howls and screams that were neither human nor wolf.

Soon, the cries were answered, and these were unmistakably the howls of the lobos. Only a few at first, they soon grew in number, until they came from every side. Every lobo in the country seemed to be gathering around that little two-room shack. The men inside were mostly hard-riding Mexican *vaqueros*, who had heard wolves howling often enough—but never anything like this. The wolves howled in unison, as if someone was conducting them like an orchestra, and in between they fell silent, as if listening to the answering howls from the wolf-girl held prisoner in the shack.

Then, from out of the night, they attacked. There seemed to be hundreds of them, racing down on the corrals to attack the goats, cows, and horses. No man who knows lobos is afraid of them but, on this occasion, the men kept together in a bunch, close to the shack, and fired off their guns at random.

They did succeed in driving off the wolves. But when they got back to the shack, they found that the plank over the window had been wrenched off, and the wolf-girl had gone.

People supposed that she had rejoined the wolves, although no tracks could be found. And strangely, the wolves themselves seemed to have disappeared for a while. Not one was seen in the district for many months.

Six years went by, and the trails were becoming a little busier since the discovery of gold in California. In 1852, a party of frontiersmen prospecting for a new trail reached the Rio Grande, a few miles above the mouth of Devil's River. At the place they approached the river, they were out of sight until they appeared on the edge of the bluff. Sitting on a sandbar below they saw a young woman cuddling two young wolf whelps. She was up in an instant, gathering the whelps one under each arm, and was off faster than a horse could follow.

She was never seen again—or, if she was, the sighting was not recorded. But, 50 and more years later, it was not uncommon to hear of a wolf—and they were killed off in quick time by the ranchers—which had a face peculiarly resembling the human.

Time Runs Out

A long time ago in West Virginia, a coal miner was killed in a fall of coal. His body was dug out but his pocket watch, which he had hung up somewhere while he worked, was left behind.

Some time later, the watch suddenly appeared, ticking hard although it ought to have run down long before, near a miner by the name of Murphy. The following day, a prop gave way just as Murphy was passing, and he was killed by a collapsing beam.

This was just the first appearance of the watch. Many times after that, it would appear, ticking loudly, in different parts of the mine. And every time, the miner working nearest to it would be dead by the evening of the day following. The watch was a herald of death. Men tried to grab it, they tried to smash it with a shovel, they tried to blow it up with dynamite. But nothing had any effect. The watch might disappear for months at a time, and the miners sometimes forgot all about it—until it returned, ticking a little louder than any ordinary watch ticks, and, sure as the sun rises, signaling a death the following day.

One day the fire boss was making his usual tour of inspection after the men had gone home when he heard the watch ticking some way ahead of him. The mine was empty, and it made an eerie sound—its inhuman tick, tick, tick, louder than ever in the long dark galleries of the mine. The fire boss felt fear and, as he moved along farther, he felt pity too, pity for a young miner named Jim, in whose workplace the watch was ticking.

The next morning, as the miners came to work, Jim was stopped by the fire boss. "Don't go to work today, Jim," he told him. "Go home to your family."

"Now why in the world should I do that?" Jim inquired.

"Don't argue with me, man. Just go!"

But Jim, who was a family man with many mouths to feed, did argue. He could not afford to give up a day's pay and risk dismissal as well. He insisted the fire boss tell him why he should not go to work.

"Well, if you must know, Jim, I heard the watch last night and it was ticking at the place you are working."

At that, Jim's face turned pale—even paler than working underground for six days a week had made it. "The death watch!" he gasped, and without further argument, he turned away from the mine.

As he walked away, Jim felt gratitude in his heart—gratitude to the fire boss for warning him, gratitude to the Lord for sparing him. He was

a religious man, and he decided he would go to church to give thanks. But first he would have to go home to change his clothes, and if he were to arrive in time for the service, he would have to hurry. So he took the shortcut across the railroad tracks.

The 7.55 came along at 60 miles an hour and knocked him into kingdom come.

The Family Who Couldn't Blow Out the Candle

There was once a family which consisted of a mother, a father, a son, a daughter, and an old grandma. All of them had mouths that were twisted out of shape in one way or another. One evening they sat up late celebrating Grandma's 90th birthday. When they were ready to go to bed, Mother said, "Father, will you blow out the candle?"

"Yes, I will," Father replied.

"Well, I wish you would," said Mother.

"Well, I will," he said.

And he blew. But his lower jaw stuck out so much farther than his top teeth that when he blew, he blew straight up his own nose. He couldn't blow out the candle. So he said, "Mother, will you blow out the candle?"

"Yes, I will," Mother replied.

"Well, I wish you would," said Father.

"Well, I will," said Mother.

And she blew. But her front teeth stuck out so much farther than her chin that when she blew, she blew straight down toward her feet. She couldn't blow out the candle. "Son, will you blow out the candle?"

"Yes, I will," said Son.

"Well, I wish you would," said Mother.

"Well, I will," said Son.

And he blew. But he had a mouth that was twisted over to the right, and when he blew, he blew toward his right ear. He couldn't blow out the candle. So he said, "Sister, will you blow out the candle?"

"Yes, I will," said Daughter.

"Well, I wish you would," said Son.

"Well, I will," said Daughter.

And she blew. But she had a mouth that was twisted over to the left, and when she blew, she blew toward her left ear. She couldn't blow out the candle. So she said, "Grandma, will you blow out the candle?"

"Yes, I will," said Grandma.

"Well, I wish you would," said Daughter.

"Well, I will," said Grandma.

Now the Grandma had a mouth that was twisted worse than the others. It waggled all around her face so it was never pointing in the same direction for more than a moment. She lent toward the candle, with her mouth going around and around and her breath going up and down and left and right—and she snuffed out the candle with her finger and thumb. Then they all went to bed.

270

The Phantom Train of Marshall Pass

Soon after the rails were laid across Marshall Pass, Colorado, where they go over a height of 12,000 feet above the sea, an old engineer named Nelson Edwards was assigned to a train. He had traveled the road with passengers behind him for a couple of months and met with no accident, but one night as he set off for the divide he fancied that the silence was deeper, the canon darker, and the air frostier than usual. A defective rail and an unsafe bridge had been reported that morning, and he began the long ascent with some misgivings. As he left the first line of snow sheds, he heard a whistle echoing somewhere among the ice and rocks, and at the same time the gong in his cab sounded and he applied the brakes. The conductor ran up and asked, "What did you stop for?"

"Why did you signal to stop?"

"I gave no signal. Pull her open and light out, for we've got to pass No. 19 at the switches, and there's a wild train climbing behind us."

Edwards drew the lever, sanded the track, and the heavy train got under way again; but the whistles behind grew nearer, sounding danger-signals, and in turning a curve he looked out and saw a train speeding after him at a rate that must bring it against the rear of his own train if something were not done. He broke into a sweat as he pulled the throttle wide open and lunged into a snowbank. The cars lurched, but the snow was flung off and the train went roaring through another shed. Here was where the defective rail had been reported. No matter. A greater danger was pressing behind. The fireman piled on coal until his clothes were wet with perspiration, and fire belched from the smokestack. The passengers, too, having been warned of their peril, had dressed themselves and were anxiously watching at the windows, for talk went among them that a mad engineer was driving the train behind.

As Edwards crossed the summit he shut off steam and surrendered his train to the force of gravity. Looking back, he could see by the faint light from new snow that the driving-wheels on the rear engine were bigger than his own, and that a a tall figure stood atop of the cars and gestured frantically. At a sharp turn in the track he found the other train but 200 yards behind, and as he swept around the curve the engineer who was chasing him leaned from his window and laughed. His face was like dough. Snow was falling and had begun to drift in the hollows, but the trains flew on; bridges shook as they thundered across

them; wind screamed in the ears of the passengers; the suspected bridge was reached; Edwards's heart was in his throat, but he seemed to clear the chasm by a bound. Now the switch was in sight, but No. 19 was not there, and as the brakes were freed the train shot by like a flash. Suddenly a red light appeared ahead, swinging to and fro on the track. As well be run into behind as to crash into an obstacle ahead. He heard the whistle of the pursuing locomotive yelp behind him, yet he reversed the lever and put on brakes, and for a few seconds lived in a hell of dread.

Hearing no sound, now, he glanced back and saw the wild train almost leap upon his own—yet just before it touched it the track seemed to spread, the engine toppled from the bank, the whole train rolled into the canon and vanished. Edwards shuddered and listened. No cry of hurt men or hiss of steam came up—nothing but the groan of the wind as it rolled through the black depth. The lantern ahead, too, disappeared. Now another danger impended, and there was no time to linger, for No. 19 might be on its way ahead if he did not reach the second switch before it moved out. The mad run was resumed and the second switch was reached in time. As Edwards was finishing the run to Green River, which he reached in the morning ahead of schedule, he found

written in the frost of his cab-window these words:

"A frate train was recked as yu saw. Now that yu saw it yu will never make another run. The enjine was not ounder control and four sexshun men wor killed. If yu ever run on this road again yu will be recked."

Edwards quit the road that morning, and returning to Denver found employment on the Union Pacific. No wreck was discovered next day in the canon where he had seen it, nor has the phantom train been in chase of any engineer who has crossed the divide since that night.

Peter Rugg Rides to Boston

This story was written by William Austin (1778–1841) who was a successful Boston lawyer besides being the writer of stories often in the form of letters. This is his most famous story, and it has become one of the legends of New England. The narrator of the story is a New York businessman who, in the summer of 1820, rode on a stagecoach from Providence to Boston.

As every seat in the coach was taken, I rode beside the driver, an intelligent and communicative man. When he had gone about ten miles, he asked me if I had a waterproof topcoat with me.

"No," I said, "Why do you ask?"

"Well, you will want one soon," the driver replied. "Do you see the ears of the horses?"

The horses had flattened their ears back on their heads, like a running hare.

"They can see the storm-breeder," said the driver, "and we shall see him soon."

I was puzzled by this as there was not a cloud in the sky.

Soon afterward a black speck appeared on the road far ahead, and the driver said, "Here comes the storm-breeder. I remember him from many a soaking. I suppose the poor fellow suffers much himself—more than anyone knows."

The speck became a man with a child beside him, in a two-wheeled carriage drawn by a large black horse. They passed us at great speed. The man looked worried, and he gave us a hard look as he passed. I noticed that after he had gone, the horses at once pricked up their ears again.

"Who is that man?" I asked. "He seems to be in trouble."

"Nobody knows who he is, but I have seen him, driving like that with his child alongside him, more than a hundred times. He always used to ask me the way to Boston, even when he was traveling in the opposite direction, so that I eventually stopped answering him. That is why he gave us such a look as he passed."

"Does he never stop anywhere?"

"I have known him to stop at all, except to ask the way to Boston. And wherever he happens to be, he always says that he cannot stop a moment because he has to be in Boston that night."

We were now climbing a hill, but the sky above us was still completely cloudless. I said as much to the driver.

"You must look," said he, "in the direction the man was coming from, for the storm never meets him—it always follows him."

When we reached the top of the hill I saw a patch in the sky no bigger than a hat. "There," said the driver, "that is the seed storm. But with luck, we may reach the tavern before it arrives."

By the time we reached the tavern, the sky was black all around, and thunder and lightning warned of the approaching rain. It came down in a torrent as we rushed for shelter, but did not last long. The black clouds passed over, rolling rapidly toward Providence.

Another traveler arrived soon after us, and we asked him if he had seen the man and child in the carriage. He said he had indeed met them, that the man had seemed bewildered and had asked him the way to Boston. He was driving at great speed, as if he were hoping to out-race the storm.

Then a pedlar, with his cart of tin goods, arrived. When we asked him about the man and the child, he replied that he had met him in four different states within the past two weeks. Each time he had asked the way to Boston, and each time he had been followed by a thunderstorm. The pedlar's goods had been soaked and his horse frightened. "So I hope I never see that man and horse again," the pedlar said, "for they do not look to me as though they belong to this world."

That was all I could find out at the time, and I might have forgotten all about it. But a long time later, as I was standing outside a hotel in Hartford, I heard a man say, "There goes Peter Rugg and his child! He looks wet and weary, and farther from Boston than ever." I looked across the road and there he was: I was certain it was the same man I had seen some three years before on the road from Providence.

I asked the stranger who had spoken, "Who *is* Peter Rugg?"

"That," he replied, "is more than anyone can say for certain. He is a famous traveler, although the innkeepers are not fond of him as he never stops to eat, drink, or sleep. The Government should get him to carry the Mail!"

"That would never do," said another bystander, "for suppose you wanted to send a letter to Boston? Peter Rugg has, to my knowledge, spent more than twenty years on the road without reaching it."

"But does he never stop anywhere?" I asked. "Can you tell me any more about him? If he has been traveling for twenty years, does he not look any older?"

They told me he did indeed look older, his child also, though his horse seemed to grow fatter and livelier.

"The last time Rugg spoke to me," the stranger continued, "he asked how far it was to Boston. I told him it was about one hundred miles."

"'Why!' he exclaimed. 'How can you tell me such a lie. It is a cruel trick to mislead a traveler. I have lost my way. Please tell me the shortest way to Boston.'

"I repeated that it was one hundred miles. 'How can you say that?' said he, 'I was told last night it was only fifty miles, and I have been traveling all night.'

"But,' I said, 'you are now traveling *away* from Boston. You must turn back.'

"'Alas!' said he, 'it is always "turn back". Boston shifts like the wind. One man tells me it is to the east, another to the west, and the signposts all point the wrong way.'

"'Why not stop and rest a while?' I said. 'You seem to be wet and tired.'

"'Yes,' he agreed, 'it has been foul weather since I left home.'

"'Why not stop then?'

"'I must not stop. I must reach home tonight. I think you must be mistaken in the distance to Boston.'

"He then gave rein to his horse, which he had been holding in with some difficulty, and disappeared in a moment. A few days afterward, I met him again in another place, going at a good twelve miles an hour."

"Is Peter Rugg his real name, or is it some nickname that has been given to him?" I asked the stranger.

"I can't say," he replied "but, look, why not ask him, for he is coming this way."

The black, high-spirited horse approached, and would have passed us, but I stepped into the road and stopped him. "Sir," I said, "may I be so bold as to inquire if you are not Mr. Rugg? For I think I have seen you before."

"My name is Peter Rugg," he replied. "I have unfortunately lost my way. I am wet, tired, and would take it kindly if you will direct me to Boston."

"Do you live in Boston? In what street?" I asked.

"In Middle Street."

"When did you leave Boston?" I asked.

"I cannot say—it seems a considerable time."

I told him that he was in Hartford and 100 miles or so from Boston, but he was reluctant to believe me. He thought he was in Newburyport and that the river he had been following was not the Connecticut River but the Merrimac.

"Have the rivers changed their courses, just as the cities have changed their places?" he exclaimed. "And look—the clouds are gathering in the south; we shall have a rainy night. Ah, that fatal oath!"

He would not wait a moment longer, and flicked the reins, whereupon his impatient horse set off at his usual great rate and in a few moments they were out of sight.

Next time business took me to Boston, I made up my mind to seek further information about Peter Rugg, and in Middle Street I found an old lady named Mrs. Croft, who had lived there for 20 years.

She told me that, the summer before, she had been summoned to her front door by a knock. On opening it, she saw a strange man, weary-looking, with a child in a battered two-wheeled carriage drawn by a large black horse. To her astonishment, the stranger asked to see Mrs. Rugg.

She told him that a Mrs. Rugg had indeed once lived in the house, but that she had died, at a great age, some 20 years before.

"How can you tell me such lies?" the stranger exclaimed. "Please ask Mrs. Rugg to step to the door."

"Sir, I assure you," she said, "Mrs. Rugg has not lived here for 20 years. No one lives here but me, and my name is Betsy Croft."

The stranger paused, and looked up and down the street. "The paint is rather faded," he said, "but this looks like my house."

Then the child spoke: "That is the stone by the door where I used to sit and eat my bread and milk."

"But," said the stranger, "it seems to be in the wrong place. Indeed, everything here seems to be in the wrong place. The streets are all changed, the people changed, the town itself seems changed. But what is strangest of all is that Catherine Rugg would desert her husband and child..."

Then he asked after John Foy, his cousin, who had been a seaman, and he asked after his brother, William Rugg, who had lived in King Street. Mrs. Croft had heard of none of these names, neither people nor streets. It was hardly likely, in Boston, that they would have a "King Street," she said, but the stranger did not understand her.

"No King Street?" he said, "Why, woman, you mock me. You might as well tell me there is no king!"

At length, the stranger decided that he had mistaken the place. "Strange mistake," he murmured. "How much this looks like the town of Boston! There is certainly a great resemblance, but I see my error now. If I were in Boston, my horse would carry me to my own front door, but he shows by his impatience that he is not at home. How absurd of me to mistake this town for Boston! Ah well," he sighed, "no home tonight."

And without another word, he drove off up the street. Mrs. Croft saw no more of him.

However, she directed me to an old man who lived nearby, who told me that, as a boy, he had known a man named Peter Rugg. The man had caused some surprise by suddenly disappearing, and taking his child with him, but people supposed that he had some reason for flight, and in time his disappearance was forgotten.

"Sir," I told him, "Peter Rugg is living still. I have seen him lately with his child, in his carriage drawn by his black horse."

The old man replied that Peter Rugg might well be still living, and his daughter too, "But you cannot have seen a *child*. Why, let me see, Jenny Rugg must be at least—hmm—the Boston Massacre was in 1770—she would have been about ten then... Why, sir, Jenny Rugg would be at least sixty years of age!"

The old man himself admitted to being over 80, and his mind was no longer clear. I saw I would learn no more in Middle Street.

In the hotel that evening, I repeated what I had learned to the company assembled in the bar. One of the men present smiled at this.

"So you think you have seen Peter Rugg?" he said. "My grandfather used to tell a story about him, which he told as though he believed it was true."

I asked him to tell his grandfather's story, and this is what he said.

"Peter Rugg, sir, once lived in Middle Street in this city. He was a well-off man with a wife and one daughter, and he was well respected by everyone for his sober life and good manners. But he had one fault. He had a terrible temper, and when he was in one of his fits of rage he would swear mightily, kick down a door, or bite a nail in half. While the fit was on him, he respected neither God nor man. Yet, at all other times he was a good man and a perfect gentleman.

"One morning in late autumn, Rugg took his daughter in his two-wheeled carriage drawn by his fine black horse and journeyed to Concord. On the return, he was overtaken by a violent storm, and he stopped at the house of a friend of his, who tried to persuade him to stay the night. This he would not do. His friend was astounded by his determination to travel on. 'Why,' he said, 'it is pitch dark, a terrible storm is raging, you are in an open carriage... It is madness to go on.'

"But Rugg swore a tremendous oath, and roared: 'I care nothing for the storm. I will see my home tonight in spite of the storm, or—*may I never see it again!*' And he cracked his whip and drove off into the storm and darkness.

"He did not come home that night, nor the next night. Inquiries were made, but no trace could be found of him after he had left his friend's house. His wife thought she heard the sound of the carriage wheels and the tread of the horse in the street outside the house, and the neighbors, watching from their windows by lamplight, saw him ride past at a great pace, unable to stop.

"Some time later there was a rumor that Peter Rugg had been seen near Hartford, passing through the country at headlong speed. This made his friends reopen their inquiries, but they were bewildered by the number of reports they received that Rugg had been seen all over New England, with his child beside him in his two-wheeled carriage, occasionally stopping to ask the way to Boston.

"The tollkeeper at the Charlestown Bridge said that sometimes, on the darkest, stormiest nights, a horse and carriage would rattle over the bridge at midnight, not stopping to pay the toll. This happened so often that on one night the tollkeeper lay in wait and, as the carriage passed, he threw a stool at the horse. But the stool seemed to pass through the horse's body, and Peter Rugg drove on, without stopping."

Two Pairs of Drawers

Once there was a man who always wore two pairs of drawers, but when he died his wife only laid out one pair for him to be buried in.

After the funeral, he came back and haunted her. Every night he walked right in through the front door. She moved house to get away from the ghost, but he came to the new house, too. She moved four or five times, but the ghost kept coming back every single night.

In the end she told her trouble to her friends. They asked her why she didn't talk to the ghost. She replied that she was too scared to. They told her that next time she should say, "What in the name of the Lord do you want?"

That night the ghost came again. She walked right up to him and said, "What in the name of the Lord do you want?"

He stared at her a long time, but she never moved, just stood there, and in the end he said, "Honey, just give me another pair of drawers, please."

She said, "All right, I'll give 'em to you," and from that day to this he has never come back again.

The Girl in the Lavender Dress

We think of legends and folk tales as stories that were first told a long time ago, but of course they are still being created at this day, so not all such tales are very old. A few years ago, for example, a story was going around about a student who attended college about the time of the Vietnam War. The strange thing about it was that the same story, with the same student, was told in many different colleges and universities throughout the U.S.A. As he could not possibly have attended more than a small fraction of them, and the story could already be classed as a legend.

The legend of the Girl in the Lavender Dress dates from less than 50 years ago, and the supposed events it describes took place about 1949, when the first, known, written version of the legend appeared in *Trees to the Wind*, by Carl Carmer. The Ramapo Mountains are not far from New York City. Even 50 years ago, on a clear day, you could just about see the skyscrapers in the distance. All the same, at that time the area was still mostly inhabited by real mountain people.

Back in the 1930s, there lived in the Ramapo Valley a girl with skin like gold, eyes like hyacinths and hair like the ripening corn. There was a lot of talk about her in the neighborhood. She seems to have been the kind of girl who does not take kindly to the rules and restrictions that most people live by. She was, they said, a wild one, but nobody knew much about her—except her own people I suppose, and they hardly came into the story.

The girl was very poor, and was usually seen in a patched and dirty dress that was too small for her, with no shoes on her feet. One day, some city church sent three barrels of old clothes to be given away to the poor folk of the Ramapo Valley. The local preacher announced that the clothes would be given out one Wednesday evening, and at the time he said there were quite a number of people in the church. Not all the clothes of the city folk were suitable, and the preacher was a little shocked when he pulled out an evening dress, which did not cover the shoulders, colored like lavender and covered with sequins. He held it up scrunched into a bundle, and at first no one wanted it. Then, from the back of the church came the girl with hair like the corn and eyes like the hyacinths. She walked right up to the preacher, took the dress, and walked out with it, not saying a word.

From that time on she wore that dress and no other.

They say it was that dress, in a way, that killed her. She had been to visit some cousins in Jersey City, and getting off the bus on the way home, late on a winter night, she had set off to walk through the woods. But she never arrived, and she was found next day frozen to death.

And that was that. One story ends right there. But about 10 years later, another story begins.

Two juniors from Hamilton College, up in Clinton, NY, were driving through the Ramapo Valley on their way to a dance. It was a lovely, warm evening in late summer, and they were in no great hurry, admiring the scenery. By the roadside they saw a girl with hair the color of ripening corn and eyes the color of hyacinths, who was wearing a lavender dress. Naturally, they stopped and asked her if she would like a lift.

She got in, sitting between them in their little two-seater car, and she proved to be as amusing as she was pretty. Or at least, she charmed those two young fellows, and they were delighted when she agreed to go to the dance with them. She had the right kind of dress for a party; she had told them she was on the way to a square dance at Sterling Furnace.

The boys had a fine time at the dance, and everyone agreed that their friend was a delightful girl, quiet but friendly, a beautiful dancer and a good companion. When they asked her what her name was, she said, "Call me Lavender. Other people do, because of the color of my dress."

It was quite late when the boys set out to drive her home. As it was an open car and she was wearing a dress that did not cover her shoulders, one of them lent her his topcoat to wear in the car.

She directed them along bumpy woodland back lanes for some miles, until she told them to stop at a small, dirty, half-ruined shack. The boys were shocked to the marrow at the sight of the place, although, of course, they were too polite to show it. The girl stood by the roadside waving until they had driven out of sight. They had gone a long way before they remembered the girl still had the topcoat and, as they were staying the night not far away, they decided to go back for it next day.

They had some trouble finding the shack again, among all those unposted backwoods tracks, but at last they did, and it looked no better on a sunny afternoon than it had looked on a dark night. The only window in it was a glass panel in the door, covered with one torn lace curtain.

They knocked on the door and it was opened by a shabby old woman, with white hair and piercing blue eyes. They asked for Lavender. She looked surprised and inquired if they were old friends of hers. They didn't like to say that they had only met her the previous evening, so

they agreed that they were old friends.

"Then you'll not have heard she's dead. Been in the graveyard just down the road there for 10 years."

The boys shook their heads. It couldn't be the same girl, they said. They had seen her quite recently.

The old woman insisted that no one else by the name of Lavender lived in the neighborhood. "Wasn't her real name anyhow. Her Pa named her Lily when she was born. Only some folk took to calling her Lavender on account of that dress she always wore."

The boys mumbled something about making a mistake and returned in silence to their car. They drove off slowly, and about 100 yards down the track they stopped. They had noticed a little clearing by the road with a few old gravestones sticking up among the long grass. "I'm going to look," one said, and they both got out.

They found the gravestone marked "Lily" right away, not by the name, because the stone was weathered and worn, but because on top of it, neatly folded, lay the missing topcoat.

More Superheroes

Paul Bunyan

Some people say Paul Bunyan, the king of the lumberjacks, was invented by an advertising man who worked for a timber company. But most of the tales about Paul have been around too long for that. He belongs to the legends of the lumber camps of the north-west. They had no books there, but you could hear stories about Paul around the camp fires. Some people say, if you go to Alaska today, you will find Paul up there, swinging his great axe.

Paul was born in Maine a long while ago. When he was in his cradle, he rocked it around so much he knocked down all the trees for two miles around. So they made him a cradle that floated and anchored it in the sea. He went on rocking and set up a wave that flooded half the villages along the coast. They decided then that they'd better bring him home again, but they couldn't wake him up. The British navy helped, and after they'd let of all their guns around Paul for seven hours, he woke up. He climbed out of his cradle and, oh dear, the wave that he caused sank half the British fleet.

Paul grew up and became a logger. He cleared the forests from Maine to the Pacific. Of course, he had some help. There was Johnny Inkslinger, his accountant, who used up nine barrels of ink a day trying to keep the books straight. And there was Babe, Paul's Blue Ox, who grew two feet every time Paul looked at him when he was young.

Babe measured 42 axe handles between the eyes—or was it between the horns?—with a bit over just enough to accommodate a tobacco box or a Size 7 Derby hat. Babe was so big they had to start a new iron mine to make shoes for him.

It was Babe who made the roads straight in the west. When Paul came upon a crooked road, full of bends that just slowed you down, he hitched Babe to one end of the road and Babe pulled it straight. A tidy piece of road was left over, which could be used somewhere else.

Paul Bunyan in North Dakota

One time soon after Paul had dug the St. Lawrence River, he had a letter from the King of Sweden. The King asked Paul to cut down all the trees in North Dakota so the Swedes could go there and farm. It was near seed time, and the King said the job must be finished in one month so the farmers could sow their seeds.

Paul called all his men together and set up the biggest camp that had ever been seen. The bunks in the bunkhouse were 18 decks high, and the men on the top bunks had to get up an hour earlier than the men on the bottom or else they couldn't climb down in time for breakfast. The boy who drove the salt and pepper wagon around the tables couldn't make it in a day. He stayed the night at the other end and started back next morning.

As this was a rush job, Paul asked the Seven Axemen to help. They were the fastest loggers after Paul himself. They were all named Frank, and this caused some problems because whenever Paul yelled out "Frank!" each one of them would drop his axe and hurry over.

The Seven Axemen had double-edged axes that were so heavy no one could lift them. To sharpen the blades they would roll a big stone down a hill and run alongside, holding the edge of the axe against the stone.

Paul had a few delays on that job. The fog was the worst. It covered everything. It even got in the coffee and made it too weak to drink. The Seven Axemen had to chop a tunnel through the fog to the bunkhouse.

The fog went away at last and the job was finished on time. All the trees were split up to make toothpicks for the Swedish army. But the King of Sweden wasn't happy. He wrote another letter to Paul, complaining that the land was covered with stumps. "My farmers can't plow land like that," he wrote. Paul called in Johnny Inkslinger. "You are a thinking man," he said. "What are we going to do about these stumps?"

Johnny Inkslinger went away and thought for seven days and seven nights without stopping. "We'll flood the ground," he said. "You know how Babe the Blue Ox hates to get his feet wet? He will walk on the stumps, and his weight will push them into the ground."

So they flooded the land with fire hoses, and set Babe loose. He picked his way from stump to stump all over North Dakota. He was so heavy, each time he put a hoof on a stump he drove it six feet underground. And that's why you won't see trees or stumps in North Dakota today.

The King of Sweden said Paul had done a good job, and the Swedish farmers moved in right away and started plowing.

Paul Bunyan and the Whistling River

Some years ago Paul was logging on what was then known as the Whistling River. It got its name from the fact that every morning, right on the dot at 19 minutes after five, and every night at 10 minutes past six, it reared up to a height of 273 feet and let loose a whistle that could be heard for a distance of 603 miles in any direction.

Of course, if one man listening by himself could hear that far, it seems reasonable to suppose that two men listening together could hear it twice as far. Up in Alaska, most every camp had three or four whistle listeners.

However, the river was famous for more than its whistling. It was known as the orneriest river that ever ran between two banks. It seemed to take a fiendish delight in tying whole rafts of good saw logs into more plain and fancy knots than the oldest sailor ever knew. Even so, it is unlikely that Paul would have bothered with it if it had left his beard alone.

Paul was sitting on a low hill one afternoon, combing his great curly beard with a pine tree, while he planned his winter operations. All of a sudden, and without a word of warning, the river hoist itself up on its hind legs and squirted about 4,519 gallons of river water straight in the center of Paul's whiskers.

Naturally, Paul was considerably startled, but he said nothing, figuring that if he paid it no mind, it would go away and leave him be. But no sooner did he get settled back with his thinking and combing, than the durn river squirted some more. This time, along with the water, it threw in for good measure a batch of mud turtles, 13 large carp, a couple of drowned muskrats, and half a raft of last year's saw logs. This made Paul pretty mad, and he jumped up with a yell that caused a landslide near Pike's Peak. He stomped around waving his arms, and swore he would tame that river or break his back trying.

He went over to another hill and sat down to think out a way to tame a river, forgetting his winter operations entirely. He sat there for three days and 47 hours without moving, thinking at top speed all the while, and finally came to the conclusion that the best thing to do was to take out the kinks. But he knew that taking the kinks out of a river as tricky as this one was apt to be quite a chore. Of course, he could dig a new channel and run the river through that, but that was never Paul's way. He liked to figure out new ways of doing things, even if they were harder.

Meanwhile, he had gotten a mite hungry, so he hollered down to camp for Sourdough Sam to bring him up a little popcorn, of which he was very fond. Sam hitched up a four-horse team while his helpers were popping the corn, and soon he arrived at Paul's feet with a wagon load.

Paul ate popcorn and thought. The faster he thought, the faster he ate, and the faster he ate the faster he thought, until finally his hands were moving so fast that nothing showed but a blur, and they made a wind that uprooted trees all around him. In practically no time at all, the ground three miles and a quarter around was covered to a depth of 18 inches with popcorn scraps, and several thousand small birds and animals, seeing the ground all white and the air filled with what looked like snowflakes, concluded that a blizzard was upon them and immediately froze to death, providing the men with pot pies for some days.

But to get back to Paul's problem. Just before the popcorn was all gone, he decided that the only practical solution was to hitch Babe, the Mighty Blue Ox, to the river and let him yank it straight.

But the problem was how to hitch Babe to the river, as it is a fact well known that an ordinary log-chain and skid hook will not hold water. So after a light lunch of three sides of barbecued beef, half a wagon load of potatoes, carrots and a few other odds and ends, Paul went down to the blacksmith's shop and got Ole, the Big Swede, to help him look through a big instruction book that told how to do most everything under the sun. But although Paul read the book through from front to back twice while Ole read it from back to front, and they both read it once from bottom to top, they found nary a word about how to hook on to a river. So Paul decided that the only practical thing to do was to invent a rigging of some kind himself.

He had to do something, as every time he heard the river whistle it made him so mad he was fit to be tied.

As he always thought best when he walked, Paul had the men survey a circle about 30 miles in diameter to walk around. This was so if he was quite a while thinking it out, he wouldn't be finding himself way down in Australia when he'd finished.

When everything was ready, he set his old fur cap on his head, clasped his hands behind him, and started walking and thinking. He thought and walked. The faster he walked, the faster he thought.

He made a complete circle every half-hour. By morning he had worn a path that was knee-deep even on him, and he had to call the men to herd the stock away and keep them from falling and getting crippled. Three days later he had thought it out, but he'd worn himself so deep that it took a day and a half to get a ladder built that would reach down that far. When he did get out, he didn't even wait for breakfast, but whistled for Babe and tore off across the hills to the north.

Paul and the Ox traveled plenty fast, covering 24 townships at a stride, and the wind from their passing raised a dust that didn't settle for some months. About noon, as they neared the North Pole, they began to see blizzard tracks, and in a short time were in the middle of their summer feeding grounds. Taking a sack from his shoulder, Paul dug out material for a box trap, which he set near a well-traveled blizzard trail, and baited with fresh icicles from the top of the North Pole. Then he went away to eat his lunch, but not before he'd carefully brushed out his tracks (a trick he later taught the Indians).

About two o'clock he went back to his blizzard trap and discovered that he had caught seven half-grown blizzards and one grizzled nor'wester, which was raising considerable fuss and bidding fair to trample the young ones before he could get them out. But he finally managed to get a pair of half-grown blizzards in his sack and turned the others loose.

About midnight he got back to camp, and hollered at Ole, the Big Swede: "Build me the biggest log chain that's ever been built, while I stake out these dadblasted blizzards."

He went down to the foot of the river and picketed one of the blizzards to a tree on the bank, then crossed and tied the other directly opposite. Right away the river began to freeze. In 10 minutes the slush ice reached nearly from bank to bank, and the blizzards were not yet really warmed to their work, either. Paul watched for a few minutes, and then went back to camp to warm up, feeling mighty well satisfied with the way things were working out.

In the morning the river had a tough time rearing up for what it maybe knew to be its last whistle, for its foot was frozen solid for more than 17 miles. The blizzards had really done their business.

By the time breakfast was over, the great chain was ready and Babe all harnessed. Paul wrapped one end of the chain around the foot of the river, and hitched Babe to the other. Warning the men to stand clear, he shouted at Babe to pull. But though the great Ox strained till his tongue hung out, pulling the chain into a solid bar some seven and a half miles long, and sank knee-deep into the solid rock, the river stubbornly refused to budge, hanging on to its kinks like a snake in a gopher hole.

Seeing this, Paul grabbed the chain and, letting loose a holler that blew the tarpaper off the shacks in the Nebraska foothills, he and the Ox together gave a mighty yank that jerked the river loose from end to end, and started hauling it out across the prairie so fast that it smoked.

After a time Paul came back and sighted along the river, which was now as straight as a gun barrel. But he didn't have long to admire his work, for he soon found he had another problem on his hands. A straight river is naturally much shorter than a crooked one, and now all the miles and miles of extra river that used to be in the kinks was running wild out on the prairie. That galled the farmers in those parts not a little, and Paul could already see clouds of dust, which the prairie folk were raising as they came at top speed to complain.

After three minutes of extra-deep thought, Paul sent a crew to camp to bring his big cross-cut saw and a lot of baling wire. He sawed the river into nine-mile lengths and the men rolled it up like linoleum and tied it with wire. He used these later when logging off the desert, rolling out as many lengths as he needed to float his logs.

But his troubles with the Whistling River were not all over. It seems that being straightened out that way took the whistle out of the river, and from that day on it refused to whistle so much as a bird call. And as Paul had gotten into the habit of depending on the whistle to wake up the men in the morning, things were a mite upset.

It's hard to say what might have happened if Squeaky Swanson hadn't showed up about that time. His speaking voice was a thin squeak, but when he hollered he could be heard clear out to Kansas on a still day. So every morning he stood outside the cookshack and hollered the blankets off every bunk in camp. Naturally the men didn't stay in bed long after the blankets were off them, what with the cold wind and all, so Squeaky was a great success.

Two mosquitoes once lighted on one of Paul's oxen, killed it, ate it, cleaned the bones, and sat on a log picking their teeth as Paul came along. He sent to Australia for two special bumble bees to kill those mosquitoes, but the bees and the mosquitoes got married and their children had stingers at both ends.

Things went from bad to worse, till Paul figured out a way to get rid of them. He brought a big boat-load of sorghum up from Louisiana, and while all the insects were eating on the sweet sorghum, he floated them back down to the Gulf of Mexico. They got so fat that it was easy to drown them all between New Orleans and Galveston.

One summer it rained and rained. It started on St. Patrick's Day and it went on raining till the Fourth of July. Paul was disgusted because it spoiled his celebrations on Independence Day. So he dived into Lake Superior and swam to where a solid pillar of water was coming down. He swam up it with powerful strokes and was gone about an hour. By the time he came back, the rain stopped. "I turned the damn thing off," he explained.

One time Paul gave a party for the Seven Axemen. He fixed a granite floor 200 feet deep for them to dance on. Still it tipped and tilted some as they danced. No women being present in the camp at the time, the Seven Axemen danced with each other. Paul danced with the one left over.

The Seven Axemen refused to take off their hob-nailed boots when they danced, and the sparks from the nails on their dancing feet lit up the place so that Paul didn't have to light the kerosene lamps. The commotion caused an earthquake, however, and the Big Onion River moved over three counties to the east.

That was the winter of the Blue Snow, which when it melted turned to ink. The Pacific froze over, and Paul had teams of oxen bringing genuine white snow from China.

As you know, the Black Hills of South Dakota were once a single mountain, which stood upside down. Except on the top of the mountain, where there was a forest 19 miles wide, the trees also grew upside down. Paul logged the trees on the top easily enough, but his men weren't so keen on logging the rest because they had to stand on their heads. Paul got into an argument with his foreman, Hels Helsen, and the two started throwing bits of the mountain at each other. Those pieces are the Black Hills of South Dakota.

Feeding his men was always a problem for Paul Bunyan. They were mighty fond of pea soup, and one time Paul got a lot of pea soup for them by accident. A team of oxen were pulling a load of peas across a frozen lake when the ice broke. The oxen were drowned, and made a good meaty base for the soup. Paul dammed the lake and threw in some salt. Then he set fire to the bush around the shore, and when the soup was cooked he opened the dam and sluiced the soup down river to the camp.

One day Paul was out hunting when he spied a fine buck standing on the edge of a bluff. He fired at it, then ran to catch it before it fell over the cliff. He ran a little too fast and as a result he received his own charge of buckshot in the back. The buck, however, had died of fright anyway.

There was never any liquor in the camp, because whenever one of the men went to town for applejack he drank it all on the way back. But one day the cook was paring potatoes and he heard a sizzling noise. The potatoes were fermenting where they lay. Sour-face Murphy was standing in the door at the time, and the cook reckoned it was his face as had soured the potatoes. When he drained them, he had a quart of Irish whiskey in the pan. The cook told Paul about this, and Paul gave Sour-face Murphy a job as camp distillery.

Febold Feboldson

Febold Feboldson is the hero of the Scandinavian settlers of the prairies. Stories about him first appeared in print 60 or 70 years ago and, like Paul Bunyan, a good many of them were probably made up by clever writers. Febold Feboldson, however, was a character in stories told in Nebraska at an earlier time, and there may be a distant historical origin for him in one of the leaders of the Swedish pioneers, Olof Bergstrom, founder of Gothenburg, Nebraska. Febold appears to be a close relation of Paul Bunyan, but he is not a logger because, of course, there are no trees on the Great Plains!

Febold Feboldson was the first white settler west of the Mississippi, except for some Spaniards and Frenchmen. Of course, he emigrated to California in the end, thus setting an example which all good middle-westerners have followed ever since.

Febold Feboldson was often bothered by the weather. Have you ever thought that the trouble with American weather is it comes from foreign countries? Sure. Florida and California have Mediterranean sunshine. The winter restorts in the Adirondacks are imitations of those in Switzerland. The famous blizzard of 1888 came from Siberia— and you know who runs things in Siberia, don't you? There is only one place where you get real American weather, and that is the Great Plains between the Mississippi River and the Rockies.

Once, the weather was even more American than it is now. They had some mighty big weather in the old days. Like in the year 1848, the year when the Petrified Snow covered the plains all summer long. It held up the '48ers, who were going to the Gold Rush in California, and that was how they became '49ers.

Febold Feboldson was running an ox train that year between Kansas City and San Francisco. Well, there wasn't anything else to do, what with the snow all over the plains. Febold was the only one to make the trip, and he found an answer to the problem of the Petrified Snow.

Coming through Death Valley, California, Febold loaded up with sand from the desert. Now the desert sand never grows cold, and neither did Febold and his oxen. He sold it to the gold rushers at $1 a bushel, and they were gratified to have it.

Pretty soon the prairie schooners were on their way west again, over the snow-covered prairies. The jolting of the wagons scattered the sand, which covered all the snow. And that's why the prairies stayed so darn hot ever afterward.

Yes, sir, Febold often regretted selling that sand to the '49ers.

But Febold was a find drought-buster. There was never a drought came out of Kansas that he couldn't bust in 24 hours. One year, though, it took a little longer.

Febold wanted to go fishing, but every day the weather go hotter and drier. He decided something must be done. At that time there were many lakes in the north of the country, even more than there are now. The settlers took to soaking themselves in the lakes every day, just to keep from drying up and blowing away. Febold made fires all around the lakes and kept them burning for three weeks. By that time the lakes got so hot that the water vaporized and made clouds. The clouds banged into each other trying to get away from the lakes, and it started to rain.

This didn't make Febold popular with everyone. The Indians complained they had no place to swim.

Febold also noticed it often started raining after some big noise, like a battle or a political meeting. The problem was: How to make a big enough noise? The Indians were still sulking and they wouldn't help. The white settlers were so dry they couldn't even speak. Then Febold thought of the frogs. Now, frogs make a good loud noise when they get to croaking, but the trouble was, they have to be good and wet before they croak.

So Febold hypnotized a couple of frogs and told them it was raining. They began to croak, saying how lovely and wet they were.

The news spread fast, and sooner than you could spit, every frog in the country was croaking loud enough to give the Indian's rain god a headache. The rain fair poured down.

This method could only be used once a year. It rained so much all the frogs were carried away right down to the Gulf of Mexico, and it took them a year to get back up again.

In between the Year of the Big Rain and the Year of the Great Heat came the Year of the Striped Weather. That year it was both hot and rainy at once. For one mile you had scorching sunshine, for the next mile solid rain. On Febolds farm, the sun shone on his cornfield until the corn began to pop, and the rain fell on the sugar cane and washed all the syrup out of it.

The canefield was on a hill and the corn field was in a valley. So the syrup flowed downhill into the popped corn and rolled it into great balls.

Some of them were hundreds of feet high. (They have all gone now because the grasshoppers ate them.)

After the Year of the Great Heat came the Year of the Great Fog. That was the biggest piece of weather that ever hit the Great Plains. Toward the end of the Year of the Great Heat it began to rain, and it rained for 40 days and 40 nights without stopping. But not a drop of rain hit the ground.

Why? Because it turned into steam, of course. And when the steam cooled, it turned into a fog. The fog was so thick that people had to go around in pairs, one opening up the fog so the other could walk through. The ranchers didn't have to water their stock. The cattle just drank the fog. It looked funny to see pigs with their noses up in the air, rooting for fish and frogs. But, although the stockmen were happy, the farmers were not. Because the sun never shone, the seeds didn't know which way to grow, and most of 'em grew downward.

Febold sent for some fog cutters from England. But they didn't get here till Thanksgiving. By that time most of the fog had turned to slush, which Febold cut up in long strips and laid on the road, so it wouldn't mess up the fields. The trouble was the dust came along later and got all mixed up with the slush, and that is why country roads are so darned muddy.

In the Year of the Big Rains, the chickens were dying of starvation. It was so wet their feet just stuck into the mud. They could not get about to forage for grub. Febold solved that one all right. He made big flat webbed feet for the chickens, so they wouldn't sink in, and he flattened out their bills so they could probe around in the mud and the water. The chickens were mighty pleased with their new equipment, and took to living on the water full time. The Indians laughed at the way these birds kept tipping up to feed under the water, and they named them ducks.

Febold Feboldson was passing through a swamp one day and stopped to light his pipe. There was a terrific explosion. He got to thinking about the cause of it, and decided it was marsh gas escaping from the swamp. Well, Febold never liked to see energy going to waste, so he made a huge cover for the swamp out of old buffalo robes. With the help of his pet gopher, Lizzie, he dug tiny tunnels from the swamp to the tepees in the Indians' village. Those tepees were the first centrally-heated homes in America. A little gas was lost when some moles linked up to the gas lines without permission, but it wasn't much.

A suburb of the Indian village lay on the other side of the Dismal

River, so Febold froze a number of gopher holes and laid them across the frozen ice of the river.

Febold was a wonderful man of inventions. He had water pumped into a big tank on his farm by dogs working a kind of treadmill. He had noticed that dogs always turn around three times before they lay down to sleep, so he made them sleepy by telling them stories like this one, woke 'em up as soon as they lay down, told 'em another story till they got sleepy again, and so on.

Bowleg Bill

You can think of Bowleg Bill as a sort of cross between Pecos Bill and Old Stormalong. Yarns of the "sea-going cowboy" are supposed to have been told by the old sailors in east-coast ports who sat around gently drinking away their declining years and trying to out-do each other in the telling of tall stories.

Judging by the number of stories about Bowleg Bill, he must have spent quite some time at sea, but he never grew to like it or understand it, and most of the jokes come from the effect of putting a Wyoming cowboy on a ship where he still treats every incident as he would if he were home on the range. The sea always disgusted him, and he never learned not to spit into the wind.

But how did Bowleg Bill ever get to sea in the first place? In the old days of whaling, it was difficult to get a crew, because the job was so hard and dangerous. One way to do it was to find a likely looking man in a saloon, buy him a few drinks, and when he wasn't looking slip something into his drink that had the effect of putting him soundly to sleep for some hours. By the time he awoke he was on the ship and out at sea.

That was what happened to Bill. He woke up one morning on the deck of the *Sawdust Sal*, with deep water all around him. Rising to his full height of 8'4" (without his high-heeled boots) he looked out on each side and said, "Durned if I ain't flooded the range in my sleep."

When the mate saw that Bowleg Bill was up and about, he came across to him, carrying a marlin spike and expecting trouble. Bill greeted him courteously and asked him if he'd seen a chestnut gelding tethered nearby. The mate told him to get aloft and take in the staysails. Bill didn't know what he was talking about but he didn't like the tone of his voice.

In any case, he was more concerned about his horse. The mate advanced on him hefting the marlin spike, and Bill reached for his gun. But it wasn't there, having been prudently removed when he was brought on board. So he grabbed hold of the marlin spike and twisted it in a knot. "Don't you know a thing like that is dangerous?" he said, and he threw it overboard. The mate yelled for help and a great scrimmage began, with Bill's fists prevailing over the saliors' and what he called their damned tent pegs.

Finally the Captain appeared, carrying a pistol. "Are you the foreman here?" Bill asked him. The Captain only said, "Clap him in irons!" but no one was anxious to carry out the order. Instead, he found himself looking down the barrel of a big six-shooter—for Bill kept another gun hidden in his high-heeled boot.

"Put that little parlor-piece away, boss," said Bill. "Why, you might put somebody's eye out with that."

The Captain was a little slow to take Bill's advice, and *Bang*! One half of his mustache was clipped clean off. *Bang*! There went the other half.

After that, the Captain agreed that the best thing was to do what Bill said, which was to "wheel this thing around for home." So Bowleg's first experience of sea going was a short one. It's a little surprising that he ever went to sea again, but he did.

One day Yank Dagget, skipper of the *Tossup*, and his crew were getting ready for the annual catch of horse-mackerel, which is what the Cape Cod fishermen call tuna. Every summer, the tuna would pass through and get caught in the nets in the harbor which were set for smaller fish. Then the fishermen would go out with harpoons and gaffs and, with any luck, make a valuable catch.

Bowleg Bill appeared on the waterfront. The people there had heard tales of him, but he'd never been seen before. He listened to the talk for a while, then he went up to Yank. "This here hoss-mackerel," he said, "he's a sassy varmint, is he?"

Yank nodded. "There's a big run of 'em this season, and each one is a long streak of hell."

"Work for a corn-fed man, is it?" said Bill, "riding herd on 'em?"

"Well, you got to know how to gaff 'em. Horse-mackereling is no business for a greenhand."

"What do you reckon the critturs will weigh on the hoof?"

"Most of 'em come a hundred to eight-nine hundred pounds."

"Now ain't that a shame", said Bill. "Not enough to kick dust in your eye. I was figgering I might admire to rope in a few, but where I come from, we don't bother with a rope on nothing under a couple of ton."

"You just throw back the small fry, do you?" Yank grinned.

"Well, them little fellers we pick up bare-handed by the slack of the belly and toss 'em into the pens."

Yank nodded. "With a horse-mackerel," he said, "you got to look out for the tail. A horse-mackerel's tail ain't like no slack hawser hanging astern. You got to make certain sure you don't get slapped over the side with his tail."

"Huh!" said Bowleg Bill. "I have yet to meet up with a crittur—two-legged or four-legged—which I couldn't take care of in that section. Where's your foreman? I see I'll have to show you fellers how to haze your herd the way it's done back in Wyoming."

"I'm skipper here," said Yank, "and I ain't taking on no greenhand while there's a run of horse-mackerel."

"Mister," said Bowleg, "if you're a betting man, I'll hit the trail with you to them corrals out yonder. And if I don't cut out one of your full-growed hoss-mackerel and bring him in bare-handed, without using none of them pointed sticks, I'll pay you twenty dollars."

Well, like any other man, Yank couldn't resist a bet he knew he would win, so he agreed. The news spread fast, and soon the whole town was talking about the crazy foreigner who was going after horse-mackerel bare-handed.

Next morning the whole harbor was cluttered up with boats. Anything that would float was there and there was hardly a single citizen left on land. The town had taken Bowleg Bill's bet as an insult, and Bowleg was hooted as he went out.

Even poor old Captain Dyer, shorebound for 20 years, was out in an ancient rowboat. "Better go back, young feller," he shouted. "You don't know what's waiting for you in that net."

"Don't you fret over me, grandpa," said Bowleg. "That's a mighty shaky caboose you're driving there. You make for cover pronto if I start a stampede!"

At the first trap the *Tossup* reached, there was great thrashing and white water, as if a hurricane were trying to get out of the net. Right in the middle of it was the biggest horse-mackerel Yank Daggett had ever seen. And the minute Yank saw him, he forgot all about Bowleg Bill and his bet, he forgot about everything expect the silver-blue tuna and his six feet of slapping, thrashing tail. The boys began to haul in the net while Yank got ready with his gaff.

Bowleg Bill climbed over, alongside Yank. "That one over yonder," he said, "will he weigh up to our bet?"

"What? He's two-thousand pounds if he's a Scotch ounce, you lubber!"

"All right, boys," Bowleg shouted, "give me a clear field!" He pushed Yank and a couple of others out of the way and yelled to the Horse-mackerel, "Come along, little dogie!"

"Hey! Get aft, you blasted pig-farmer!" Yank hollered. "That fish is big money, and I ain't leaving it to no damned greenhand to lose him!"

"Now, just keep your britches dry, boss," said Bowleg," and lift that doggone spear out of my road. I've picked my animal and I'm a-going after him for all creation and a barbed-wire fence! *Hy-up*! Come along, little dogie, come along!"

He reached out and got hold of the fish in the narrow part near the tail, and he heaved. How in eternity he figured to swing aboard 2,000 pounds of game fish that way, only an inland foreigner might know! The tail slipped out of his hands, and the horse-mackerel slipped clear of the net.

"Look out!" Yank hollered, "He's clear away!"

"No, he ain't," Bowleg answered. Over the side he went, boots and all, and before the fish had got under way he was sitting astride it, whipping it astern with his hat, and hollering:

"*Whoooop-eee*! *Hyee-up*! Show some buck now, you white-livered coyote, or I'll sell you to a livery stable! Come on, now, *hy-up*!"

And away went that silver devil, kicking up the spray like a dust storm. He jumped clean out of the water like a porpoise, but when he came down again, Bill was still astride and still fanning away behind with his wide-brimmed hat.

Yank groaned. "There goes the biggest catch—and the damnedest fool—that was ever set loose in these waters!"

But one or two began to cheer: "Ride him, cowboy!" And other folk took it up, till all over the harbor they were cheering for Bowleg Bill.

And the Loudest yells came from Bill himself, who was whooping like an Indian with the hooping cough. "*Yippee*! Come on, you two-dollar fly-roost—ain't you going to throw no sand in their eyes?"

Somehow that cowboy had a hold on the dorsal fin, and no matter how the horse-mackerel jumped, he couldn't shake Bill loose. They went scudding across the harbor in a wide circle, with the big horse-mackerel getting madder every minute. He dove to starboard, he dove to larboard, he all but somersaulted right over. But Bowledg hung on with his knees pressed tight against its sides, riding as easy as grandma in her Sunday rocker. Then the tuna made one last big leap, up in the air and clean over the *Tossup*.

"Buck away, you overgrowed sardine!" yelled Bowleg. "I'll tame you if it takes to Kansas City."

But after that last jump, it was plain the big fish was losing wind. He stopped pitching, and jogged along easy among the harbor craft. Bowleg sat there, his top half out of the water, and he started stroking the fish behind the gills and talking to him, and little by little teaching him to go where Bill wanted him. He hauled one way on the fin, and the fish turned that way; he hauled the other way, and the fish turned again. And when he had ridden all the wildness out of him, Bowleg headed in for the beach.

They came in slow, till the horse-mackerel was almost touching bottom. The whole town was ready to send up a cheer for the landing of the biggest fish in its history, when that big beef farmer did something that no one in a fishing town would ever understand.

Instead of riding the fish right into the beach, he turned him around and jumped off. The fish slowly started to make for the open sea, and Bowleg chivvied him on, smacking the water with his hat and yelling.

By that time there was a crowd on the beach, and they were as mad as a school of bees in a tar barrel. Bowleg Bill had some explaining to do.

He shook his head at them, and there was a sad look in his eye as he said to them, "That poor old wind-broke waterbug! I tell you, folks, there ain't nothing that'll break a cowhand's heart so quick as to find a crittur with the rough all rode out of him at first mount."

Tony Beaver

In West Virginia you could hear the same sort of tales about a mighty lumberjack as were told of Paul Bunyan, but there he had the name of Tony Beaver.

Tony Beaver had a horse that was very quick, but it wasn't so much its speed that was unusual but because of the way it was saddled. Tony had a boy in his camp who looked after the horse and wasn't too bright in the head. He brought the horse around for Tony one day with the saddle facing the wrong way. "I saddled him that way," he explained, "so you can ride him both going and coming."

"Well," said Tony, "there's no sense to that, so I believe it's true." He jumped on the horse and did just like the boy said—he rode both going and coming. It was a swift way of traveling, and about the only way a man could be in two places at once.

Another time Tony Beaver jumped over a white oak tree, only he jumped a mite too high and landed on top of a cloud. The cloud got such a fright it raced away off up into the sky, and things looked bad for Tony. As it was, the cloud was getting thinner and Tony was sinking through it. Sometimes you could see his boots sticking out the bottom. It seemed that he was bound to fall and be bust into fractions.

But Tony started stomping around in the cloud until he made it so mad it turned black and fired up in a terrible thunderstorm. Tony waited for a good big streak of lightning, and slid safely down to the ground. (Some say he learned that trick from Pecos Bill.)

One year Tony Beaver raised some watermelons. They were so big he had to build a cart that covered more than an acre to take 'em to market. One of the watermelons fell in the Eel River and broke up. Tony's men used the seeds as canoes.

Little Audrey

Young sisters and brothers can be embarrassing sometimes. If you meet a man with a big red nose, you don't say anything about it, do you? Maybe you talk about the weather, or who will win the Superbowl, or the rising price of milk shakes. Then along comes little sister, points her four-year-old finger at the man and says, "Why have you got a big red nose?"

The Little Audrey (who laughed and laughed) stories are about a little girl something like that, only worse. (It doesn't have to be Little Audrey; it can be Little Frannie or Little Caroline or whoever.) They seem to have been told mainly in high schools and colleges. They are nonsense stories, although they have something of the cold, hard, embarrassing logic that small children often show. Many of them are, in a way, savage or cruel, but again it is the unthinking cruelty of small children.

The following stories were collected on campuses in the south-west and published by the Texas Folk-Lore Society over 50 years ago. But you may know some more recent Little Audrey stories, for she is still around, under one name or another.

Once upon a time, Little Audrey got lost on a desert island. Along came some cannibals and captured her. They tied her up to a tree and put a big pot on to boil. They were going to make a stew out of her. Little Audrey looked around at those lean, hungry cannibals and counted them. There were 19. Little Audrey laughed and laughed, because she knew she was not nearly big enough to make a stew for 19 people.

One day while her mama was in town, Little Audrey decided to bake a cake. She got down the recipe book and mixed the cake as it said. She sifted flour, she creamed butter, she mixed in sugar, she beat eggs, and she stirred them all together. Then she was ready to cook the cake. She looked in the recipe book again, and it said: "Now set in the oven for forty minutes." So Little Audrey crawled into the oven and closed the door. When her mama came home, she looked everywhere for Little Audrey, but she couldn't find her. Then she smelled something burning. She opened the door and there was Little Audrey, burned to a crisp. Her mother laughed and laughed, because she didn't know Little Audrey could read.

Witches and Other Devilry

You probably remember about the witches of Salem, in colonial times. Back then in the Seventeenth Century, most people believed in witches. Two centuries later, many still did, and even now, in the space age, some people do. Maybe witches exist if you think they do. As the old rhyme says:

> Where folk believe in witches, witches are,
> And when they don't believe, not one is thar.

Witches are sometimes frightening, sometimes gruesome, sometimes just plain irritating, and sometimes funny. And of course sometimes they just ain't thar, like the witch in our first story *The Cave of Gold*, a tale from the Ozarks.

The Cave of Gold

"I ain't superstitious, neither," said Uncle Bill mildly, "but a lot of things what some folks *call* superstitions is just as true as God's own gospel. And as for witches, it ain't no manner of use to tell me there ain't none, because I know better. Why, I've been rode by 'em myself, many the time!

"I was just dozing off in the old cabin, when in come the purtiest girl I ever seen, with a brand new bridle in her hand. She fetched a whoop and jumped plumb astraddle of my back, and the first thing I knowed she had that there bridle on to me, with the big cold bit a-cutting into my gums. And the next thing I knowed she tured me into a flea-bit gray pony, and we was a-tearing down the road with the spurs a-socking into my hams at every jump.

"Up hills and down hollows and across branches and through berry patches we went, till we met up with some foreigners a-packing big sacks full of money—bank robbers, I reckon they was or something. The witch-woman, she lit down and help them fellers, and danged if they didn't pile all them big pokes on my back. Purty soon we come to a big cave under a cliff, and she tied me up to a white oak sapling whilst they took the money inside for to hide it, I reckon. After a while the foreigners come out, a-talking and a-laughing amongst theirselves, and purty soon she come out too, and rid me back home again.

"Well, the next night she come and rid me some more, and we met up with the same fellers, and they drug in another terrible big load of money.

"And the next night the same, and more of it, and the next night too—it seemed like there weren't no end to the money we toted into that there cave hole. Every morning I'd wake up plumb tuckered out and briar-scratched, and my mouth a-tasting like a cat had done littered in it.

"I never said nothing to the old woman about this here witch-riding and all, but I sure done a heap of studying over it. I spent a lot of time a-looking for that there cave too, but I couldn't make out to find it no ways, so one morning I hobbled off down to old Pap Jennin's shanty and told him the whle story. Pap, he was a witch-master, and I knowed he'd tell me what I better do.

"The old man, he just pondered a while, a-shaking of his head, and then he says, 'Well, Bill, I reckon you-all better mark that there cave so we can find it easy. When you get it marked, I'll just lay for this here witch-woman and kill her with a silver bullet. Then we'll get the gold money, of course.'

"The next night, when she hitched me outside the cave, I just dropped as many droppings as I could, and started to chew me a good big blaze on the white oak sapling, like Pap told me. I chewed and chewed...

"All of a sudden come a hell of a noise and a big flash of light, and then I heard a lot of hollering. My old woman was doing the hollering. I seen I was home again, and it seemed like I'd went and benastied the bed-blankets bad, and dang near chewed the old woman's leg off!"

The Witch and the Spinning Wheel

Besides needing a silver bullet to kill them, another old belief about witches was that they shed their skin after midnight, when they perform dark, mysterious acts. There is a story about that from Louisiana.

One time a man rid up at night to a cabin on the edge of the swamp. He was that hungry and tired that he say to hisself, "If I can get a hunk of corn-pone and a slice of baking, I don't care what I pays." At that moment a yellow woman comes out of the cabin. She was spry on her feet as a catbird, and her eyes was soft and shiny. She ask the man for to alight and come in and get some supper. And Lord! How his mouth do water when he catch a glimpse of the skillet on the coals! He like it so well that he stay until he get so fat the grease run out of his jaws when he look at the sun. The yellow woman, she spends her time cooking for him, waiting on him, and at last the man marries the yellow woman.

At first they get along tolerable well, but he begin to notice that there's something curious about that yellow woman. She ain't never in the cabin when he wake up in the night! So he make up his mind to spy on her. He lay down one night and pretends like he's asleep. The yellow woman watches him out of the corner of her eye, till she hear him snore. Then she reach down a big gridiron from the wall, and rake out some coals, and haul the big spinning wheel close to the hearth. Then she set herself down on that gridiron, and soon as it was red-hot, she begin to spin her skin off her body on the spinning wheel... "Turn and spin, come off skin." And the skin come off that witch-woman's body, beginning at the top of her head. And when it was off, then she was a great big yellow cat. Then, she take the skin and chuck it on the bed. "Lay there, skin," she say, "with that fool asleep in the bed, until I come back. I is going to have some fun, I is!"

With that she jump out of the window and lope off. Soon as she is gone, the man, he jump out of the bed and take the skin and fill it plumb full of salt and pepper. Then he throw it back on to the bed. Then he creep out and watch through the keyhole until the witch-woman come home. She laugh while she is picking up the skin and shaking herself back into it, but when she feels the salt and pepper, she laugh on the other side of her mouth. She moan and groan so you can hear her a mile! But she ain't able to get out of that skin, and the man watch through the keyhole till she fall down and die on the floor.

The Bell Witch

The legend of the Bell Witch comes in different shapes and sizes. This version was written down from accounts by several different people, and probably that is why it changes in mood now and then, with some parts grim and gruesome, and some parts humorous. (The joke about the man under the Stetson hat is a *very* old one.)

Back in the days before the Civil War there lived somewhere in North Carolina a man named John Bell. He was a planter and was well-fixed. He had a good-sized plantation, a dozen black field hands, and mules and cows and hogs a-plenty. His family was made up of his wife, a daughter called Mary, about 14 years old (who, they say, was mighty pretty), and two or three young 'uns who don't figure much in the story. John Bell got along fine—until he hired him an overseer.

The overseer was a quarrelsome sort of fellow, always at sixes and sevens with other folks, especially with the Blacks, although he didn't mind jawing his boss neither. John Bell was of half a mind to fire the scoundrel and hire another one. But Mrs. Bell stood up for him. He stayed on a good while, and the longer he stayed the more uppity he got. He was the worst kind of bully, a man of high temper, and the rows between him and Bell got bigger and bigger.

Mr. Bell had a tall temper too, and the men did not spend a lot of time patting each other on the back and bragging about each other's good points. A stand-up fight was bound to come off.

It did. Some say it was about the way the overseer had beat up one of the Blacks. Some say it was about something Mr. Bell heard and saw from behind a cotton-house one day when Mary rode through the field where the overseer was working. Bell went away blowing smoke from his pistol barrel, and mumbling something about white trash. The overseer didn't go away at all.

Of course Bell was brought into court, but he pleaded self-defense, and the jury let him off. He went home, hired him another overseer, and allowed that everything was settled. But the truth was that everything was now plumb unsettled.

That year and the next and the next, the crops on the Bell place were an out-and-out failure. His mules died of colic or some strange disease like it. His cows and hogs got sick of something the horse-doctor couldn't cure. He had to sell his slaves one by one, all except an old woman. Finally he went broke. He got what he could for his land, and moved with his family to Tennessee. They say that where he settled down, the town of Bell, Tennessee, was named for him. Anyway, he bought him a house and a patch of land near the home of old Andy Jackson, who had knocked off from being President and was living in a big house nearby.

Not long after the move to Tennessee, strange things began to happen in the Bell home. The children gtt into the habit of tumbling, or being tumbled, out of bed at least once a week, and of waking up every morning with every stitch of the bed-clothes snatched off and their hair all tangled and mussed up. Now for young-uns to tumble out of bed and to wake up in the morning with their heads uncombed is a mighty strange thing, and the Bells realized it. The children couldn't explain this carrying-on, for they were always asleep till they hit the floor; and it was a peculiar fact that they were never tumbled out while awake.

The old black woman told them it was the ghost of the overseer Mr. Bell had killed that was pestering the children. She had spunk, and one day she allowed she would find out whether she was right by spending the night under the young-uns' bed. In the middle of the night Mr. and Mrs. Bell were fetched out of their bed by a squeal like a panther's. When they lit a lamp and ran into the room, they found the old woman sprawled in the middle of the floor, dripping cold sweat, her face gray-blue as sugar-cane peeling, and her eyes like saucers. She was stiff-jointed and tongue-tied. when they got her sitting up and her tongue loosened, she screeched: "Hits him! Hit's him! He pinched me all over, stuck pins in me, whupped me! I ain't going back there no more!"

It seems like the witch could get hungry like folks, and was satisfied with folks' grub. But it had to be the best. One day the old black woman came tearing into the front room where Mrs. Bell was quilting and said the witch was back in the kitchen drinking up all the sweet milk.

Mrs. Bell was scared and said the old woman was lying.

"Come see for yourself, missus! Come see for yourself! I was back there mixin biscuit and I reached over to get a cup o' milk an the cup was in the air, an the milk was runnin out of it, an it weren't going nowhere! Just runnin out of the cup, an then I couldn't see it no more."

"You're just seeing things," said Mrs. Bell.

"Just what I ain't—I ain't seeing the milk! Go back there in the kitchen if you don't believe it. Go on back and look for yourself. No, ma'am, that ghost can guzzle all the milk the cows ever give before I raise my finger to stop it."

Mrs. Bell went back into the kitchen and looked. There was a cup there that had had milk in it, and the milk was gone, sure as shootin.

She was now as scared as the old woman, and sent right away for her husband to come out of the field.

They couldn't figure out how a ghost could drink milk, or what becomes of the milk if he does. Does the milk dry up into the ghost of itself? If not, where does it go when the ghost swallows it? Ghosts can't be seen. At least, this one couldn't. They could see through where it was. If they could see through it, why couldn't they see the milk as plain when it was inside the ghost as when it was outside? The old woman, said the milk was running out of the cup, but it "weren't going nowhere." An old Holy Roller preacher from down in Tallahatchie Bottom who rode over to talk about it argued that if the old woman's tale was so, milk must be of a higher class than folks. When it turns into the soul of itself, it leaves nothing behind; but folks leave behind a corpse that must be covered up with dirt right away. Folks argued about it on front galleries in the summer time and around the fire in winter—but they didn't argue about it on the Bells' front gallery or by the Bells' fire.

But the witch didn't let up on the Bells' grub. No one ever saw it, but lots of times some member of the family would see something to eat dive out of the cupboard or pop out of the safe. The witch's favorite was cream, and he got to skimming it from every pan in the spring-house. The Bells were never able to get any butter from the churning.

Mr. Bell might have stood for having his young-uns' rest disturbed and his old black woman all tore up this way, but he couldn't stand for letting the ghost eat him out of house and home. So he called the family together and allowed he would move again—this time to Mississippi, where land was rich and cheap.

Mrs. Bell raised up. "Pa," said she, "it seems like to me we have been getting along tolerable well here. I don't see any use moving away. What would keep the witch from following us down there?"

"Nothing in the world," spoke up a hide-bottomed chair from a corner of the room. "I'll follow you wherever you go," the chair went on, "And I'll tell you what: If you stay on here, I won't bother you much; but if you go traipsing off to Mississippi—well, you'll wish you hadn't."

Mr. Bell was scared and bothered, but he screwed up his courage enough to ask the witch why he couldn't live where he pleased. But there was no answer. He asked some more questions. But the chair had lapsed into the habit of silence that chairs have.

Mary, Mr. Bells' daughter, was now old enough to argue with the old folks about things. She was pretty as a spotted puppy, they say, and had lots of spunk and took after her Pa. She sided with him. Girls always like to be moving. So when the family got over its scare about the chair they argued back and forth. But finally Mrs. Bell and what they remembered about the witch got the upper hand. Mr. Bell and Mary gave up the idea of moving to Mississippi—for a while anyway.

And for a while the witch eased up on them. It even did some good turns. One day Mr. Bell was talking of visiting a family across the creek where he had heard everybody was sick. "I have just come from there" said a voice from the eight-day clock, and went on to tell how well everybody was and what everybody was doing. Later Mr. Bell met up with a member of the family and learned that everything the witch said was so.

Maybe because she had taken side with the witch in the argument about going to Mississippi, the witch was partial to Mrs. Bell.

One Christmas, the family was invited to a party. Mrs. Bell was sick and couldn't go but she told them to go ahead, she didn't need them and could make out all right.

Before they got far one of the wagon wheels flew off and let the axle down into the road with a bump. It looked like a common accident, and the old man climbed down and put the wheel back on the axle and stuck the linchpin in. He looked at all the other linchpins and saw they were on all right. Before long another wheel flew off. They looked on the ground for the linchpin but couldn't find it there. Mr. Bell whittled a new one, and when he went to put the wheel back on he found the old one in place. He fixed the wheel and drove off again, telling all of the children to watch all of the wheels. Soon they saw something like a streak of moonshine dart around the wagon, and all four wheels flew off, and the wagon dropped kersplash into a mud-hole. They put them back on, turned round, and drove back home, going quiet and easy, like sitting on eggs.

When they got there, they found their mammy sitting up by the Christmas tree eating a plate of fresh strawberries, and feeling lots better.

Other pranks were laid to the witch. Often when the old man and the boys would go to the stable to catch the horses and mules for the day's plowing or a trip to town, the critters would back their ears and rear and kick and stomp like hornets or yellow-jackets were after them. Some mornings they would be puny as chickens with the pip, and caked with sweat and mud, and their manes and tails tangled in witch-locks. The neighbors said that off and on they met an unbridled and bare-backed horse, and the horse would stop, and something on his back that they couldn't see would talk to them—but not long—they had business the other way.

Mary was now mighty near grown. She had turned out to be a

beautiful woman. She had lots of beaux. But whenever one of them screwed himself up to the point of popping the question he always found that the words stuck in his throat and his face and ears burned. For young fellows these were strange signs. But it was always that way. And none of them seemed to be able to ask Mary the question. They blamed it on the witch, and finally quit hitching their horses to the Bell fence.

All but one. His name was Gardner. He was a catch for any girl smart as a briar, good-looking, easy-going and open-hearted, and the owner of a home as big as the court-house, with columns as tall and white. He got all wrapped up in Mary and Mary was leaning to him.

The way of the witch with him was different, more businesslike. Maybe it was because the witch realized this was the man Mary was setting her heart on. One night when Gardner was walking up the row of cedars in the Bell yard to see Mary, something he couldn't see reached out from a big cedar and touched him on the shoulder, and a voice said, "Wait a minute." Gardner was afraid to wait, but he was more afraid to run. So he waited.

"You might as well understand, here and now, that you are not going to have Mary Bell."

"Why not?" Gardner asked.

"You might have guessed from all that's happened around here. I'm in love with her myself. It's going to be hard to get her consent, and it may be harder to get the old man's. But she's not going to marry you, I'll see to that. If you open your mouth about it tonight, you'll be dead as a doornail before morning."

Gardner studied a while and said, "If you'd only come out like a man."

The cedar tree stepped out and snatched his hat off and stomped it.

"Well, I reckon I'll have to lay off for a while," says Gardner. "But I do love her, and I'd go to the end of the world for her."

"Well, you don't have to go that far, and it wouldn't do you no good if you did, and if you love her the only way you can keep her out of hell is to get out yourself. If you keep on hanging around here, I'll make it hell for you. Now this is how far you go. Pack up your traps and get out of the country, hide and hair. Go any place you think the Bells won't hear tell of you—and go before breakfast. If you slip out quiet without raising any rookus, I'll never pester you again. What's more, on the day you get married I'll give you a pair of new boots you'll be proud of all your life."

Gardner couldn't see why the witch's promise of a pair of wedding boots was in the same class as the threat of death before breakfast. But he didn't split hairs, and he didn't argue any more. He picked up his hat, sneaked back to his horse, and rode off.

He left the neighborhood before sunup and moved to the western part of the state. After he had been there a while he fell in love with a girl and got engaged to her. When he was dressing for the wedding he couldn't find his boots. He looked high and low, but no boots could he find. He was about to give up and go to his wedding in his sock feet, when a voice told him to look in the bed. And there between the sheets he found a pair of shiny new boots. He put them on and went his way rejoicing and thinking of how well a ghost kept his word, and wondering if the boots would ever wear out and if they were like the Seven-League boots he had read about.

But they looked like natural boots. He told some of his friends how he had got them. They thought he was a liar. But they had to own up they were wrong. One day Gardner's house-boy made a mistake and carried them instead of another pair to a cobbler. The cobbler said they were in perfect shape, that they were not made by mortal hands, and that the soles were sewed on in a way that no man or man-made machine could have stitched them.

Meanwhile, Mr. Bell decided again to move to Mississippi. It looked like his move from North Carolina was jumping from the frying pan into the fire, but he figured maybe the skillet wouldn't be any hotter. Gardner's break-up with Mary and Mary not marrying hung heavy on his mind. Mrs. Bell raised up again, telling him about rolling stones. And the witch horned in. By this time the family had got used to the witch and would talk free with him, but respectful. Every time the question came up there was a row between Mr. Bell and Mary on one side and Mrs. Bell and the witch on the other. The old black woman told Mr. Bell the haunt didn't want him to move because he was afraid of witch hunters in Mississippi. She said there were powerful ones down there.

And so one winter after the crops had petered out on him again, he sold his place dirt cheap. The old woman told him to wait till spring to start. Good Friday would be a good day to leave, she said, for the haunt would have to go back to his grave and stay three days under the ground and would be puny-like several days more. While he was in good working order he could be in two or three places at once and be in any of them in the bat of an eye, but then he would have to lie low, and that would give them plenty of start. So Mr. Bell, early on Good Friday, stacked his furniture and duds in a couple of wagons, climbed into the front one with Mary, put the old woman and his biggest boy into the hind one, and told Mrs. Bell, "Get in if you're a-comin, and don't forget the young-uns."

And that was the way the Bell family came to Mississippi. Mr. Bell bought him a little place in Panola County, 10 miles east of Batesville on the Oxford road. He was all ready to begin life over again without supernatural interference.

But the witch made a quick comeback, not before the family got there, but before they moved into their new home.

When Mr. Bell first got to Batesville, he left the family there and went out to look at the land he aimed to buy. When he got a place that suited him, he went back to town for his family and stuff. There was some sort of hitch, and the wagons did not get started till late in the evening. As the wagons moved slowly out of town, dark clouds began to roll up in the south and west, and before they had gone three miles the storm broke. Dark came on earlier than usual, for the clouds hid the sun. The rain beat down on the wagon covers. Every now and then the lightning flashes lit up the swaying trees on each side of the road, the draggle-tailed horses, and the road itself—a long, muddy creek—and then it was dark as a stack of black cats. The folks all stopped talking. There was nothing to listen to but the beating rain and the thunder and the suck of the horses' feet and the wheels in the mud.

All at once the hind wagon, with the family in it, slid to the side of the road and sunk into the mud up to the bed. Mr. Bell saw it in a lightning flash and came back. It couldn't be moved; the horses had not foothold, and the wheels were in too deep. The fix they were in wasn't dangerous, but it was mighty uncomfortable.

And then the witch took a hand.

"If you'll go back to your wagon and stop your cussin'," said the empty dark beside the wagon, "I'll get you out. Hump it back to your wagon now."

Mr. Bell waded back and crawled in.

And then the horses and the wagon and the furniture and the family and the dog under the wagon and the calf tied behind and everything else but the mud on the wheels rose up about eight feet high and floated down the road till they were just behind the front wagon, and then they settled down easy and went on home without any trouble.

The family got settled down in their two-story double-loghouse amongest the cedars on the Oxford road.

A few nights later, the witch spoke up from one of the andirons and told Mr. Bell and Mrs. Bell he was in love with Mary. He said he wanted to marry her. Mr. Bell was shocked and surprised. He explained, respectful but emphatic like, that he could never dream of letting a daughter of his marry a ghost, not even so noble a ghost like the one he was talking with.

"I got a claim on you, John Bell," said the witch. "I got a claim on you and yours. I got a claim." And his voice was deep and hollowlike.

This was a point Mr. Bell maybe didn't want to hear any more about. So he said, "Have you spoken to Mary?"

"No, not spoken."

"Well, how do you know she would have you?"

"I don't. But I haven't got any reason to believe she wouldn't love me. She's never seen me. She doesn't know whether she would or not. Maybe she would consider it an honor to be married to a ghost. Not many girls are, you know. Why, it would make her famous."

"I don't want any daughter of mine getting famous that way. And besides, what if you were to have children? What in the world do you reckon they'd be like? Like you or her? Maybe half good human meat and bone, and the other half sight unseen. No, I reckon plain flesh and blood's good enough for Mary."

"But, John Bell, I love Mary. And remember. Remember."

"So do I, and that's why I'm not a-goin' to let you marry her. Why, when she got old I reckon you'd quit her for some young girl. When Mary marries, she marries a man that's solid and alive in body."

"I gather, John Bell, that you're opposed to me courting your daughter. But she's the one to say, and I'm going to talk to her about it. You'll be my father-in-law yet, or you'll be a-mourning, a-mourning."

"But what kind of wedding would it be like?" Mrs. Bell put in. "Think of it. Mary standing in front of the preacher and the preacher saying, 'Do you take this woman?' to a vase of flowers. I won't stand for it. I've stood for a lot of things, and you can't say I haven't been a friend to you. But I won't stand for Mary being a laughing-stock and disgrace to the family."

"If we're a-goin to add to this family," Mr. Bell took up, "we're a-goin to be able to see what we're addin. I don't even know what shape you've got, if any."

"Oh, I can give you some idea what shape I have. I'll let you shake hands with me. But you must promise not to squeeze. We're very delicate, especially when we touch folks. Here, hold out your hand, and I'll put mine in it."

Mr. Bell held out his hand, felt something and grabbed it. It was, he said later, like the hand of a new-born baby—soft and crinkly and warm and just about the size of a new-born baby's hand.

"How big are you all over?" he asked.

"I can't tell you that."

"Well, there's one other thing I want to know. How do you get into this house any time you want to when every window and door is locked and barred? Do you ooze through the walls?"

"No. It's a lot easier than that. If you'll watch the corner of the ceiling up there, you'll see."

And all the rest of his life Mr. Bell swore to trustworthy witnesses that he saw the corner of the ceiling raised a good three feet and then let down again—all without the slightest racket.

"Do you mean to tell me that anything with a hand like that can hoist the top off of the house that way?"

"Sure," came the answer. "But—about Mary. I'm going to talk to her right off."

"Don't," said Mr. Bell. "Do you want to drive her crazy?"

But the meeting was over, for there was no answer. And the fire had died down, and the andiron looked glum.

The story is kind of skimpy here. Nobody seems to know what the witch said to Mary or what Mary said to the witch.

But the family noticed next day that she was drooping and wasn't minding what was going on around her. For days she wandered about the house and up and down the yard under the gloomy old cedars, like somebody sleep-walking. And the color left her face, and deep in her wide-open black eyes was a far-away look, like she was trying to see something that ought to be but wasn't there. Every day she got up later and went to bed earlier.

And finally there came a day when she didn't get up at all. In the evening a screech-owl hollered in a cedar right by the gallery.

That night her fever was high, and by midnight she was raving. "We've put off seeing a doctor too long," said Mrs. Bell.

"No use," said a voice. "All the doctors and medicines in the world won't cure her. But if you want one, I'll get him, and get him a lot quicker than you can."

The doctor got there just as the old eight-day clock struck one. "I heard somebody hollering at my window about midnight, telling me to come out here right away. When I got to the door, nobody was there; but I thought I'd better come anyway." He was a young doctor just starting

317

out. "Say, what kind of road overseer and gang do you fellows have out this way? Last time I came over this road, it was the worst I ever saw. Why, I picked up a Stetson hat in the middle of a mud-hole near the four-mile board, and by George there was a man under it. 'You're in a bad fix, old man,' I said. 'Hell,' he said, 'that ain't nothin to the fix this mule's in under me.' I had to lift up my feet half the way to keep them from dragging in the mud by the horse's belly. But tonight my horse skimmed over it in an hour. Well, who's sick out here?"

"It's her mind and nerves," he told them after he had questioned them and examined Mary. "I won't conceal from you, she's in pretty bad shape. And medicine won't do her any good. You've just got to be gentle and careful with her. Humor her and be patient with her. I'll give her something to put her to sleep when she gets like this. Watch her close and don't let her get lonesome. She's young and strong and ought to come round in time."

But she never did. For a month she lay there on the bed, looking at nothing and yet straining to see something. Something too far off. At night her Pa and Ma took turns sitting up. They didn't want the neighbors in. They called the doctor back a few times, but he shook his head and said he couldn't do any more. So they would watch and wait, wanting to do something, but helpless.

One night her Ma was sitting there holding Mary's hand and stroking the dark hair back from her forehead. Suddenly Mary pushed her mother away and sat up and looked across the foot of the bed, as if somebody was standing there.

"Mamma," she whispered, "Mamma . . . I see him . . . at last. . . . And I think . . . I think . . . I'm going . . . to love him."

And she died with the only expression of happiness they had seen on her face in months.

They say that on the day of the funeral, when the coffin was carried from the house to a wagon, a great black bird flew down from the sky and hung in the air just above the wagon. And around its neck was a bell that tolled in the mournfullest tone ever heard by the ear of man. And when the funeral procession began to move, the great bird floated just in front of it all the way to the graveyard and circled round and round the grave during the burial, the bell tolling all the while. And when the mound was rounded up, the bird swung high up in the air and flew away to the west and finally became just a little speck above the treetops and disappeared. But long after it was gone the mourning notes of the bell floated back to those who stood and watched.

The New Jersey Dragon

The stamping ground of the New Jersey dragon was (is?) anywhere between the Trenton area and Cape May, but mostly near the coast.

It was in the town of Burlington, about 1735, that Mother Leeds gave birth to a baby. Mother Leeds looked like a respectable Quaker lady, but she had been suspected of witchcraft in the past and when she had that baby, it turned out the suspicions were true.

A lot of old women were there, as they always are at births, deaths, and marriages, so there was no lack of witnesses. They said at first the baby was like other babies, but it soon began to change before their eyes. It grew long and brown, and presently took the shape of a dragon, with a body like a snake and a head like a horse, a pig's feet and wings like a bat. It grew very fast, and as its size increased, so did its strength. When it was as big as a man, it turned on the people there, even its own mother, thumping them with its great, leathery, forked tail. Finally it disappeared up the chimney, and its harsh cries mingled with the noise of the storm that was raging outside.

Soon afterward several children disappeared. They had been eaten by the dragon. For several years it roamed the country, sometimes glimpsed in the woods at nightfall. It would wing its way from farm to farm, though it generally did less mischief than it did when it first escaped. It would sour the milk by breathing on it, and people said it made the cows dry and scorched the growing corn. On a still night, you could follow its progress by the howling of dogs, the hoots of owls, and the squawks of chickens, as it made its way across country.

It was often seen on the coast before a ship was wrecked, and even though it did not do a great deal of harm itself, its coming meant that bad luck was on the way. On the coast it kept company with ghosts, like the golden-haired woman in white, or the black-muzzled pirate, or the robber whose head had been cut off by Captain Kidd and who used to stump along the beach without it.

Sometimes the Jersey Dragon would breathe on the waters of the creeks and pools, poisoning all the fish and making them unfit for human beings to eat.

In 1740, a clergyman was brought in to see what he could do about it. He was a man famous for his piety and good deeds, who had a fine record against fiends and had even stopped his congregation drinking applejack, which some said was the main cause of the fiends anyway. The clergyman took bell, book, and candle, and he banned the dragon from the neighborhood for 100 years.

In all that time, not a hen was lost, not a creek poisoned. But exactly 100 years later, in the year 1840, the dragon came back. By that time, people had almost forgotten all about it; it was remembered only through dim legends. But now it was whiffling among the pines again, eating sheep and other animals, and threatening children who were unwise enough to play outdoors around twilight.

It was seen again more than once after that, but it seemed to be becoming less vigorous, and no one has seen it for a good many years now. They say its life has run its course, and that it will not return again. Perhaps. You never can tell with dragons.

Rachel's Curse

A long time ago, on the waterfront of a town in Massachusetts, lived an old woman by the name of Rachel. She was an ancient, dirty, and penniless hag, dressed in rags, and she had a rough tongue in her head, which she didn't mind using. Respectable people usually avoided her, although now and then a schoolmaster or a physician, or even a minister, consulted her before going on a journey.

She used to wander around alone, late at night, especially when there was no moon. You might see her stumbling along the rocky foreshore, watching the sea. Sometimes she seemed to be looking for something.

Her eye was keen, and she had a wonderful knowledge of the weather. It was this which brought her the only friends she had. For the local fishermen respected her knowledge of the sea, the wind and the weather, and they would always ask her advice before they set out from the harbor. It was good advice, too, and when they returned they would leave one of their best fish on her doorstep as a sign of gratitude. It was this cooperation with the fishermen that was the only purpose in her life, so far as anyone knew.

One day a Boston ship, the *Betsy*, put into the harbor. The sailors on the *Betsy* had heard tell of Rachel, but they didn't believe in her powers and considered the local fishermen simple-minded to listen to an old hag. They went to ask her advice too, but they went only to make fun of her. She saw through them right away, and grew angry, accusing them of being wreckers, who lure a ship on to the rocks with a light so they can steal her cargo.

Rachel put a curse on the *Betsy* and warned the local sailors not to sail in her. Now the Boston men got irritated in their turn, and maybe just a little scared, which can often make men angry. Early next morning, one of them set fire to Rachel's hut. When they saw the flames, nearly everybody in town rushed to the waterfront. They found Rachel on a rock, wrapped in an old sail cloth, with her matted hair flying wild in the wind and her long, bony arms gesturing. She seemed madder than ever. As the crew of the *Betsy* went aboard, she stared at them, with a hellish glint in her keen eyes. As the ship passed the rock, she cursed it and those who sailed on it from Hell to high water. Outside the harbor, the ship hit a reef, sank quickly, but only one sailor drowned— the man who had set fire to Rachel's house.

Everyone was so occupied with the shipwreck that they forgot about Rachel for the minute. When someone went to look at the pile of old rags on the rock, they found her dead. They buried her where her hut once stood, and named the reef that sank the *Betsy* "Rachel's Curse."

Polly Grundy's Dead

Cats, especially black cats, often play a part in stories about witches. In this story, first published by J. Frank Dobie for the Texas Folk Lore Society, there are more cats than witches.

An old wood-cutter was coming home one evening when he saw a passel of black cats out in the road. He looked to see what they were doing, and there was nine black cats toting a little dead cat on a stretcher. He thought to himself, "Well, I never heard of such a thing as this: Nine black cats toting a little dead cat on a stretcher."

Just then one of them cats called out to the old man and said, "Say, mister, please tell Aunt Kan that Polly Grundy's dead."

The old man never answered; he just walked on a little faster, but he thought: "Hmm-mm! If this don't beat everything, them cats a-telling me to tell Aunt Kan that Polly Grundy's dead. Who in tarnation is Aunt Kan, I wonder? And who is Polly Grundy?"

Well, he just walked on again, getting a little faster all the time, and presently another of 'em hollered out, "Say, old man, please tell Aunt Kan that Polly Grundy's dead."

He walked on a little faster yet, and presently all of 'em squalled out, "Hey there, old man, please tell Aunt Kan that Polly Grundy's dead."

Then the old man broke into a run, and he never stopped till he got to his house. He thought he wouldn't tell his old woman nothing about it. But that night he was setting by the fire eating his supper, and he said to his wife, "Well, Old Woman, I guess I'll tell you something that I didn't think I would tell you."

When he said that, the old yellow cat got up from the corner where she was a-laying and come over and set down right by his chair, a-looking up at him.

His old woman said, "Well, what is it, Old Man? I knowed there was something on your mind when you come in at that door."

He said, "Well, when I was coming in from the woods this evening, walking down the road, right there in the road I seen a whole passel of black cats. When I went over and looked, there was nine black cats toting a little dead cat on a stretcher. And them cats squall out to me three times and tell me to tell Aunt Kan that Polly Grundy's dead."

When he said that, the old yellow cat jumped up and said, "Is she? By God, I must go to the burying!", and out that door she flew.

The Devil and Tom Walker

This is one of the many picturesque tales told by Washington Irving, and was first published in 1824 in a collection named *Tales of a Traveler*. Strangely, the book was fiercely criticized when it first came out, which almost put Irving off writing any more. Irving spent much of his life in Europe, and he was one of the first American writers to gain international fame. His re-telling of old folk tales, American and European, was perhaps his greatest work. This tale of the Devil in New England also brings up the subject of Captain Kidd's buried treasure, which comes into other stories by Irving.

A few miles from Boston in Massachusetts, there is a deep inlet, winding several miles into the interior of the country from Charles Bay, and terminating in a thickly-wooded swamp or morass. On one side of this inlet is a beautiful dark grove: On the opposite side the land rises abruptly from the water's edge into a high ridge, on which grow a few scattered oaks of great age and immense size. Under one of these gigantic trees, according to old stories, there was a great amount of treasure buried by Kidd the pirate. The inlet allowed a facility to bring the money in a boat secretly and at night to the very foot of the hill; the elevation of the place permitted a good lookout to be kept that no one was at hand; while the remarkable trees formed good landmarks by which the place might easily be found again. The old stories add, moreover, that the Devil presided at the hiding of the money, and took it under his guardianship: But this it is well known he always does with buried treasure, particularly when it has been ill-gotten. Be that as it may, Kidd never returned to recover his wealth, being shortly after seized at Boston, sent out to England, and there hanged for a pirate.

About the year 1727, just at the time that earthquakes were prevalent in New England, and shook many tall sinners down upon their knees, there lived near this place a meagre, miserly fellow of the name of Tom Walker. He had a wife as miserly as himself: They were so miserly that they even conspired to cheat each other. Whatever the woman could lay hands on, she hid away; a hen could not cackle but she was on the alert to secure the new-laid egg. Her husband continually prying about to detect her secret hoards, and many and fierce were the conflicts that took place about what ought to have been common property. They lived in a forlorn-looking house that stood alone, and had an air of starvation. A few straggling savin-trees, emblems of sterility, grew near it; no smoke ever curled from its chimney; no traveler stopped at its door. A miserable horse, whose ribs were as articulate as the bars of gridiron, stalked about a field, where a thin carpet of moss, scarcely covering the ragged beds of puddingstone, tantalized and balked his hunger; and sometimes he would lean his head over the fence, look piteously at the passer-by, and seem to petition deliverance from this land of famine.

The house and its inmates had altogether a bad name. Tom's wife was a tall termagant, fierce of temper, loud of tongue, and strong of arm. Her voice was often heard in wordy warfare with her husband; and his face sometimes showed signs that their conflicts were not confined to words. No one ventured, however, to interfere between them. The lonely wayfarer shrunk within himself at the horrid clamour and clapper-clawing; eyed the den of discord askance; and hurried on his way, rejoicing, if a bachelor, in his celibacy.

One day that Tom Walker had been to a distant part of the neighborhood, he took what he considered a short cut homeward, through the swamp. Like most short cuts, it was an ill-chosen route. The swamp was thickly grown with great gloomy pines and hemlocks, some of them 90 feet high, which made it dark at noonday, and a retreat for all the owls of the neighborhood. It was full of pits and quagmires, partly covered with weeds and mosses, where the green surface often betrayed the traveler into a gulf of black, smothering mud: There were also dark and stagnant pools, the abodes of the tadpole, the bullfrog, and the water snake; where the trunks of pines and hemlocks lay half drowned, half rotting, looking like alligators sleeping in the mire.

Tom had long been picking his way cautiously through this treacherous forest; stepping from tuft to tuft of rushes and roots, which afforded precarious footholds among deep sloughs; or pacing carefully, like a cat, along the prostrate trunks of trees; startled now and then by the sudden screaming of the bittern, or the quacking of a wild duck, rising on the wing from some solitary pool. At length he arrived at a piece of firm ground, which ran out like a peninsula into the deep bosom of the swamp. It had been one of the strongholds of the Indians during their wars with the first colonists. Here they had thrown up a kind of fort, which they had looked upon as almost impregnable, and had used as a place of refuge for their squaws and children. Nothing remained of the old Indian fort but a few embankments, gradually sinking to the level of the surrounding earth, and already overgrown in part by oaks and other forest trees, the foliage of which formed a contrast to the dark pines and hemlocks of the swamp.

It was late in the dusk of evening when Tom Walker reached the old fort, and he paused there a while to rest himself. Anyone but he would have felt unwilling to linger in this lonely, melancholy place, for the common people had a bad opinion of it, from the stories handed down from the time of the Indian wars; when it was asserted that the savages held incantations here, and made sacrifices to the evil spirits.

Tom Walker, however, was not a man to be troubled with any fears of the kind. He reposed himself for some time on the trunk of a fallen hemlock, listening to the boding cry of the tree toad, and delving with his walking staff into a mound of black mould at his feet. As he turned up the soil unconsciously, his staff struck against something hard. He raked it out of the vegetable mould, and lo! a cloven skull, with an Indian tomahawk buried deep in it, lay before him. The rust on the weapon showed the time that had elapsed since this death blow had been given. It was a dreary memento of the fierce struggle that had taken place in this last foothold of the Indian warriors.

"Humph!" said Tom Walker, as he gave it a kick to shake the dirt from it.

"Let that skull alone!" said a gruff voice. Tom lifted up his eyes, and beheld a great black man seated directly opposite him, on the stump of a tree. He was exceedingly surprised, having neither heard nor seen any

one approach, and he was still more perplexed on observing, as well as the gathering gloom would permit, that the stranger was neither Negro nor Indian. It is true he was dressed in a rude half Indian garb, and had a red belt or sash swathed around his body; but his face was neither black nor copper-color, but swarthy and dingy, and begrimed with soot, as if he had been accustomed to toil among fires and forges. He had a shock of coarse black hair, that stood out from his head in all directions, and bore an axe on his shoulder.

He scowled for a moment at Tom with a pair of great red eyes.

"What are you doing on my grounds?" said the black man, with a hoarse growling voice.

"Your grounds!" said Tom with a sneer, "no more your grounds than mine; they belong to Deacon Peabody."

"Deacon Peabody be damned," said the stranger, "as I flatter myself he will be, if he does not look more to his own sins and less to those of his neighbors. Look yonder, and see how Deacon Peabody is faring."

Tom looked in the direction that the stranger pointed, and beheld one of the great trees, fair and flourishing without, but rotten at the core, and saw that it had been nearly hewn through, so that the first high wind was likely to blow it down. On the bark of the tree was scored the name of Deacon Peabody, an eminent man, who had waxed wealthy by driving shrewd bargains with the Indians. He now looked around, and found most of the tall trees marked with the name of some great man of the colony, and all more or less scored with an axe. The one on which he had been seated, and which had evidently just been hewn down, bore the name of Crowninshield; and he recollected a mighty rich man of that name, who made a vulgar display of wealth, which it was whispered he had acquired by buccaneering.

"He's just ready for burning!" said the black man, with a growl of triumph. "You see I am likely to have a good stock of firewood for winter."

"But what right have you," said Tom, "to cut down Deacon Peabody's timber?"

"The right of a prior claim," said the other. "This woodland belonged to me long before one of your white-faced race put foot upon the soil."

"And pray, who are you, if I may be so bold?" said Tom.

"Oh, I go by various names. I am the wild huntsman in some countries; the black miner in others. In this neighborhood I am known by the name of the black woodsman. I am he to whom the red men consecrated this spot, and in honor of whom they now and then roasted a white man, by way of sweet-smelling sacrifice. Since the red men have been exterminated by you white savages. I amuse myself by presiding at the persecutions of Quakers and Anabaptists; I am the great patron and prompter of slave-dealers, and the grand master of the Salem witches."

"The upshot of all which is that, if I mistake not," said Tom sturdily, "you are he commonly called Old Scratch."

"The same, at your service!" replied the black man, with a half civil nod.

Such was the opening of this interview, according to the old story; although it has almost too familiar an air to be credited. One would think that to meet with such a singular personage, in this wild, lonely place, would have shaken any man's nerves; but Tom was a hard-minded fellow, not easily daunted, and he had lived so long with a termagant wife, that he did not even fear the Devil.

It is said that after this commencement they had a long and earnest conversation together, as Tom returned homeward. The black man told him of great sums of money buried by Kidd the pirate, under the oak-trees on the high ridge, not far from the morass. All these were under his command, and protected by his power, so that none could find them but such as propitiated his favor. These he offered to place within Tom Walker's reach, having conceived an especial kindness for him; but they were to be had only on certain conditions. What these conditions were may easily be surmised, though Tom never disclosed them publicly. They must have been very hard, for he required time to think of them, and he was not a man to stick at trifles where money was in view. When they had reached the edge of the swamp, the stranger paused.—"What proof have I that all you have been telling me is true?" said Tom. "There is my signature," said the black man, pressing his finger on Tom's forehead. So saying, he turned off among the thickets of the swamp, and seemed, as Tom said, to go down, down, down, into the earth, until nothing but his head and shoulders could be seen, and so on, until he totally disappeared.

When Tom reached home, he found the black print of a finger, burnt, as it were, into his forehead, which nothing could obliterate.

The first news his wife had to tell him was the sudden death of Absalom Crowninshield, the rich buccaneer. It was announced in the paper with the usual flourish, that "A great man had fallen in Israel."

Tom recollected the tree which his black friend had just hewn down, and which was ready for burning. "Let the freebooter roast," said Tom, "who cares!" He now felt convinced that all he had heard and seen was no illusion.

He was not prone to let his wife into his confidence; but as this was an uneasy secret, he willingly shared it with her. All her avarice was awakened at the mention of hidden gold, and she urged her husband to comply with the black man's terms, and secure what would make them wealthy for life. However Tom might have felt disposed to sell himself to the Devil, he was determined not to do so to oblige his wife; so he flatly refused, out of the mere spirit of contradiction. Many and bitter were the quarrels they had on the subject, but the more she talked, the more resolute was Tom not to be damned to please her.

At length she determined to drive the bargain on her own account, and, if she succeeded, to keep all the gain to herself. Being of the same fearless temper as her husband, she set off for the old Indian fort toward the close of a summer's day. She was many hours absent. When she came back, she was reserved and sullen in her replies. She spoke something of a black man, whom she had met about twilight, hewing at the root of a tall tree. He was sulky, however, and would not come to terms: She was to go again with a propitiatory offering, but what it was she forbore to say.

The next evening she set off again for the swamp, with her apron heavily laden. Tom waited and waited for her, but in vain; midnight came, but she did not make her appearance: Morning, noon, night returned, but still she did not come. Tom now grew uneasy for her safety, especially as he found she had carried off in her apron the silver teapot and spoons, and every portable article of value. Another night elapsed, another morning came; but no wife. In a word, she was never heard of more.

What was her real fate nobody knows, in consequence of so many pretending to know. It is one of those facts which have become confounded by a variety of historians. Some asserted that she lost her way among the tangled mazes of the swamp, and sank into some pit or slough; others, more uncharitable, hinted that she had eloped with the household booty, and made off to some other province; while others surmised that the tempter had decoyed her into a dismal quagmire, on the top of which her hat was found lying. In confirmation of this, it was said a great black man, with an axe on his shoulder, was seen late that very evening coming out of the swamp, carrying a bundle tied in a check apron, with an air of surly triumph.

The most current and probable story, however, observes that Tom Walker grew so anxious about the fate of his wife and his property, that he set out at length to seek them both at the Indian fort. During a long summer's afternoon he searched about the gloomy place, but no wife was to be seen. He called her name repeatedly, but she was nowhere to be heard. The bittern alone responded to his voice, as he flew screaming by; or the bullfrog croaked dolefully from a neighboring pool. At length, it is said, just in the brown hour of twilight, when the owls began to hoot, and the bats to flit about, his attention was attracted by the clamor of carrion crows hovering about a Cypress tree. He looked up, and beheld a bundle tied in a check apron, and hanging in the branches of the tree, with a great vulture perched hard by, as if keeping watch upon it. He leaped with joy; for he recognized his wife's apron, and supposed it to contain the household valuables.

"Let us get hold of the property," said he, consolingly to himself, "and we will endeavor to do without the woman."

As he scrambled up the tree, the vulture spread its wide wings, and sailed off screaming into the deep shadows of the forest. Tom seized the check apron, but, woeful sight! found nothing but a heart and liver tied up in it!

Such, according to the most authentic old story, was all that was to be found of Tom's wife. She had probably attempted to deal with the black man as she had been accustomed to deal with her husband; but though a female scold is generally considered a match for the Devil, yet in this instance she appears to have had the worst of it. She must have died game, however; for it is said Tom noticed many prints of cloven feet deeply stamped about the tree, and found handfuls of hair, that looked as if they had been plucked from the coarse black shock of the woodman. Tom knew his wife's prowess by experience. He shrugged his shoulders, as he looked at the signs of a fierce clapper-clawing. "Egad," said he to himself, "Old Scratch must have had a tough time of it!"

Tom consoled himself for the loss of his property, with the loss of his wife, for he was a man of fortitude. He even felt something like gratitude toward the black woodman, who, he considered, had done him a kindness. He sought, therefore, to cultivate a further acquaintance with him, but for some time without success; the old blacklegs played shy, for, whatever people may think, he is not always to be had for calling for: He knows how to play his cards when pretty sure of his game.

At length, it is said, when delay had whetted Tom's eagerness to the quick, and prepared him to agree to anything rather than not gain the promised treasure, he met the black man one evening in his usual woodman's dress, with his axe on his shoulder, sauntering along the swamp, and humming a tune. He affected to receive Tom's advances with great indifference, made brief replies, and went on humming his tune.

By degrees, however, Tom brought him to business, and they began to haggle about the terms on which the former was to have the pirate's treasure. There was one condition which need not be mentioned, being generally understood in all cases where the Devil grants favors; but there were others about which, though of less importance, he was inflexibly obstinate. He insisted that the money found through his means should be employed in his service. He proposed, therefore, that Tom should employ it in the black traffic; that is to say, that he should fit out a slave ship. This, however, Tom resolutely refused: He was bad enough in all conscience; but the Devil himself could not tempt him to turn slave trader.

Finding Tom so squeamish on this point, he did not insist upon it, but proposed, instead, that he should turn usurer; the Devil being extremely anxious for the increase of usurers, looking upon them as his peculiar people.

To this no objections were made, for it was just to Tom's taste.

"You shall open a broker's shop in Boston next month," said the black man.

"I'll do it tomorrow, if you wish," said Tom Walker.

"You shall lend money at two per cent a month."

"Egad, I'll charge four!" replied Tom Walker.

"You shall extort bonds, foreclose mortgages, drive the merchant to bankruptcy..."

"I'll drive him to the Devil," cried Tom Walker.

"You are the usurer for my money!" said the blacklegs with delight. "When will you want the rhino?"

"This very night."

"Done!" said the Devil.

"Done!" said Tom Walker. So they shook hands and struck a bargain.

A few days' time saw Tom Walker seated behind his desk in a counting house in Boston.

His reputation for a ready-moneyed man, who would lend money out for a good consideration, soon spread abroad. Everybody remembers the time of Governor Belcher, when money was particularly scarce. It was a time of paper credit. The country had been deluged with government bills; the famous Land Bank had been established; there had been a rage for speculating; the people had run mad with schemes for new settlements; for building cities in the wilderness; land jobbers went about with maps of grants, and townships, and Eldorados, lying nobody knew where, but which everybody was ready to purchase. In a word, the great speculating fever which breaks out every now and then in the country, had raged to an alarming degree, and everybody was dreaming of making sudden fortunes from nothing. As usual the fever had subsided; the dream had gone off, and the imaginary fortunes with it; the patients were left in doleful plight, and the whole country resounded with the consequent cry of "hard times."

At this propitious time of public distress did Tom Walker set up as usurer in Boston. His door was soon thronged by customers. The needy and adventurous; the gambling speculator; the dreaming land jobber; the thriftless tradesman; the merchant with cracked credit; in short, everyone driven to raise money by desperate means and desperate sacrifices, hurried to Tom Walker.

Thus Tom was the universal friend of the needy, and acted like a "friend in need;" that is to say, he always exacted good pay and good security. In proportion to the distress of the applicant was the hardness of his terms. He accumulated bonds and mortgages; gradually squeezed his customers closer and closer: And sent them at length, dry as a sponge, from his door.

In this way he made money hand over hand; became a rich and mighty man, and exalted his cocked hat upon change. He built himself, as usual, a vast house, out of ostentation; but left the greater part of it unfinished and unfurnished, out of parsimony. He even set up a carriage in the fullness of his vainglory, though he nearly starved the horses which drew it; and, as the ungreased wheels groaned and screeched on the axle-trees, you would have thought you heard the souls of the poor debtors he was squeezing.

As Tom waxed old, however, he grew thoughtful. Having secured the good things of this world, he began to feel anxious about those of the next. He thought with regret on the bargain he had made with his black friend, and set his wits to work to cheat him out of the conditions. He became, therefore, all of a sudden, a violent church-goer. He prayed loudly and strenuously, as if heaven were to be taken by force of lungs. Indeed, one might always tell when he had sinned most during the week, by the clamor of his Sunday devotion. The quiet Christians, who had been modestly and steadfastly traveling Zion-ward, were struck with self-reproach at seeing themselves so suddenly outstripped in their career by this new convert. Tom was as rigid in religious as in money matters; he was a stern supervisor and censurer of his neighbors, and seemed to think every sin entered up to their account became a credit on his own side of the page. He even talked of the expediency of reviving the persecution of Quakers and Anabaptists. In a word, Tom's zeal became as notorious as his riches.

Still, in spite of all this strenuous attention to forms. Tom had a lurking dread that the Devil, after all, would have his due. That he might not be taken unawares, therefore, it is said he always carried a small Bible in his coat-pocket. He had also a great folio Bible on his counting house desk, and would frequently be found reading it when people called on business; on such occasions he would lay his green spectacles in the book, to mark the place, while he turned around to drive some usurious bargain.

Some say that Tom grew a little crack-brained in his old days, and that, fancying his end approaching, he had his horse new shod, saddled and bridled, and buried with his feet uppermost; because he supposed that at the last day the world would be turned upside down; in which case he should find his horse standing ready for mounting, and he was determined at the worst to give his old friend a run for it. This, however, is probably a mere old wives' fable. If he really did take such a precaution, it was totally superfluous; at least so says the authentic old legend, which closes his story in the following manner.

One hot summer afternoon in the dog days, just as a terrible black thundergust was coming up, Tom sat in his counting house in his white linen cap and India silk morning gown. He was on the point of foreclosing a mortgage, by which he would complete the ruin of an unlucky land speculator for whom he had professed the greatest friendship. The poor land jobber begged him grant a few months' indulgence. But Tom had grown testy and irritated, and he refused another day.

"My family will be ruined and brought upon the parish," said the land jobber. "Charity begins at home," replied Tom; "I must take care of myself in these hard times."

"You have made so much money out of me," said the speculator.

Tom lost his patience and his piety—"The Devil take me," said he, "if I have made a farthing!"

Just then there were three loud knocks at the street door. He stepped out to see who was there. A black man was holding a black horse, which neighed and stamped with impatience.

"Tom, you're come for," said the black fellow, gruffly. Tom shrunk back, but too late. He had left his little Bible at the bottom of his coat pocket, and his big Bible on the desk buried under the mortgage he was about to foreclose: Never was sinner taken more unawares. The black man whisked him like a child into the saddle, gave the horse a lash, and away he galloped, with Tom on his back, in the midst of the thunderstorm. The clerks stuck their pens behind their ears, and stared after him from the windows. Away went Tom Walker, dashing down the streets; his white cap bobbing up and down; his morning gown fluttering in the wind, and his steed striking fire out of the pavement at every bound. When the clerks turned to look for the black man he had disappeared.

Tom Walker never returned to foreclose the mortgage. A countryman who lived on the border of the swamp, reported that in the height of the thundergust he had heard a great clattering of hoofs and a howling along the road, and running to the window caught sight of a figure, such as I have described, on a horse that galloped like mad across the fields, over the hills and down into the black hemlock swamp toward the old Indian fort; and that, shortly after, a thunderbolt falling in that direction seemed to set the whole forest in a blaze.

The good people of Boston shook their heads and shrugged their shoulders, but had been so much accustomed to witches and goblins and tricks of the Devil, in all kinds of shapes from the first settlement of the colony, that they were not so much horror struck as might have been expected. Trustees were appointed to take charge of Tom's effects. There was nothing, however, to administer upon. On searching his coffers, all his bonds and mortgages were found reduced to cinders. In place of gold and silver his iron chest was filled with chips and shavings; two skeletons lay in his stable instead of his half-starved horses, and the very next day his great house took fire and was burnt to the ground.

Such was the end of Tom Walker and his ill-gotten wealth. Let all griping money brokers lay this story to heart. The truth of it is not to be doubted. The very hole under the oak trees, whence he dug Kidd's money, is to be seen to this day; and the neighboring swamp and old Indian fort are often haunted in stormy nights by a figure on horseback, in morning gown and white cap, which is doubtless the troubled spirit of the usurer. In fact, the story has resolved itself into a proverb, and is the origin of that popular saying, so prevalent throughout New England, of "The Devil and Tom Walker."

Feathertop

Nathaniel Hawthorne (1804—64), the author of this story, was born in Salem, Massachusetts, and was a Salem descendant of one of the judges in the famous witchcraft trials in the Seventeenth Century. (This judge comes into Hawthorne's novel, *The House of the Seven Gables*.) Although most famous as a great American novelist, Hawthorne wrote many stories for children, published in books such as *Grandfather's Chair* and *Tanglewood Tales*. The witch in this story, however, is a very different sort of witch from the unfortunate women who were accused at Salem.

"Dickon," cried Mother Rigby, "a coal for my pipe!"

The pipe was in the old dame's mouth when she said these words. She had thrust it there after filling it with tobacco, but without stooping to light it at the hearth, where indeed there was no appearance of a fire having been kindled that morning. Forthwith, however, as soon as the order was given, there was an intense red glow out of the bowl of the pipe, and a whiff of smoke from Mother Rigby's lips. Whence the coal came, and how brought thither by an invisible hand, I have never been able to discover. "Good!" quoth Mother Rigby, with a nod of her head. "Thank ye, Dickon! And now for making this scarecrow. Be within call, Dickon, in case I need you again."

The good woman had risen thus early (for as yet it was scarcely sunrise) in order to set about making a scarecrow, which she intended to put in the middle of her corn patch. It was now the latter week of May, and the crows and blackbirds had already discovered the little, green, rolled-up leaf of the Indian corn just peeping out of the soil. She was determined, therefore, to contrive as lifelike a scarecrow as ever was seen, and to finish it immediately from top to toe, so that it should begin its sentinel's duty that very morning. Now Mother Rigby (as everybody must have heard) was one of the most cunning and potent witches in New England, and might, with very little trouble, have made a scarecrow ugly enough to frighten the minister himself. But on this occasion, as she had awakened in an uncommonly pleasant humor, and was further dulcified by her pipe of tobacco, she resolved to produce something fine, beautiful, and splendid, rather than hideous and horrible.

"I don't want to set up a hobgoblin in my own corn patch, and almost at my own doorstep," said Mother Rigby to herself, puffing out a whiff of smoke, "I could do it if I pleased, but I'm tired of doing marvelous things, and so I'll keep within the bounds of everyday business, just for variety's sake. Besides, there is no use in scaring the little children for a mile roundabout, though 'tis true I'm a witch."

It was settled therefore in her own mind, that the scarecrow should represent a fine gentleman of the period, so far as the materials at hand would allow. Perhaps it may be as well to enumerate the chief of the articles that went to the composition of this figure.

The most important item of all, probably, although it made so little show, was a certain broomstick, on which Mother Rigby had taken many an airy gallop at midnight, and which now served the scarecrow by way of a spinal column, or, as the unlearned phrase it, a backbone. One of its arms was a disabled flail, which used to be wielded by Goodman Rigby, before his spouse worried him out of this troublesome world; the other, if I mistake not, was composed of the pudding stick and a broken rung of a chair, tied loosely together at the elbow. As for its legs, the right one was a hoe handle, and the left an undistinguished and miscellaneous stick from the woodpile. Its lungs, stomach, and other affairs of that kind were nothing better than a meal bag stuffed with straw. Thus we have made out the skeleton and entire corporeity of the scarecrow, with the exception of its head; and this was admirably supplied by a somewhat withered and shriveled pumpkin, in which

Mother Rigby cut two holes for the eyes, and a slit for the mouth, leaving a bluish-colored knob in the middle to pass for a nose. It was really quite a respectable face.

"I've seen worse ones on human shoulders, at any rate," said Mother Rigby. "And many a fine gentleman has a pumpkin head, as well as my scarecrow."

But the clothes in this case were to be the making of the man. So the good old woman took down from from a peg an ancient plum-colored coat of London make, and with relics of embroidery on its seams, cuffs, pocket flaps, and buttonholes, but lamentably worn and faded, patched at the elbows, tattered at the skirts, and threadbare all over. On the left breast was a round hole, whence either a star of nobility had been rent away, or else the hot heart of some former wearer had scorched it through and through. The neighbors said this rich garment belonged to the black man's wardrobe, and that he kept it at Mother Rigby's cottage for the convenience of slipping it on whenever he wished to make a grand appearance at the governor's table. To match the coat there was a velvet waistcoat of very ample size and formerly embroidered with foliage that had been as brightly golden as the maple leaves in October, but which had now quite vanished out of the substance of the velvet. Next came a pair of scarlet breeches once worn by the French Governor of Louisbourg, and the knees of which had touched the lower step of the throne of Louis le Grand. The Frenchman had given these small clothes to an Indian pow wow, who parted with them to the old witch for a gill of strong waters at one of their dances in the forest. Furthermore, Mother Rigby produced a pair of silk stockings and put them on the figure's legs, where they showed as unsubstantial as a dream with the wooden reality of the two sticks making itself miserably apparent through the holes. Lastly, she put her dead husband's wig on the bare scalp of the pumpkin, and surmounted the whole with a dusty three-cornered hat, in which was stuck the longest tail-feather of a rooster.

Then the old dame stood the figure up in a corner of her cottage and chuckled to behold its yellow semblance of a visage, with its nobby little nose thrust into the air. It had a strangely self-satisfied aspect, and seemed to say, "Come look at me!"

"And you are well worth looking at, that's a fact!" quoth Mother Rigby, in admiration at her own handiwork. "I've made many a puppet since I've been a witch; but me-thinks this is the finest of them all. Tis almost too good for a scarecrow. And, by the by, I'll just fill a fresh pipe of tobacco, and then take him out to the corn patch."

While filling her pipe, the old woman continued to gaze with almost motherly affection at the figure in the corner. To say the truth, whether it were chance, or skill, or downright witchcraft, there was something wonderfully human in this ridiculous shape, bedizened with its tattered finery, and as for the countenance, it appeared to shrivel its yellow surface into a grin,—a funny kind of expression betwixt scorn and merriment, as if it understood itself to be a jest at mankind. The more Mother Rigby looked, the better she was pleased.

"Dickon," cried she, sharply, "another coal for my pipe!"

Hardly had she spoken, than, just as before, there was a red-glowing coal on the top of the tobacco. She drew in a long whiff and puffed it forth again into the bar of morning sunshine which struggled through the one dusty pane of her cottage-window. Mother Rigby always liked to flavor her pipe with a coal of fire from the particular chimney corner whence this had been brought. But where the chimney corner might be, or who brought the coal from it—further than that the invisible messenger seemed to respond to the name of Dickon—I cannot tell.

"That puppet yonder," thought Mother Rigby, still with her eyes fixed on the scarecrow, "is too good a piece of work to stand all summer in a corn patch, frightening away the crows and blackbirds. He's capable of better things. Why, I've danced with a worse one, when partners happened to be scarce, at our witch meetings in the forest! What if I should let him take his chance among the other men of straw and empty fellows who go bustling about the world?"

The old witch took three or four more whiffs of her pipe and smiled.

"He'll meet plenty of his brethren at every street corner!" continued she. "Well, I didn't mean to dabble in witchcraft today, further than the lighting of my pipe; but a witch I am, and a witch I'm likely to be, and there's no use in trying to shirk it. I'll make a man of my scarecrow, were it only for the joke's sake!"

While muttering these words, Mother Rigby took the pipe from her own mouth and thrust it into the crevice which represented the same feature in the pumpkin visage of the scarecrow.

"Puff, darling, puff!" said she. "Puff away, my fine fellow! Your life depends on it!"

This was a strange exhortation, undoubtedly, to be addressed to a mere thing of sticks, straw, and old clothes, with nothing better than a shriveled pumpkin for a head; as we know to have been the scarecrow's case. Nevertheless, as we must carefully hold in remembrance, Mother Rigby was a witch of singular power and dexterity; and keeping this fact duly before our minds, we shall see nothing beyond credibility in the remarkable incidents of our story. Indeed, the great difficulty will be at once got over if we can only bring ourselves to believe that as soon as the old dame bade him puff, there came a whiff of smoke from the scarecrow's mouth. It was the very feeblest of whiffs, to be sure; but it was followed by another and another, each more decided than the preceding one.

"Puff away, my pet! Puff away, my pretty one!" Mother Rigby kept repeating, with her pleasantest smile. "It is the breath of life to ye; and that you may take my word for."

Beyond all question the pipe was bewitched. There must have been a spell either in the tobacco or in the fiercely glowing coal that so mysteriously burned on top of it, or in the pungently aromatic smoke which exhaled from the kindled weed. The figure, after a few doubtful attempts, at length blew forth a volley of smoke extending all the way from the obscure corner into the bar of sunshine. There it eddied and melted away among the motes of dust. It seemed a convulsive effort; for the two or three next whiffs were fainter, although the coal still glowed and threw a gleam over the scarecrow's visage. The old witch clapped her skinny hands together, and smiled encouragingly upon her handiwork. She saw that the charm worked well. The shriveled, yellow face, which heretofore had been no face at all, had already a thin, fantastic haze, as it were, of human likeness, shifting to and fro across it; sometimes vanishing entirely, but growing more perceptible than ever with the next whiff from the pipe. The whole figure, in like manner, assumed a show of life, such as we impart to ill-defined shapes among the clouds, and half deceive ourselves with the pastime of our own fancy.

If we must needs pry closely into the matter, it may be doubted whether there was any real change, after all, in the sordid, worn out, worthless, and ill-jointed substance of the scarecrow; but merely a spectral illusion, and a cunning effect of light and shade so colored and contrived as to delude the eyes of most men. The miracles of witchcraft seem always to have had a very shallow subtlety; and, at least, if the above explanation do not hit the truth of the process, I can suggest no better.

"Well puffed, my pretty lad!" still cried old Mother Rigby. "Come, another good stout whiff, and let it be with might and main. Puff for thy life, I tell thee! Puff out of the very bottom of thy heart; if any heart thou hast, or any bottom to it! Well done, again! Thou didst suck in that mouthful as if for the love of it."

And then the witch beckoned to the scarecrow, throwing so much magnetic potency into her gesture that it seemed as if it must inevitably be obeyed, like the mystic call of the loadstone when it summons the iron.

"Why lurkest thou in the corner, lazy one?" said she. "Step forth! Thou hast the world before thee!"

Upon my word, if the legend were not one which I heard on my grandmother's knee, and which had established its place among things credible before my childish judgement could analyse its probability, I question whether I should have the face to tell it now.

In obedience to Mother Rigby's word, and extending its arm as if to reach her outstretched hand, the figure made a step forward—a kind of hitch and jerk, however, rather than a step—then tottered and almost lost is balance. What could the witch expect? It was nothing after all, but a scarecrow stuck upon two sticks. But the strong willed old beldam scowled and beckoned, and flung the energy of her purpose so forcibly at this poor combination of rotten wood and musty straw and ragged garments, that it was compelled to show itself a man, in spite of the reality of things. So it stepped into the bar of sunshine. There it stood— poor devil of a contrivance that it was!—with only the thinnest vesture of human similitude about it, through which was evident the stiff, rickety, incongruous, faded, tattered, good-for-nothing patchwork of its substance, ready to sink in a heap on the floor, as conscious of its own unworthiness to be erect. Shall I confess the truth? At its present point of vivification, the scarecrow reminds me of some of the lukewarm and abortive characters, composed of heterogeneous materials, used for the thousandth time, and never worth using, with which romance writers (and myself, no doubt, among the rest) have so overpeopled the world of fiction.

But the fierce old hag began to get angry and show a glimpse of her diabolic nature (like a snake's head peeping with a hiss out of her bosom) at this pusillanimous behavior of the thing which she had taken the trouble to put together.

"Puff away, wretch!" cried she, wrathfully. "Puff, puff, puff, thou thing of straw and emptiness! Thou rag or two! Thou meal bag! Thou pumpkin head! Thou nothing! Where shall I find a name vile enough to call thee by? Puff, I say, and suck in thy fantastic life along with the smoke; else I snatch the pipe from thy mouth and hurl thee where that red coal came from."

Thus threatened, the unhappy scarecrow had nothing for it but to puff away for dear life. As need was, therefore, it applied itself lustily to the pipe and sent forth such abundant volleys of tobacco smoke that the small cottage kitchen became all vaporous. The one sunbeam struggled mistily through, and could but imperfectly define the image of the cracked and dusty windowpane on the opposite wall.

Mother Rigby, meanwhile, with one brown arm akimbo and the other stretched toward the figure, loomed grimly amid the obscurity with such port and expression as when she was wont to heave a ponderous nightmare on her victims and stand at the bedside to enjoy their agony. In fear and trembling did this poor scarecrow puff. But its efforts, it must be acknowledged, served an excellent purpose; for, with each successive whiff, the figure lost more and more of its dizzy and perplexing tenuity and seemed to take denser substance. Its very garments, moreover, partook of the magical change, and shone with the gloss of novelty and glistened with the skilfully embroidered gold that had long ago been rent away. And, half revealed among the smoke, a yellow visage bent its lustreless eyes on Mother Rigby.

At last the old witch clinched her fist and shook it at the figure. Not that she was positively angry, but merely acting on the principle— perhaps untrue, or not the only truth, though as high a one as Mother Rigby could be expected to attain—that feeble and torpid natures, being incapable of better inspiration, must be stirred up by fear. But here was the crisis. Should she fail in what she now sought to effect, it was her ruthless purpose to scatter the miserable simulacre into its original elements.

"Thou hast a man's aspect," said she, sternly. "Have also the echo and mockery of a voice! I bid thee speak!"

The scarecrow gasped, struggled, and at length emitted a murmur, which was so incorporated with its smoky breath that you could scarcely tell whether it were indeed a voice or only a whiff of tobacco. Some narrators of this legend held the opinion that Mother Rigby's conjurations, and the fierceness of her will had compelled a familiar spirit into the figure, and that the voice was his.

"Mother," mumbled the poor stifled voice, "be not so awful with me! I would fain speak; but being without wits, what can I say?"

"Thou canst speak, darling, canst thou?" cried Mother Rigby, relaxing her grim countenance into a smile. "And what shalt thou say, quotha! Say, indeed! Art thou of the brotherhood of the empty skull, and demandest of me what thou shalt say? Thou shalt say a thousand things, and saying them a thousand times over, thou shalt still have said nothing! Be not afraid, I tell thee! When thou comest into the world (whither I purpose sending thee forthwith), thou shalt not lack the wherewithal to talk. Talk! Why, thou shalt babble like a millstream if thou wilt. Thou hast brains enough for that, I trow!"

"At your service, mother," responded the figure.

"And that was well said, my pretty one," answered Mother Rigby. "Then thou spakest like thyself, and meant nothing. Thou shalt have a hundred such set phrases, and five hundred to the boot of them. And now, darling, I have taken so much pains with thee, and thou art so beautiful, that, by my troth, I love thee better than any witch's puppet in the world; and I've made them of all sorts—clay, wax, straw, sticks, night fog, morning mist, sea foam, and chimney smoke. But thou art the very best. So give heed to what I say."

"Yes, kind mother," said the figure, "with all my heart!"

"With all thy heart!" cried the old witch, setting her hands to her sides and laughing loudly. "Thou hast such a pretty way of speaking. With all thy heart! And thou didst put thy hand to the left side of thy waistcoat, as if thou really hadst one!"

So now, in high good humor with this fantastic contrivance of hers, Mother Rigby told the scarecrow that it must go and play its part in the great world, where not one man in a hundred, she affirmed, was gifted with more real substance than itself. And, that he might hold up his head with the best of them, she endowed him, on the spot, with an unreckonable amount of wealth. It consisted partly of a gold mine in Eldorado, and of 10,000 shares in a broken bubble, and 500,000 acres of vineyard at the North Pole, and of a castle in the air, and a chateau in Spain, together with all the rents and income therefrom accruing. She further made over to him the cargo of a certain ship, laden with salt of Cadiz, which she herself, by her necromantic arts, had caused to founder, 10 years before, in the deepest part of mid ocean. If the salt were not dissolved, and could be brought to market, it would fetch a pretty penny among the fishermen. That he might not lack ready money, she gave him a copper farthing of Birmingham manufacture, being all the coin she had about her, and likewise a great deal of brass, which she applied to his forehead, thus making it yellower than ever.

"With that brass alone," quoth Mother Rigby, "thou canst pay thy way all over the earth. Kiss me, pretty darling! I have done my best for thee."

Furthermore, that the adventurer might lack no possible advantage toward a fair start in life, this excellent old dame gave him a token by which he was to introduce himself to a certain magistrate, member of the council, merchant, and elder of the church (the four capacities constituting but one man), who stood at the head of society in the neighboring metropolis. The token was neither more nor less than a single word which Mother Rigby whispered to the scarecrow, and which the scarecrow was to whisper to the merchant.

"Gouty as the old fellow is, he'll run thy errands for thee, when once thou hast given him that word in his ear," said the old witch. "Mother Rigby knows the worshipful Justice Gookin, and the worshipful Justice knows Mother Rigby!"

Here the witch thrust her wrinkled face close to the puppet's, chuckling irrepressibly, and fidgeting all through her system, with delight at the idea which she meant to communicate.

"The worshipful Master Gookin," whispered she, "hath a comely maiden to his daughter. And hark ye, my pet! Thou hast a fair outside, and a pretty wit enough of thine own. Yea, a pretty wit enough! Thou wilt think better of it when thou hast seen more of other people's wits. Now, with thy outside and thy inside, thou art the very man to win a young girl's heart. Never doubt it! I tell thee it shall be so. Put but a bold face on the matter, sigh, smile, flourish thy hat, thrust forth thy leg like a dancing master, put they right hand to the left side of thy waistcoat, and pretty Polly Gookin is thine own!"

All this while the new creature had been sucking in and exhaling the vapory fragrance of his pipe, and seemed now to continue this occupation as much for the enjoyment it afforded as because it was an essential condition of his existence. It was wonderful to see how exceedingly like a human being it behaved. Its eyes (for it appeared to possess a pair) were bent on Mother Rigby, and at suitable junctures it nodded or shook its head. Neither did it lack words proper for the occasion: "Really! Indeed! Pray tell me! It is possible! Upon my word! By no means! Oh! Ah! Hem!" and other such weighty utterances as imply attention, inquiry, acquiescence, or dissent on the part of the auditor. Even had you stood by and seen the scarecrow made, you could scarcely have resisted the conviction that it perfectly understood the cunning counsels which the old witch poured into its counterfeit of an ear. The more earnestly it applied its lips to the pipe the more distinctly was its human likeness stamped among visible realities, the more sagacious grew its expression, the more lifelike its gestures and movements, and the more intelligibly audible its voice. Its garments, too, glistened so much the brighter with an illusionary magnificence. The very pipe, in which burned the spell of all this wonder-work, ceased to appear as a smoke-blackened earthen stump, and became a meerschaum, with painted bowl and amber mouthpiece.

It might be apprehended, however, that as the life of the illusion seemed indentical with the vapor of the pipe, it would terminate simultaneously with the reduction of the tobacco to ashes. But the beldam foresaw the difficulty.

"Hold thou the pipe, my precious one," said she, "while I fill it for thee again."

It was sorrowful to behold how the fine gentleman began to fade back into a scarecrow while Mother Rigby shook the ashes out of the pipe and proceeded to replenish it from her tobacco box.

"Dickon," cried she, in her high, sharp tone, "another coal for this pipe!"

No sooner said than the intensely red speck of fire was glowing within the pipe bowl; and the scarecrow, without waiting for the witch's bidding, applied the tube to his lips and drew in a few short, convulsive whiffs, which soon, however, became regular and equable.

"Now, mine own heart's darling," quoth Mother Rigby, "whatever may happen to thee, thou must stick to thy pipe. Thy life is in it; and that, at least, thou knowest well, if thou knowest nought besides. Stick to thy pipe, I say! Smoke, puff, blow thy cloud; and tell the people, if any question be made, that it is for thy health, and that so the physician orders thee to do. And, sweet one, when thou shalt find thy pipe getting low, go apart into some corner and (first filling thyself with smoke) cry sharply, 'Dickon, a fresh pipe of tobacco!' and 'Dickon, another coal for my pipe!' and have it into thy petty mouth as speedily as may be. Else, instead of a gallant gentleman in a gold-laced coat, thou wilt be but a jumble of sticks and tattered clothes, and a bag of straw, and a withered pumpkin! Now depart, my treasure, and good luck go with thee!"

"Never fear, mother!" said the figure, in a stout voice, and sending forth a courageous whiff of smoke. "I will thrive, if an honest man and a gentleman may!"

"Oh, thou wilt be the death of me!" cried the old witch, convulsed with laughter. "That was well said. If an honest man and a gentleman may! Thou playest thy part to perfection. Get along with thee for a smart fellow; and I will wager on thy head, as a man of pith and substance, with a brain, and what they call a heart, and all else that a man should have, against any other thing on two legs. I hold myself a better witch than yesterday, for thy sake. Did not I make thee? And I defy any witch in New England to make such another! Here; take my staff along with thee!"

The staff, though it was but a plain oaken stick, immediately took the aspect of a gold-headed cane.

"That gold head has as much sense in it as thine own," said Mother Rigby, "and it will guide thee straight to worshipful Master Gookin's door. Get thee gone, my pretty pet, my darling, my precious one, my treasure; and if any ask thy name, it is Feathertop. For thou has a feather in thy hat, and I have thrust a handful of feathers into the hollow of thy head, and thy wig too is of the fashion they call Feathertop—so be Feathertop thy name!"

And, issuing from the cottage, Feathertop strode manfully toward town. Mother Rigby stood at the threshold, well pleased to see how the sunbeams glistened on him, as if all his magnificence were real, and how diligently and lovingly he smoked his pipe, and how handsomely he walked, in spite of a little stiffness of his legs. She watched him until out of sight, and threw a witch benediction after her darling, when a turn of the road snatched him from her view.

Betimes in the forenoon, when the principal street of the neighboring town was just at its acme of life and bustle, a stranger of very distinguished figure was seen on the sidewalk. His port as well as his garments betokened nothing short of nobility. He wore a richly

embroidered plum-colored coat, a waistcoat of costly velvet magnificiently adorned with golden foliage, a pair of splendid scarlet breeches, and the finest and glossiest of white silk stockings. His head was covered with a peruke, so daintily powdered and adjusted that it would have been sacrilege to disorder it with a hat; which therefore (and it was a gold-laced hat, set off with a snowy feather) he carried beneath his arm. On the breast of his coat glistened a star. He managed his gold-headed cane with an airy grace peculiar to the fine gentlemen of the period; and, to give the highest possible finish to his equipment, he had lace ruffles at his wrist, of a most ethereal delicacy, sufficiently avouching how idle and aristocratic must be the hands which they half concealed.

It was a remarkable point in the accoutrement of this brilliant personage, that he held in his left hand a fantastic kind of a pipe, with an exquisitely painted bowl and an amber mouthpiece. This he applied to his lips as often as every five or six paces, and inhaled a deep whiff of smoke, which, after being retained a moment in his lungs, might be seen to eddy gracefully from his mouth and nostrils.

As may well be supposed, the street was all astir to find out the stranger's name.

"It is some great nobleman, beyond question," said one of the townspeople. "Do you see the star at his breast?"

"Nay, it is too bright to be seen," said another. "Yes, he must needs be a nobleman, as you say. But by what conveyance, think you, can his lordship have voyaged or traveled hither? There has been no vessel from the old country for a month past; and if he have arrived overland from the southward, pray where are his attendants and equipage?"

"He needs no quipage to set off his rank," remarked a third. "If he came among us in rags, nobility would shine through a hole in his elbow. I never saw such dignity of aspect. He has the old Norman blood in his veins, I warrant him."

"I rather take him to be a Dutchman, or one of your high Germans," said another citizen. "The men of those countries have always the pipe at their mouths."

"And so has a Turk," answered his companion. "But, in my judgement, this stranger hath been bred at the French court, and hath there learned politeness and grace of manner, which none understand so well as the nobility of France. That gait, now! A vulgar spectator might deem it stiff—he might call it a hitch and jerk—but, to my eye, it hath an unspeakable majesty, and must have been acquired by constant observation of the deportment of the Grand Monarque. The stranger's character and office are evident enough. He is a French Ambassador, come to treat with our rulers about the cession of Canada."

"More probably a Spaniard," said another, "and hence his yellow complexion; or, most likely, he is from the Havana, or from some port on the spanish main, and comes to make investigation about the piracies which our governor is thought to connive at. Those settlers in Peru and Mexico have skins as yellow as the gold which they dig out of their mines."

"Yellow or not," cried a lady, "he is a beautiful man!—so tall, so slender! Such a fine, noble face, with so well-shaped a nose, and all that delicacy of expression about the mouth! And, bless me, how bright his star is! It positively shoots out flames!"

"So do your eyes, fair lady," said the stranger, with a bow and a flourish of his pipe, for he was just passing at the instant. "Upon my honor, they have quite dazzled me."

"Was ever so original and exquisite a compliment?" murmured the lady, in an ecstacy of delight.

Amid the general admiration excited by the stranger's appearance, there were only two dissenting voices. One was that of an impertinent cur, which, after snuffing at the heels of the glittering figure, put its tail between its legs and skulked into its master's backyard, vociferating an execrable howl. The other dissentient was a young child, who squaled at the fullest stretch of his lungs, and babbled some unintelligible nonsense about a pumpkin.

Feathertop, meanwhile, pursued his way along the street. Except for the few complimentary words to the lady, and now and then a slight inclination of the head in requital of the profound reverences of the bystanders he seemed wholly absorbed in his pipe. There needed no other proof of his rank and consequence than the perfect equanimity with which he comported himself, while the curiosity and admiration of the town swelled almost into clamor around him. With a crowd gathering behind his footsteps, he finally reached the mansion house of the worshipful Justice Gookin, entered the gate, ascended the steps of the front door, and knocked. In the interim, before his summons was answered, the stranger was observed to shake the ashes out of his pipe.

"What did he say in that sharp voice?" inquired one of the spectators.

"Nay, I know not," answered his friend. "But the sun dazzles my eyes strangely. How dim and faded his lordship looks all of a sudden! Bless my wits, what is the matter with me?"

"The wonder is," said the other, "that his pipe, which was out only an instant ago, should be all alight again, and with the reddest coal I ever saw. There is something mysterious about this stranger. What a whiff of smoke was that! Dim and faded did you call him? Why, as he turns about, the star on his breast is all ablaze."

"It is, indeed," said his companions, "and it will go near to dazzle pretty Polly Gookin, whom I can now see peeping at it from out of the chamber window."

The door being now opened, Feathertop turned to the crowd, made a stately bend of his body like a great man acknowledging the reverence of the meaner sort, and vanished into the house. There was a mysterious kind of a smile, if it might not better be called a grin or grimace, upon his visage; but of all the throng that beheld him not an individual appears to have possessed insight enough to detect the illusive character of the stranger except a little child and a cur dog.

Our legend here loses somewhat of its continuity, and, passing over the preliminary explanations between Feathertop and the merchant, goes in quest of the pretty Polly Gookin. She was a damsel of a soft, round figure, with light hair and blue eyes, and a fair, rosy face, which seemed neither very shrewd nor very simple. This young lady had caught a glimpse of the glistening stranger while standing at the threshold, and had forthwith put on a laced cap, a string of beads, her finest kerchief, and her stiffest damask petticoat, in preparation for the interview. Hurrying from her chamber to the parlor, she had ever since been viewing herself in the large looking glass and practicing pretty airs—now a smile, now a ceremonious dignity of aspect, and now a softer smile than the former, kissing her hand likewise, tossing her head, and managing her fan, while within the mirror an unsubstantial little maid repeated every gesture and did all the foolish things that Polly did, but without making her ashamed of them. In short, it was the fault of pretty Polly's ability rather than her will if she failed to be as complete an artifice as the illustrious Feathertop himself; and, when she thus tampered with her own simplicity, the witch's phantom might well hope to win her.

No sooner did Polly hear her father's gouty footsteps approaching the parlor door, accompanied with the stiff clatter of Feathertop's high-heeled shoes, than she seated herself bolt upright and innocently began warbling a song.

"Polly! Daughter Polly!" cried the old merchant. "Come hither, child."

Master Gookin's aspect, as he opened the door, was doubtful and somewhat troubled.

"This gentleman," continued he, presenting the stranger, "is the Chevalier Feathertop—nay, I beg his pardon, my Lord Feathertop—who hath brought me a token of remembrance from an ancient friend of mine. Pay your duty to his lordship, child, and honor him as his quality deserves."

After these few words of introduction, the worshipful magistrate immediately quitted the room. But, even in that brief moment, had the fair Polly glanced aside at her father instead of devoting herself wholly to the brilliant guest, she might have taken warning of some mischief nigh at hand. The old man was nervous, fidgety, and very pale. Purposing a smile of courtesy, he had deformed his face with a sort of galvanic grin, which, when Feathertop's back was turned, he exchanged for a scowl, at the same time shaking his fist and stamping his gouty foot—an incivility which brought its retribution along with it. The truth appears to have been, that Mother Rigby's word of introduction, whatever it might be, had operated far more on the rich merchant's fears than on his goodwill. Moreover, being a man of wonderfully acute observation, he had noticed that the painted figures on the bowl of Feathertop's pipe were in motion. Looking more closely, he became convinced that these figures were a party of little demons, each duly provided with horns and a tail, and dancing hand in hand, with gestures of diabolical merriment, around the circumference of the pipe bowl. As if to confirm his supicions, while Master Gookin ushered his guest along a dusky passage from his private room to the parlor, the star on Feathertop's breast had scintillated actual flames, and threw a flickering gleam upon the wall, the ceiling, and the floor.

With such sinister prognostics manifesting themselves on all hands, it is not to be marveled at that the merchant should have felt that he was commiting his daughter to a very questionable acquaintance. He cursed, in his secret soul, the insinuating elegance of Feathertop's manners, as this brilliant personage bowed, smiled, put his hand on his heart, inhaled a long whiff from his pipe, and enriched the atmosphere with the smoky vapor of a fragrant and visible sigh. Gladly would poor Master Gookin have thrust his dangerous guest into the street; but there was a constraint and terror within him. This respectable old gentleman, we fear, at an earlier period of life, had given some pledge or other to the evil principle, and perhaps was now to redeem it by the sacrifice of his daughter.

It so happened that the parlor-door was partly of glass, shaded by a silken curtain, the folds of which hung a little awry. So strong was the merchant's interest in witnessing what was to ensue between the fair Polly and the gallant Feathertop, that after quitting the room he could by no means refrain from peeping through the crevice of the curtain.

But there was nothing very miraculous to be seen; nothing—except the trifles previously noticed—to confirm the idea of a supernatural peril environing the pretty Polly. The stranger, it is true, was evidently a thorough and practiced man of the world, systematic and self-possessed, and therefore the sort of a person to whom a parent ought not to confide a simple young girl, without due watchfulness for the result. The worthy magistrate, who had been conversant with all degrees and qualities of mankind, could not but perceive every motion and gesture of the distinguished Feathertop came in its proper place; nothing had been left rude or native in him; a well-digested conventionalism had incorporated itself thoroughly with his substance and transformed him into a work of art. Perhaps it was this peculiarity that invested him with a species of ghastliness and awe. It is the effect of anything completely and consummately artificial, in human shape, that the person impresses us as an unreality and as having hardly pith enough to cast a shadow upon the floor. As regarded Feathertop, all this resulted in a wild, extravagant, and fantastical impression, as if his life and being were akin to the smoke that curled upward from his pipe.

But pretty Polly Gookin felt not thus. The pair were now promenading the room; Feathertop with his dainty stride and no less dainty grimace; the girl with a native maidenly grace, just touched, not spoiled, by a slightly affected manner, which seemed caught from the perfect artifice of her companion. The longer the interview continued, the more charmed was pretty Polly, until, within the first quarter of an hour (as the old magistrate noted by his watch), she was evidently beginning to be in love. Nor need it have been witchcraft that subdued her in such a hurry; the poor child's heart, it may be, was so very fervent that it melted her with its own warmth as reflected from the hollow semblance of a lover. No matter what Feathertop said, his words found depth and reverberation in her ear; no matter what he did, his action was heroic to her eye. And by this time it is to be supposed there was a blush on Polly's cheek, a tender smile about her mouth, and a liquid softness in her glance; while the star kept coruscating on Feathertop's breast, and the little demons careered with more frantic merriment than ever about the circumference of his pipe bowl. O pretty Polly Gookin, why should these imps rejoice so madly that a silly maiden's heart was about to be given to a shadow! Is it so unusual a misfortune, so rare a triumph?

By and by Feathertop paused, and, throwing himself into an imposing attitude, seemed to summon the fair girl to survey his figure and resist him longer if she could. His star, his embroidery, his buckles, glowed at that instant with unutterable splendor; the picturesque hues of his attire took a richer depth of coloring; there was a gleam and polish over his whole presence betokening the perfect witchery of well-ordered manners. The maiden raised her eyes and suffered them to linger upon her companion with a bashful and admiring gaze. Then, as if desirous of judging what value her own simple comeliness might have side by side with so much brilliancy, she cast a glance toward the full-length looking glass in front of which they happened to be standing. It was one of the truest plates in the world, and incapable of flattery. No sooner did the images therein reflected meet Polly's eye than she shrieked, shrank from the wildest dismay, and sank insensible upon the floor. Feathertop likewise had looked toward the mirror, and there beheld, not the glittering mockery of his outside show, but a picture of the sordid patchwork of his real composition, stripped of all witchcraft.

The wretched simulacrum! We almost pity him. He threw up his arms with an expression of despair that went further than any of his previous manifestations towards vindicating his claims to be reckoned human: For perchance the only time since this so often empty and deceptive life of mortals began its course, an illusion had seen and fully recognized itself.

Mother Rigby was seated by her kitchen hearth in the twilight of this eventful day, and had just shaken the ashes out of a new pipe, when she heard a hurried tramp along the road. Yet it did not seem so much the tramp of human footsteps as the clatter of sticks or the rattling of dry bones.

"Ha!" thought the old witch, "what step is that? Whose skeleton is out of its grave now, I wonder?"

A figure burst headlong into the cottage door. It was Feathertop! His pipe was still alight; the star still flamed upon his breast; the embroidery still glowed upon his garmets; nor had he lost, in any degree or manner that could be estimated, the aspect that assimilated him with our mortal brotherhood. But yet, in some indescribable way (as is the case with all that has deluded us when once found out), the poor reality was felt beneath the cunning artifice.

"What has gone wrong?" demanded the witch. "Did yonder sniffling hypocrite thrust my darling from his door? The Villain! I'll set twenty fiends to torment him till he offer thee his daughter on his bended knees!"

"No, mother," said Feathertop, despondingly. "It was not that."

"Did the girl scorn my precious one?" asked Mother Rigby, her fierce eyes glowing like two coals of Tophet. "I'll cover her face with pimples! Her nose shall be as red as the coal in thy pipe! Her front teeth shall drop out! In a week hence she shall not be worth thy having!"

"Let her alone, mother," answered poor Feathertop, "the girl was half won; and methinks a kiss from her sweet lips might have made me altogether human. But, he added, after a brief pause and then a howl of self-contempt, "I've seen myself, mother! I've seen myself for the wretched, ragged, empty thing I am! I'll exist no longer!"

Snatching the pipe from his mouth, he flung it with all his might against the chimney, and at the same instant sank upon the floor a medley of straw and tattered garments, with some sticks protruding from the heap and a shriveled pumpkin in the midst. The eyeholes were now lustreless; but the rudely carved gap, that just before had been a mouth, still seemed to twist itself into a despairing grin, and was so far human.

"Poor fellow!" quoth Mother Rigby, with a rueful glance at the relics of her ill-fated contrivance. "My poor, dear, pretty Feathertop! There are thousand upon thousands of coxcombs and charlatans in the world, made up of just such a jumble of·worn-out, forgotten, and good-for-nothing trash as he was! Yet they live in fair repute, and never see themselves for what they are. And why should my poor puppet by the only one to know himself and perish for it?"

While thus muttering, the witch had filled a fresh pipe of tobacco, and held the stem between her fingers, as doubtful whether to thrust it into her own mouth or Feathertop's.

"Poor Feathertop!" she continued. "I could easily give him another chance and send him forth again tomorrow. But no; his feelings are too tender, his sensibilities too deep. He seems to have too much heart to bustle for his own advantage in such an empty and heartless world. Well! Well! I'll make a scarecrow of him after all. Tis an innocent and useful vocation, and will suit my darling well; and if each of his human brethren had as fit a one, twould be the better for mankind; and as for this pipe of tabacco, I need it more than he."

So saying Mother Rigby put the stem between her lips. "Dickon!" cried she, in her high, sharp tone, "another coal for my pipe!"